Promoting the health of children in public care

The essential guide for health and social work professionals and commissioners

Promoting the health of children in public care

The essential guide for health and social work professionals and commissioners

edited by Florence Merredew
and Carolyn Sampeys

Published by British Association
for Adoption & Fostering
(BAAF)
Saffron House
3rd Floor, 6–10 Kirby Street
London EC1N 8TS
www.baaf.org.uk

Charity registration 275689 (England and Wales)
and SC039337 (Scotland)

© The collection, BAAF, 2015
© Introduction, BAAF and Carolyn Sampeys, 2015

British Library Cataloguing in Publication Data
A catalogue record for this book is available
from the British Library

ISBN 978 1 910039 26 7

Project management by Jo Francis, Publications, BAAF
Designed by Helen Joubert Associates
Typeset by Avon DataSet Ltd, Bidford on Avon
Printed in Great Britain by TJ International
Trade distribution by Turnaround Publisher Services,
Unit 3, Olympia Trading Estate, Coburg Road,
London N22 6TZ

BAAF is the leading UK-wide membership
organisation for all those concerned with
adoption, fostering and child care issues.

Contents

Acknowledgements

This book has truly been a team effort, as evidenced by the number of authors who have contributed their professional experience, knowledge and expertise in a diverse range of specialist areas. There have been many drafts of each chapter and the authors have all responded generously to requests to expand or clarify sections, and to provide further references, all on top of their day jobs. Kath Burton deserves a special mention for the many occasions when she assisted with editing a difficult section, as well as for her ongoing encouragement and belief that this book would be completed!

In addition to the authors who are acknowledged at the start of each chapter, we appreciate Jennifer Driscoll's expert legal contributions to an early draft on unaccompanied asylum-seeking children, Deborah Price-Williams' helpful comments on commissioning, and Rachel Brooks for her expertise on children with autism spectrum disorder. Additionally, our thanks go to Rachel Cook who read early drafts of several chapters and offered a legal perspective as well as a fresh eye. We also extend our thanks to the many members of the Health Group who encouraged us to produce this book.

This book would not have been completed without the assistance of various BAAF colleagues. We extend heartfelt thanks to Alexandra Conroy Harris, Priscilla McLoughlin and Sarah Coldrick, who had the onerous task of providing legal advice on all chapters for England, Northern Ireland and Wales respectively, and to Leonie Jordan for responding to numerous last minute legal queries. Paul Adams, Fostering Development Consultant, provided an invaluable social care perspective which led to several interesting debates about best practice and revisions to many chapters. Danielle Sawyer provided welcome administrative support and John Simmonds was an ongoing source of expertise and all-round support. Finally, we are indebted to Shaila Shah and Jo Francis in BAAF's Publications Department for their guidance and expertise, as well as patience for a project which took much longer than expected to complete.

1 Introduction

Carolyn Sampeys
Chair, BAAF Health Group (2010–2015)

An old man was walking on the beach at dawn and noticed a young man ahead of him who was picking up starfish and flinging them into the sea. Catching up with the young man, he asked him why he was doing this. The reply was that the stranded starfish would die if left in the morning sun.

'But this beach goes on for miles and there are millions of starfish,' countered the old man. 'How can your efforts make any difference?'

The young man looked at the starfish in his hand and then threw it to safety in the waves. 'It makes a difference to this one,' he said.

This story was told by the late David Baum, President of the Royal College of Paediatrics and Child Health and Professor of Paediatrics and Child Health at the University of Bristol. He was also former President of the British Association of Community Child Health. He used it to describe the importance of the individual in community child health services and gave the incoming president of the Association, Professor Leon Polnay, a small starfish to wear as an insignia.

It is repeated here, as in a previous publication (Mather and Batty, 2000), because it contains a message to all who work with looked after children, and in memory of a dedicated paediatrician who cared deeply about the welfare of disadvantaged children all over the world.

I am delighted to introduce this much needed resource for health professionals and others working with looked after children throughout the UK and further afield. I have no doubt it will fill a gap on our bookshelves, bringing together information about quality standards, best practice, evidence, regulations and guidance.

Children and young people who are looked after are a particularly vulnerable group and both require and deserve a quality specialist multidisciplinary health service to meet their needs. Throughout this book, where the term "looked after children" is used, this applies to children and young people up to 18 years of age, currently being looked after and accommodated by local authorities (Health and Social Care Trusts in Northern Ireland), including those for whom the care plan is adoption.

We know that the majority of children enter care due to neglect and abuse and it is essential that we understand the effects of these experiences in the short and longer term.

On entering care, these children experience separation and loss of birth family, including siblings, and friends. For too many looked after children, their difficulties are further exacerbated by placement moves and lack of appropriate resources and timely interventions. For many years, health services have struggled to meet the needs of this vulnerable group of children. Their complex and diverse needs can be challenging for the children, their carers and professionals in health, education and social care. We can only hope to provide a quality health service for looked after children if we work in a multidisciplinary and multi-agency way.

The original purpose of this publication was to provide a resource for those health professionals new to the field, since there is little formal training in this specialist area. However, it soon became apparent that it is important for other professionals to gain an understanding of the wider context of health and how they can contribute to improved outcomes for looked after children. Therefore, this publication is aimed at a much wider audience, encompassing colleagues in commissioning, social care, education and Child and Adolescent Mental Health Services (CAMHS). In the changing NHS, commissioners who may have limited experience of the needs of looked after children will find this publication essential in understanding the role of health professionals in this specialist field. In some ways, commissioning is the foundation on which a child's journey rests and commissioners therefore need to have a sound understanding of the issues.

We have drawn on the considerable experience of medical advisers and specialist nurses working with looked after children across the UK to compile this book. Colleagues with particular expertise in specialist areas have also made valuable contributions, as have a number of legal advisers and social workers. This publication is not a purely medical text; rather, it addresses the challenging task of promoting the health of vulnerable children with high levels of health inequality, within a complex social care context and legal framework.

We hope that this publication will prove to be an essential guide to good practice, in providing quality health care for looked after children, and will signpost professionals to further information, research and references. In addition, information on legislation, regulations and guidance is provided for England, Northern Ireland and Wales. BAAF job descriptions (2008), which outline flexible templates for three roles held by doctors working with adoption and fostering agencies, and Intercollegiate Competencies for health care staff working with looked after children (Royal College of Nursing and Royal College of Paediatrics and Child Health, 2012, revision expected in 2015) are referenced and should be used alongside this book.

If we are to provide a quality service to meet the needs of looked after children, it is of utmost importance that health professionals lead on the development of quality standards and participate in peer review, audit and continuing professional development. We must share best practice, and both contribute to, and keep abreast of, changes in regulations. Our aim is to empower looked after children and their carers to value their own health and equip them with the skills necessary to promote their health as care leavers, or support them and their adoptive parents through their adoption journey.

As background, let us first consider who the children are, what makes them vulnerable and why they have historically had poor health, education and social outcomes. We will then explore the content of this publication. Finally, we will reflect on how BAAF, and specifically the BAAF Health Group, has evolved over the last few decades alongside the changes in adoption and permanency practice and the care of looked after children.

The children

As mentioned previously, abuse and neglect are the main reasons children enter care. Children who become looked after by the local authority are the same children who have been identified as children in need and may well have been the subject of child protection procedures. We know that chaotic family lifestyles, domestic violence, and drug and alcohol misuse often lead to poor parenting. The child's adverse experiences before entering care are compounded by separation and loss, as well as placement moves, when these occur. There may be a temporary need for foster care for families in acute distress, or where there is parental physical or mental ill-health. Short break care may be required for children with disabilities and some children with complex disabilities may require placement in specialist residential schools.

On 31 March 2013, 68,100 children in England, 5,769 in Wales and 2,807 in Northern Ireland were in the care of local authorities. This represents an increase of 12 per cent in England and 23 per cent in Wales since 2009 (Department for Education (DfE), 2013a; Welsh Government, 2014) and a 12 per cent increase in Northern Ireland since 2011 (Department of Health, Social Services and Public Safety (DHSSPS), 2013a). Most of these children (over 70 per cent) were living with foster carers. The remainder were living in residential settings, children's homes, secure units, hostels, placed for adoption or living with their parents under placement with parent regulations.

Looked after children are a diverse and mobile group, which adds to their vulnerability and exacerbates difficulties with accessing health and other services. In the year ending 31 March 2013, over 30,000 children entered care in England and Wales, with a similar number leaving the care of the local authority during this period (DfE, 2013a; Welsh Government, 2014), with many of them returning home to parents. Within this population, there are a number of sub-groups with particular needs. This includes infants and younger children who may require permanency; children from black and minority ethnic backgrounds, some of whom may be unaccompanied and seeking asylum; children with disabilities and other complex health needs; and young people who need preparation and support to leave care.

Of those children leaving care in 2013, one-third in England, over half in Northern Ireland and half in Wales returned to their birth families (DfE, 2013a; Welsh Government, 2013a; DHSSPS, 2014). A significant number of these children will return to care in the future.

A considerable level of political and media attention has directed the spotlight onto adoption recently and many reforms are under way across the UK. The number of adoptions from care for the year to 31 March 2013 increased by 15 per cent in England (DfE, 2013a), 47 per cent in Northern Ireland (DHSSPS, 2013a), and 33 per cent in Wales (Welsh Government, 2013a) since 2012 (3,980, 88 and 327 respectively).

The introduction of special guardianship orders in 2005 (Adoption and Children Act 2002) led to only a gradual increase in their usage by the courts. However, in the year to 31 March 2014 in England, there was an increase of 22 per cent in the number of special guardianship orders granted (158 per cent since 2010). Residence orders also saw a significant increase (25 per cent since 2012, 77 per cent since 2009) (DfE, 2014). These statistics show that more and more children are achieving permanent placements, which must be applauded; however, we cannot afford to be complacent.

This publication also considers children who live in private fostering arrangements who, although they are not looked after, are separated from their families and may have similar needs to those looked after. Particular concerns about private fostering led to increased awareness and a requirement to register cases. A total of 1,610 children were reported to be in private placements in England (DfE, 2013b) and 42 in Wales (Welsh Government, 2013b), although actual numbers are thought to be considerably higher. Northern Ireland does not produce statistics relating to private fostering arrangements.

An exploration of the chapters

This publication covers a wide range of topics and follows a child's journey through care. Each chapter concludes with key points and a summary of what health professionals should do. The titles of the individual chapters are self-explanatory, but it is helpful to briefly consider their content here.

The book begins with an in-depth look at who the children are and why they become looked after. We explore the health of looked after children and young people and, as you would expect, take a holistic view of health encompassing physical health, development, oral health, mental health and well-being.

We explore how risk factors, such as antenatal exposure to substances, and early life experiences of neglect and abuse can affect all parameters of a child's health and development, and focus on commonly found health issues in looked after children.

Looked after children and young people are at greater risk of mental health issues, conduct disorders and emotional disorders (Meltzer *et al*, 2003; McCann *et al*, 1996), and these are described in more detail in Chapter 4. Assessing attachment and mental/emotional health is explored, together with the effects of contact with birth family and discussion about the availability of therapeutic services and post-adoption support within health services.

To lay the foundation for statutory health provision and the statutory health assessment, in Chapter 5 we explore the various pathways of a child or young person through the care system, the accompanying legal context and issues of consent and parental responsibility.

In Chapter 7, we describe the process and requirements for statutory health assessments and the roles and responsibilities of health professionals. There is advice on the content and documentation of a holistic health assessment; collation of information; and compilation of a report and health care plan tailored to individual children/young people.

Health promotion is highlighted in Chapter 8 as an essential component of the health assessment. Indeed, any interaction with a looked after child or young person should be used as an opportunity for health education. Health promotion is essential if young people are to be equipped with the skills to make life choices with regard to their health and well-being, and to maximise their health outcomes in the long term. Areas covered in this chapter include lifestyles, sexual health, sleep, behaviour, culture and religion.

There are particular groups of looked after children/young people who may require additional resources and special expertise from their health professionals. Therefore, we look in more depth at disabled children and young people (Chapter 9), black and minority ethnic children (Chapter 10), unaccompanied asylum-seeking children (Chapter 11), and children in private fostering arrangements (Chapter 14).

Disabled children are over-represented in the looked after population (Marchant, 2011). Common disabilities are described, including Autism Spectrum Disorder, Attention Deficit Hyperactivity Disorder, learning disability, and physical disability.

Black and minority ethnic children are also over-represented in the care system. While these children have the same health issues as other children, they frequently have additional needs related to their ethnicity, and practitioners should be culturally competent. We address the importance of considering the child's ethnic, cultural, religious and linguistic identities and their impact on their health and well-being.

Chapter 11, on unaccompanied asylum-seeking and other separated children, reflects the need to understand the individual child's circumstances and therefore their additional needs. It includes the importance of awareness raising and the difficult areas of child trafficking and assessing age.

Health issues and concerns surrounding children adopted from overseas are addressed in Chapter 13, with sources of further information also provided.

We acknowledge the particular area of concern around leaving care with a dedicated chapter (Chapter 12). The transition from adolescence to adulthood is a difficult experience for the majority of young people, but when combined with the complex care histories and journeys of care leavers, this transition can become overwhelming and fraught with anxiety. Health professionals have an important role in promoting health and empowering care leavers to access universal health services and manage any health issues as they prepare to leave care.

The processes and guiding principles for the comprehensive assessment of prospective adult carers, particularly foster carers and adoptive parents, are described in Chapter 15, together with common health concerns and risks which may affect parenting ability and therefore placement stability. This can often be a challenging area for medical advisers, who need to develop a sound understanding of adult health issues relevant to substitute care.

Chapter 16 deals with the management of health records, including the principles underpinning the handling of records, confidentiality and information sharing. The BAAF Health Group continues to lobby for retention of the NHS number after adoption to ensure continuity of health information.

Finally, in Chapter 17 we discuss quality assurance, clinical governance and the importance of conducting audit and service reviews in planning for and providing quality services for looked after children and adoption. Commissioning is an increasingly important area facing health professionals, and helpful advice is given on issues to be considered by commissioners. Health professionals need to highlight to commissioners the needs of this vulnerable group of children, given their corporate parenting responsibility.

Evolution of services for adopted, fostered and looked after children

Adoption services have undergone a complete transformation. Historically, adoption was very much a service aimed at finding babies for infertile couples. Placements were shrouded in secrecy and background information on the child's birth family was extremely limited. The philosophy behind adoption, the numbers of children available for adoption, and the number of adoptions have changed considerably over the last 40 years. In the 1970s, there were in the region of 20,000 adoptions a year. Since then, numbers have fallen, due in part to changes in social attitudes, as well as availability of contraception and abortion. By the 1990s, there were around 5,000 adoptions a year and the number of adoption orders has remained fairly stable since then. Adoption is now a much more child-centred service dedicated to finding families for children, the majority of whom have come through the care system. Children for whom the plan is adoption have far more complex histories. There are a greater number of sibling groups, the children are older and they are likely to have suffered adversity, either antenatally or whilst living with their birth families.

It is important to remember that adoption is not the answer for all children who need a permanent placement. The needs of some children are more appropriately met through kinship care, special guardianship orders (England and Wales), residence orders (Northern Ireland), child arrangements orders (formerly residence orders in England and Wales until April 2014) or perhaps long-term foster care.

Perhaps the biggest impetus to improving services for looked after children was the Government's *Review of the Safeguards for Children Living Away from Home*, by Sir

William Utting (1996) and reported in *People Like Us* (Utting, 1997). This drew attention to the significant concerns regarding education, health and social outcomes for looked after children.

Government initiatives such as *Quality Protects* in England (Department of Health, 1998b) and *Children First* in Wales (Welsh Assembly Government, 1999), and the *Prime Minister's Review of Adoption* (Department of Health, 2000), helped focus on the unmet needs of looked after children and led to improvements in health services for them.

The last twenty years have seen significant changes in health provision for looked after children. This has included the development of the crucial roles of specialist nurses, specialist health visitors and designated nurses for looked after children. These health professionals are skilled at providing holistic health assessments and support for these children, promoting placement stability and empowering looked after young people and care leavers to take responsibility for their own health needs. This has been a significant contributory factor to better outcomes for looked after children.

In many regions, there are dedicated professionals with a clear remit for health provision for looked after and adopted children. There are multidisciplinary teams comprising paediatricians, specialist nurses, CAMHS and therapists helping to meet statutory and non-statutory obligations. Multi-agency working has become more effective and there is much evidence of good practice. The health service is an important partner to the local authority, but the overall responsibility for looked after children rests with the local authority.

Today, the skilled health professional for looked after children recognises their needs and those of their families, and understands the implications of antenatal drug or alcohol exposure and the effects of neglect and abuse on children. These health professionals are involved in educating other professionals and supporting families to be able to provide an environment for these children to flourish. For those children who continue to be looked after in the longer term, the role of the health professional is to enable and empower them to promote and value their own health.

The role of the medical adviser in adoption is defined in statute (Adoption Agencies Regulations 2005 (England), Adoption Agencies (Wales) Regulations 2005 and Adoption Agencies Regulations (Northern Ireland) 1989, with responsibility for providing assessments and reports on children for whom the plan is adoption, together with advice on the health of prospective adopters and information sharing about individual children with adoption agencies, adoption panels and prospective adopters. It is important that the medical adviser is skilled in carrying out this role and has access to support and further advice.

The role of the medical adviser to the fostering panel has expanded to include providing health advice on carers, and to attend the panel. The delivery of good practice means that the same scrutiny and considerations are applied to potential foster carers as to potential adoptive parents. Some children will remain with their foster carer throughout their formative years and comprehensive health assessment of foster carers is essential to assess health risk, identify needs for health promotion and support, and to ensure appropriate matching, so that decisions taken are in the best interests of children.

The evolution of BAAF and its Health Group

BAAF has gone through evolution itself. A past Chair of the Health Group, Dr Mary Mather, collated information on the history of the BAAF Health Group for a previous publication (Mather and Batty, 2000) and, with her kind permission, it is included below with updating as necessary.

History of the BAAF Health Group

The British Agencies for Adoption and Fostering (BAAF) Medical Group (now the British Association for Adoption and Fostering) was formed in 1964. At that time, adoption was largely confined to voluntary agencies. Apart from the large agencies, fostering did not appear on the agenda of the voluntary sector until later, following the Houghton Committee report on the adoption of children (Department of Health, 1972). The Medical Group is in fact considerably older than BAAF itself. It was set up by the medical members of the forerunner of the Association of British Adoption and Fostering Agencies (ABAFA), which later joined with the Adoption Resource Exchange (ARE) to become BAAF.

Those who think that excellence, quality and the pursuit of standards in clinical practice are phenomena of the 21st century would find an afternoon spent amongst the dusty files of the BAAF library extremely instructive. Over 50 years ago, the small group of dedicated medical advisers who formed the initial group were extremely concerned about the differing standards of medical practice across all the voluntary agencies involved in adoption work. They spent most of their early meetings designing and re-designing health forms in order to ensure overall continuity of practice. This process still continues today and there is no doubt that BAAF health forms, now adopted by the majority of local authorities throughout the UK, ensure that high quality standard health assessments of looked after children are achieved.

The first Chair of the Medical Group was Dr Hilda Lewis, who died three years after the group was formed. In her memory, a trust fund was set up to enable the Medical Group to hold the annual Hilda Lewis lecture. These early lectures were prestigious events and were followed by a buffet reception. Eminent speakers were invited from abroad and the lecture was held in venues such as Great Ormond Street Hospital, the Thomas Coram Foundation and the Central Hall Westminster.

As the numbers of children being placed for adoption declined during the 1980s, the interest in the Hilda Lewis lecture also declined. The tradition of continuing education in adoption practice was, however, maintained in the form of the Annual General Meeting of the Medical Group. Medical advisers in increasing numbers and from all over the country met at this two-day event to discuss new developments in practice, share problems and explore future developments. It has become generally recognised that continuing medical education and professional development are important for doctors and nurses engaged in this field, and essential to maintaining quality standards for health professionals. The medical education of doctors involved with looked after children and adoption is probably unique in that it has been carried out over the past 45 years largely by BAAF. There cannot be another area of medical practice in which the voluntary sector, as opposed to the medical profession, has been so responsible for medical training.

The Chairs of the Medical Group have been outstanding in the length of time they have committed to the group. Professor John Forefar, from Edinburgh, succeeded Dr Hilda Lewis. Dr Frank Bamford from Manchester then took the chair throughout most of the 1970s, followed by Dr Christine Cooper, Dr Anne Jepsom, Dr Marion Miles, Dr Heather Payne and, more recently, Dr Mary Mather and Dr Catherine Hill. Dr Christine (Tina) Cooper deserves a special mention. She was a much loved and respected paediatrician from Newcastle who was involved in the BAAF Medical Group from the start and was secretary of the group throughout most of the 1970s before becoming Chair in 1982. Tina's records of meetings have provided much of the history of the Medical Group.

For the medical practitioner involved in the care of looked after children, there is frequently a stark contrast between the services offered to this group and those given to every other child/patient. Those doctors who remember the FFI (Freedom from Infection) Inspections will no doubt vividly recall the extra time added onto the end of an outpatient clinic spent seeing "normal children" and their caring, anxious parents. A subdued, unresponsive child, invariably accompanied by a social worker, who knew virtually nothing about her/him, would be undressed and checked for bruises and infestation, a stethoscope would be waved in the general direction of the chest, she or he would be duly declared "free from infection" and the appropriate form would be signed. The child then disappeared, never to be seen again by that doctor or clinic. This almost veterinary procedure did nothing for the child, the doctor, the social worker or indeed human dignity, and thankfully has been abandoned. Interestingly, the usefulness of the process was never questioned or audited at the time.

The BAAF Health Group in the 21st century

The importance of the roles of the medical adviser in adoption, and health professionals for looked after children, have been recognised by our fellow paediatricians. Continued work between the BAAF Health Group and the Royal College of Paediatrics and Child Health (RCPCH) has led to adoption and looked after children becoming specialist areas of paediatrics and the BAAF Health Group is now a special interest group of the RCPCH.

Comprehensive health assessments for looked after children and children going through the adoption process are crucial to ensure that these children's health needs are addressed and met. The standardisation of health assessments and reports has contributed greatly to this and BAAF has remained at the forefront of raising standards. The almost universally used BAAF health forms are constantly reviewed and revised by the BAAF Health Group Advisory Committee.

We advocate children's full registration with a GP to ensure complete health records follow the child and any gaps in immunisation uptake or health surveillance can be identified.

The health professional for looked after children plays an important role in gathering together health information from multiple sources, conducting and recording quality health assessments, and ensuring that health needs and health promotion are addressed. Liaison with multi-agency professionals is key to ensuring that relevant health information is shared appropriately, to inform the care plan and advise on future implications.

The BAAF Health Group has long advocated that the same standard of comprehensive health and developmental assessment offered to children with an adoption plan should be undertaken for all children upon becoming looked after. The development of the specific role of nurses for looked after children has had an enormous impact on the uptake of their statutory health assessments and in their health outcomes.

The BAAF Health Group today is an active and vibrant group of paediatricians, specialist nurses, psychologists and psychiatrists throughout the UK, at the forefront of developments in the field, with a clear voice advocating and promoting the needs of looked after children and young people. Every opportunity is taken to raise the profile of the work carried out by professionals in the field.

Membership of BAAF is essential for health professionals involved in this area to keep abreast of changes in the legal framework, to contribute to setting quality standards, to be aware of the various political agendas, and to take part in continuing professional development. There are currently over 500 members of the BAAF Health Group. The Chair is supported by a Health Group Advisory Committee, which meets quarterly, and a committed BAAF Health Group Development Officer. The annual health conference attracts around 130–150 delegates and topics are varied and always relevant to members, with positive evaluations and feedback.

In conclusion, I hope you find this publication an important companion in this specialised and rewarding area of work. You may choose to dip into it, read it from cover to cover, or use it as a tool to champion the health and well-being of looked after children in your region.

The BAAF Health Group is justifiably proud of its contribution over the years to the development of health services for looked after and adopted children, and its continuing role in raising quality standards, promoting best practice and advocating for looked after children and the health professionals who are fortunate to support them.

I am indebted to everyone who has contributed to the comprehensive content of this publication, for their hard work and perseverance, and to the BAAF legal advisers for ensuring accuracy.

My warmest and heartfelt thanks go to Florence Merredew (BAAF Health Group Development Officer), who has risen to and relished the challenge of co-ordinating the collaborative input and has been indispensible as my co-editor.

Bibliography

BAAF (2008) *Model Job Descriptions and Competencies for Medical Advisers in Adoption and Fostering*, London: BAAF, available at: www.baaf.org.uk/webfm_send/348

Chambers H. with Howell S., Madge N. and Olle H. (2002) *Healthy Care: Building an evidence base for promoting the health and well-being of looked after children and young people*, London: National Children's Bureau

Department for Education (2013a) *Children Looked After in England (Including Adoption and Care Leavers)*, *Statistical First Release*, available at: www.gov.uk/government/uploads/system/uploads/attachment_data/file/244872/SFR36_2013.pdf

Department for Education (2013b) *Notifications of Private Fostering Arrangements for England Year Ending 31 March 2013*, *Statistical First Release*, available at: www.gov.uk/government/uploads/system/uploads/attachment_data/file/223576/SFR25-2013_Text.pdf

Department for Education (2014) *Children Looked After in England (Including Adoption and Care Leavers)*, available at: www.gov.uk/government/uploads/system/uploads/attachment_data/file/244872/SFR36_2013.pdf

Department of Health (1972) *Report of the Departmental Committee on the Adoption of Children (Houghton Committee)*, London: Stationery Office

Department of Health (1998a) *The Government's Response to the Children's Safeguards Review*, London: Stationery Office

Department of Health (1998b) *Quality Protects: Framework for Action*, London: Stationery Office

Department of Health (2000) *Local Authority Circular: Prime Minister's Review of Adoption: Report from the Performance and Innovation Unit*, London: Stationery Office

Department of Health, Social Services and Public Safety (2013a) *Children's Social Care Statistics for Northern Ireland 2012/13*, available at: www.dhsspsni.gov.uk/microsoft_word_-_childrens-social-care-stats-201213.pdf

Department of Health, Social Services and Public Safety (2013b) *Children Adopted From Care in Northern Ireland 2012/13*, available at: www.dhsspsni.gov.uk/index/statistics/ad1_children_adopted_from_care_in_northern_ireland_2012_13.pdf

Department of Health, Social Services and Public Safety (2014) *Children's Social Care Statistics for Northern Ireland 2012/13*, available at: www.dhsspsni.gov.uk/child-social-care-13-14.pdf

Marchant R. (2011) 'Looked after disabled children', *Community Care Inform*, available at: www.ccinform.co.uk/

Mather M. and Batty D. (2000) *Doctors for Children in Public Care* (training exercises by Heather Payne), London: BAAF

McCann J., James A., Wilson S. and Dunn G. (1996) 'Prevalence of psychiatric disorders in young people in the care system', *British Medical Journal*, 313, pp 1529–1530

Meltzer M., Corbin T., Gatward R., Goodman R. and Ford T. (2003) *The Mental Health of Young People Looked After by Local Authorities in England*, London: Stationery Office

Royal College of Nursing and Royal College of Paediatrics and Child Health (2012) *Looked After Children: Knowledge, skills and competences of health care staff*, London: RCN and RCPCH, available at: www.rcpch.ac.uk/system/files/protected/page/RCPCH_RCN_LAC_2012.pdf

Utting W. (1996) *Review of the Safeguards for Children Living Away from Home*, London: Stationery Office

Utting W. (1997) *People Like Us: The report of the review of the safeguards for children living away from home*, London: Stationery Office

Welsh Assembly Government (1999) *Children First Programme*, Cardiff: WAG

Welsh Government (2013a) *Adoptions, Outcomes and Placements of Looked After Children by Local Authorities, Wales, 2012–2013*, available at: http://wales.gov.uk/docs/statistics/2014/140327-adoptions-outcomes-placements-children-looked-after-local-authorities-2012-13a-en.pdf

Welsh Government (2013b) *Private Fostering in Wales, Year Ending 31 March 2013, Knowledge and Analytical Services*, available at: https://statswales.wales.gov.uk/Catalogue/Health-and-Social-Care/Social-Services/Childrens-Services

Welsh Government (2014) *Adoptions, Outcomes and Placements for Children Looked After by Local Authorities, Year Ending 31 March 2014*, available at: http://wales.gov.uk/statistics-and-research/adoptions-outcomes-placements-children-looked-after/?lang=en

2   The child's health

Kath Burton

Responsibility for [the health of] children in care falls between health services and children's services, because 'the health of looked after children is everybody's business, but actually it is nobody's business'.
Helen Chambers, National Children's Bureau, Principal Officer, Well-being

It has long been known that children who have been looked after by local authorities have statistically poorer outcomes in many areas of life, including health (Chambers *et al*, 2002). This is partly because when children enter care, their health may already be compromised through neglect, poverty, abuse, exposure to toxic substances before birth, parental ill health and chaotic lifestyles. Additionally, the adverse experiences of children and young people within the care system, particularly frequent placement moves, can compound their difficulties and result in further compromise to their physical and mental health, education and future economic well-being. The effects of adverse life experiences before and during care are cumulative – they have a direct effect on health in its widest sense and can be lifelong.

The principle of corporate parenting is that the local authority is the "parent" of children in care and thus has a legal and moral duty to provide the type of support any good parent would provide for their child. This should include enhancing the child's quality of life, and encouraging them to enjoy a healthy lifestyle is an important part of this. The premise of the Government's White Paper, *Care Matters* (Department for Education and Skills (DfES), 2007) was that the corporate parent's aspirations for children in care should be exactly the same as any parent would have for their own child. Section 10 of the Children Act 2004 named specific "relevant partners", including primary care trusts (now replaced in England by clinical commissioning groups) or local health boards in Wales, schools, police, probation and youth offending teams, which must co-operate with local authorities to improve children's well-being in their area. This is especially important for looked after children as the lack of a parental figure to consistently advocate for and promote the child's health is key to the difficulties these children face. It is incumbent on all, but especially professionals, to take every opportunity to identify and address any health issues a looked after child may have, to enable and encourage them to enjoy a healthy lifestyle and to prepare them to take responsibility for their health and well-being as adults. Time in care, however short, should make a positive difference to a child's life.

Children in care deserve excellent parenting – nurturing, supportive and ambitious care which provides stability, promotes resilience and respects their cultural heritage.
(DfES, 2007)

In Wales, the Social Services and Well-Being (Wales) Act 2014 repeals s.17 of the Children Act 1989 and replaces it with a new framework for the assessment for and provision of services to children and adults. This new provision comes into force in April 2016.

Private fostering arrangements

Children cared for under private fostering arrangements are not legally "looked after" but have much in common with children cared for by the State. There are no accurate data about the number of children involved; Government statistics show that there were 1,780 children known to be privately fostered at 31 March 2012, which represents an increase of eight per cent from the previous year (Department for Education (DfE), 2012a). However, this increase is attributable to a rise in notifications from just three local authorities, and, in at least one of these, relates to an awareness-raising campaign to ensure that colleges registered language students in order for these children to be recorded as privately fostered in accordance with the Children (Private Arrangements for Fostering) Regulations 2005; the actual number of children in the colleges being privately fostered had not increased, but awareness of the regulations and subsequent notification to the local authority had. This illustrates that the official statistics are unlikely to be accurate, with the true figures of privately fostered children being very much higher. The health of these children is discussed in Chapter 14.

Who are the children, and why do they become looked after?

Children looked after by a local authority may be subject to a care order under s.31 of the Children Act 1989, or s.49 of the Children (Northern Ireland) Order 1995, or may be looked after on a voluntary basis through agreement with parents under s.20 of the same Act, or under s.22 of the same Order. The issue of who holds parental responsibility (PR) is different between these two groups as the local authority/Trust (in Northern Ireland) only has PR for those children subject to care orders, but apart from this, looked after children share many characteristics.

Since the implementation of the Legal Aid, Sentencing and Punishment of Offenders Act 2012 in December 2012, all children who are remanded into custody in England and Wales automatically also become looked after. A period of remand should only last for a short time and the automatic looked after status ends upon conviction, acquittal or grant of bail. Whether a child remains looked after following the period of remand will depend on the individual circumstances of their case.

Official statistics in England show that there are increasing numbers of children looked after by local authorities: on 31 March 2013, 68,110 children were in care, which represents an increase of 12 per cent since 2009. A total of 28,830 children started to be looked after during the year ending 31 March 2013, an increase of 12 per cent from the year ending 31 March 2009. It must be remembered that due to movements in and out of care, more than a third as many children again will experience the care system in any one year. From a total population of 100,000, approximately 165 children would be expected to experience being looked after in a year. A total of 28,460 children ceased to be looked after during the year ending 31 March 2013, an increase of 14 per cent since 2009 (DfE, 2013).

In Wales, 5,769 children were in the care of local authorities on 31 March 2013. Of these, 2,023 children started to be looked after and 1,952 ceased to be looked after during the year ending 31 March 2013 (Welsh Government, 2014).

In Northern Ireland as of 31 March 2013, 2,807 children were looked after by Health and Social Care Trusts, an increase of six per cent on the previous year. A total of 26 per cent of these children were looked after for periods of less than one year, with nine per cent in care for 10 years or longer (Department of Health, Social Services and Public Safety (DHSSPS), 2013).

The following demographics provide a description of looked after children in England for the year ending 31 March 2013 (DfE, 2013). These statistics are broadly similar in Northern Ireland and Wales, although there are some variations in recording.

Age and sex
55 per cent of looked after children were boys.

- Age under 1 year   6 per cent
- Between 1 and 4 years   18 per cent
- Between 5 and 9 years   19 per cent
- Between 10 and 15 years   36 per cent
- Over 16 years   20 per cent

NB These figures have been rounded down.

Where the children live
- Foster carers   75 per cent
- Residential units (secure units, children's homes and hostels)   9 per cent
- With parents   5 per cent
- Placed for adoption   4 per cent
- Living independently   3 per cent
- Residential schools or other residential settings   4 per cent

These statistics have remained relatively stable since 2006 or earlier.

Destination of children ceasing to be looked after

- 37 per cent returned home to live with parents or relatives
- 13 per cent were adopted
- 8 per cent were subject to special guardianship orders
- 5 per cent were subject to residence orders
- 14 per cent moved to independent living with or without support
- 2 per cent moved to residential accommodation paid for by adult social services
- 2 per cent were sentenced to custody
- 1 per cent had their care transferred to another authority
- 20 per cent ceased to be in care for any other reason

NB: These figures have been rounded up.

Main category of need at time of entering care

- 62 per cent abuse or neglect
- 15 per cent family dysfunction
- 5 per cent absent parenting
- 9 per cent family in acute stress
- 4 per cent parental illness or disability
- 3 per cent child's disability
- 2 per cent socially unacceptable behaviour
- <1 per cent low income

(DfE, 2013)

Risk factors for becoming looked after

Abuse and neglect
Abuse and neglect are the principal reasons for social care services initially becoming engaged with a child; many were children in need or subject to a child protection plan before becoming looked after. Neglect and physical, sexual and emotional abuse often occur together; they may be severe and longstanding, leading to significant emotional, physical and developmental damage.

Dysfunctional family
Many looked after children's birth families are dysfunctional or suffering acute stress secondary to poverty, homelessness, bereavement or relationship breakdown. Lifestyles may be chaotic and include domestic violence or misuse of drugs and/or alcohol. Some

children need a break from their birth family or community while a package of support is put in place to try to rebuild family relationships or improve their ability to function. A child often exhibits socially unacceptable behaviour as a result of inconsistent behavioural strategies in the home, and neglect and abuse.

Poverty

A child living in a single-parent family with four or more children, living in private rented, overcrowded accommodation and relying on state benefits has a one in 10 chance of admission to care, compared with a one in 7,000 chance for a child in a family with none of these adverse factors (Bebbington and Miles, 1989).

Criminal behaviour

Under the Legal Aid, Sentencing and Punishment of Offenders Act 2012, children remanded in custody become looked after; some retain their looked after status on release, either due to inability to return to their parents or former accommodation, or as formerly relevant children. Some children are placed in secure children's homes to protect their own or others' welfare and safety. Although over two-thirds of children placed in secure homes are boys, most children placed for welfare reasons are girls (Department for Children, Schools and Families (DCSF), 2007).

Parental illness

Poor parental physical and mental health or disability, for example, terminal illness, poorly controlled schizophrenia or significant learning disability, may make it impossible for someone to parent adequately, even with appropriate wider family and professional support.

Antenatal concerns

Babies may be subject to child protection plans and brought into care at birth where there is sufficient professional concern that parents will be unable to provide safe care; this may relate to their parenting of previous children, their lifestyle, health or disability.

Childhood disability

Disabled children are over-represented in the looked after population; once in care, they tend to remain looked after for longer and suffer greater placement instability. These children are often older and have higher levels of challenging behaviour; children with such complex needs require sophisticated parenting and impose enormous demands on the most competent of families. Disabled children are also more likely to be abused or neglected; Jones *et al* (2012), in their systemic review and meta-analysis of 17 studies, found that disabled children were more likely than their peers to be victims of physical or sexual violence, although the evidence base in this area is not robust. Families may need short breaks for their children, and looked after children with the most complex impairments may require educational provision in specialist residential schools. The health needs of disabled children are discussed further in Chapter 9.

Absent parents

Some children will need care because their parents are absent; this includes children relinquished for adoption and those whose parents have died or abandoned them, but most are unaccompanied asylum-seeking children (UASC). The latter, and children adopted from abroad, often have additional physical and mental health needs; these are discussed in detail in Chapters 11 and 13 and in *Health Screening of Children Adopted from Abroad* (BAAF, 2004).

Black and minority ethnic populations

Children from black and minority ethnic populations are more likely to become looked after than their peers; they make up 23 per cent of the looked after population but only 17 per cent of the general population. The specific health needs of this population are discussed fully in Chapter 10.

The scope of looked after children's health problems

DfE (2013) figures for the year ending 31 March 2013 showed that, of the children looked after continuously for 12 months, 83 per cent were up to date with their immunisations; data for the general population shows 90 per cent of children were fully immunised to the age of five years. A total of 81.6 per cent of looked after children had visited a dentist within the previous 12 months, and four per cent had a substance misuse problem. A previous survey completed for the Office of National Statistics (ONS) (Melzer *et al*, 2003) of 1,000 looked after children and young people aged 5 to 17 years used information obtained from carers, teachers and some of the young people aged between 11 and 17 years. Two-thirds of the children had at least one physical health complaint, most frequently eye and/or sight problems, speech and/or language difficulties, bed-wetting (including among older children), co-ordination difficulties and asthma. All conditions except asthma were more common in looked after children than in the general population. A further UK study of children looked after for at least a year showed that 52 per cent had a health condition of sufficient seriousness to require out-patient treatment; 15 per cent had more than one such condition (Skuse *et al*, 2001). A study in Utah in the USA confirmed these findings: of the 6,177 medical records of children in care examined, 54 per cent showed that one or more acute or chronic medical problems were present, half of which required referral (Steele and Buchi, 2008).

Common health issues

Genetic conditions

Many children are at risk of inheriting conditions from their parents, e.g. learning disability or Huntington's disease, among many others. Testing for such diseases, where available, has been the source of much debate between social workers, medical advisers for adoption and fostering and geneticists; the general principle is that children at risk of inherited disease should have genetic testing at the same stage as children who are living with their birth families, i.e. the looked after or adopted child should be treated no differently from any other child. This applies particularly to testing for carrier states, e.g. in cystic fibrosis and in those conditions such as Huntington's chorea where symptoms are unlikely to present until adulthood and pre-symptomatic diagnosis does not lead to a change in management. In such circumstances, the child's autonomy to make their own decision about testing in adulthood should be respected, as many will choose not to test; for example, only 20 per cent of adults at risk of Huntington's proceed to testing.

It is, of course, appropriate to test children at the time when knowledge of their status would affect their management, e.g. 25–30 per cent of all patients with phaeochromocytoma have genetic mutations (Bryant *et al*, 2003; Gimenez-Roqueplo *et al*, 2008) and screening for the disease in children at risk usually commences at around five years of age, so testing the child in their fifth year would be appropriate, even though they would be unable to give informed consent themselves.

Genetic testing and adoption

There is a dilemma for adoption agencies as it is presumed that both they and prospective adopters will have all relevant information about a child to aid their decision about where a child would be best placed; some would argue that this includes genetic information. However, there is no compelling reason why adoptive parents should have genetic information about their child in circumstances where the child's birth parents would not, or why an adopted child's privacy and autonomy should be compromised by premature testing performed in a misguided attempt to make a child more adoptable. There is often much uncertainty in the information that health professionals are able to give to pro-spective adopters, for example, regarding the effect of pre-birth exposure to drugs. The agency and prospective adopters should be given a written report on the child that contains all the relevant and accurate health information available at the time and which identifies gaps in information. Prospective adopters should be offered a meeting with the agency's medical adviser to discuss the report and its possible implications for the child and their family. Consultations with relevant specialists, including geneticists, could also be held if necessary. It is important to establish a mechanism whereby genetic information discovered after adoption can be exchanged between adoptive and birth families. For further details, see *Genetic Testing and Adoption* (BAAF, 2006) and *Report on the Genetic Testing of Children* (British Society for Human Genetics, 2010).

It is not recommended to attempt to gain information about the ethnicity of an absent parent (usually the father) through DNA testing, as such testing is not validated for this purpose and provides information about ancestors over long periods of time, rather than specific information about a particular person, such as a parent. Further information is available in the BAAF and British Society for Human Genetics *Statement on the Use of DNA Testing to Determine Racial Background* (2014) (see Appendix A).

Case study

John is a three-year-old boy whose mother is severely disabled by Huntington's disease; there are no other relatives willing or able to care for John so he is to be placed for adoption. Prospective carers have come forward but insist on knowing if John will be affected; their social worker supports them in this as he knows some adults with Huntington's disease are aggressive. Two options are considered:

1. Test on the grounds that adoptive parents have the right to full information;
2. Delay testing until John can decide for himself if he wishes to know if he is affected.

The local genetics service is reluctant to arrange testing but offers to meet the prospective adopters. They explain that a diagnosis now will not change the course of John's health or alter his management in any way; they also inform the adopters that most (80 per cent) people with a family history of Huntington's choose not to be tested, so testing John now would violate his right to make his own decision later. The geneticist reassures the adopters that it is unlikely, but not impossible, that John will get symptoms before adulthood even if he does have the Huntington's gene. The adopters decide they are already prepared to take on uncertainty in any adopted child and withdraw their request for testing.

Children exposed to alcohol before birth

Exposure to alcohol before birth can have significantly deleterious effects on children but these are often overlooked, particularly when the history of the birth mother drinking alcohol in pregnancy is not known (or denied), or when the child does not have the classic dysmorphic facial features that occur when a birth mother drinks alcohol during the brief period when the foetal face is formed. As children with foetal alcohol spectrum disorders (FASD) may not be dysmorphic, can be very verbal and have normal intelligence, their serious difficulties with behaviour and learning are often misunderstood or unrecognised; they may therefore be considered to have an invisible disability.

As drinking alcohol is a socially acceptable activity in many societies, some pregnant women and professionals are less conscious of its adverse effects on the unborn child, even though there is no known safe level of drinking in pregnancy. The history of excessive consumption may be unknown or poorly recorded by professionals and therefore subsequently unavailable to doctors wondering if a child's problems may be secondary to alcohol exposure. It is therefore important to invite birth parents to initial health assessments; validated questionnaires such as the CAGE test (the name is an acronym of its four questions: Cut down, Annoyed, Guilty, Eye opener) (Dhalla and Kopec, 2007) or the Alcohol Use Disorders Identification Test (AUDIT) (Bradley *et al*, 2007) are available to screen for hazardous drinking. In the absence of parents, extended family members will often know how much a birth mother was drinking in pregnancy; for looked after children, it is important to ask for this information as early as possible, in case parents and families disengage from professionals. In addition, it is easy to underestimate the amount of alcohol being consumed – a glass of wine is commonly thought to equate to one unit of alcohol, but this only applies to 125ml of eight per cent wine, whereas many wine glasses hold 200ml or more, and many wines are at least 12 per cent alcohol (for example, 175 ml of 13 per cent wine is 2.1 units). There are similar misconceptions about beers and lagers. The Drinkaware website (www.drinkaware.co.uk) has a unit calculator and a wealth of useful information about alcohol use, and is a helpful resource tool for professionals and parents alike.

Women drinking to excess may be malnourished and this may increase the effect of alcohol on the foetal brain; also, they may not access appropriate antenatal care. It is important to realise that alcohol inflicts a permanent chemical damage on the foetal brain, even in the absence of recognisable physical abnormalities; the results of this structural damage can be ameliorated by appropriate management but the injury itself cannot be repaired and therefore the effect on the child is permanent. Carers and professionals skilled in the management of affected individuals speak of the need for them to have an "external brain", i.e. someone else to think for them and keep them safe throughout their lives.

There are several diagnostic terms used in this area of work.

Foetal Alcohol Syndrome (FAS): confirmed alcohol exposure

- Definitely known alcohol exposure plus the typical facial pattern of short palpebral fissures (10th centile or less), thin upper lip vermillion and smooth philtrum.
- Evidence of pre/postnatal growth retardation.
- Evidence of neurocognitive deficits.

FAS: no confirmed alcohol exposure

- As above but no definite evidence of alcohol exposure.

Partial FAS: confirmed alcohol exposure

- Some but not all of the above features present.
- Neurocognitive and some facial features seen.

Alcohol-Related Birth Defect (ARBD)

- Confirmed exposure to alcohol.
- Some but not all facial features present.
- Behavioural features or structural abnormalities are more pronounced.

Alcohol-Related Neurodevelopmental Disorder (ARND)

- Confirmed exposure to alcohol.
- No facial features or growth retardation.
- Neurocognitive features prominent.

(Adapted from Stratton *et al*, 1996; and Hoyme *et al*, 2005)

The term foetal alcohol spectrum disorder (FASD) is not considered to be a diagnostic term, although it remains in common use as a "catch-all" umbrella term. For children who have cognitive and behavioural difficulties compatible with pre-birth exposure to alcohol without a clear history of such exposure, Dr Mary Mather (personal communication, 2011) has proposed a working diagnosis of "Neurodevelopmental disorder of uncertain aetiology but consistent with alcohol exposure".

A number of physical abnormalities are associated with foetal alcohol exposure, including pre- and postnatal growth deficiency; abnormal facial features, including those mentioned above plus low nasal bridge, small jaw and flat mid-face; heart and kidney defects; cleft palate and hare lip; and some bone abnormalities.

Often the most disabling effects are those on the child's neurodevelopmental progress and behaviour. Early in life, babies can be extremely irritable and difficult to soothe; unlike babies experiencing withdrawal from opiates, those exposed to alcohol seem to dislike swaddling as they can be hypersensitive to touch. Later on, affected children may be impulsive and unable to suppress undesirable responses so are unable to prevent their emotions from becoming overwhelming, leading to outbursts of temper or crying; such children need a quiet space to withdraw to from a busy classroom, for example. Others may fail to recognise that present actions may lead to future consequences, making it difficult for carers to use standard methods to manage behaviour. Socially, these children often appear able but although they may be fluent, their social use of language is poor and they are socially inept, having difficulty in reading others' emotions and putting complex information together to understand a joke, for example. They often do not understand the concept of ownership, which can lead to crime.

In particular, maintaining and shifting attention appropriately is problematic so these children may be highly distractible. Working memory deficits are common and affected children may have difficulty in learning from experience and generalising learning, despite their intelligence being in the normal range. Executive functioning may be poor so there may be difficulties in planning activities, making decisions and in thinking logically or in abstract. Although most children affected by alcohol have intellectual function within the normal range, some will have a learning disability.

Some of the cognitive and behavioural effects of pre-birth exposure to alcohol are not seen until middle childhood, by which time the information about the birth mother's drinking habits in pregnancy may be forgotten or impossible to obtain. Such children may not be correctly identified as alcohol affected, with difficult behaviour being attributed to attachment disorders. Indeed, they may be co-morbid – many alcohol-affected children fit the criteria for autism and attention deficit hyperactivity disorder (ADHD) on standardised screening tests, meaning that many have multiple assessments and incorrect diagnoses, leading to trauma for both the child and carer. Conversely, where it is considered that a child was probably exposed to alcohol before birth, but he or she shows no signs in early life, it is important for carers to be aware that difficulties with learning and behaviour may develop in middle childhood or beyond. Professionals may need reminding that pre-birth exposure to alcohol may be the cause of the child's difficulties.

Secondary disabilities in children affected by alcohol before birth

- 90 per cent psychological problems
- 60 per cent disrupted schooling
- 60 per cent trouble with the law
- 50 per cent confinement
- 50 per cent inappropriate sexual behaviour

(Streissguth *et al*, 1996)

Most family, twin and adoption studies suggest that alcoholism is familial, with genetic factors being significant in this, probably because alcohol can modify how genetic material behaves. Environmental factors and personal characteristics such as age, ethnicity and the presence of psychiatric co-morbidity are also important (Agarwal-Kozlowski and Agarwal, 2000). There appears to be a greater effect of genetic risk factors among men than women, although both environment and genetic factors are important influences for both sexes (Light *et al*, 1996).

Several charitable organisations (including FAS Aware UK, FASD Trust and NOFAS) provide valuable support to those affected by exposure to alcohol before birth and their parents and carers; training for professionals is also available.

Children exposed to other toxins before birth

In addition to alcohol, looked after children are more likely to be exposed to other toxic substances before birth. These may include chemicals from cigarette smoking, street drugs such as cocaine, heroin, cannabis, benzodiazepines and amphetamines, and prescribed medication such as methadone and antidepressants. Foetuses are commonly exposed to a cocktail of substances. These may have immediate effects, such as neonatal abstinence syndrome commonly seen in babies withdrawing from opiates, or cognitive and behavioural consequences, which may become apparent only in middle childhood or beyond.

Neonatal abstinence syndrome occurs when the foetus has become addicted to substances used by the mother. When this happens after maternal opiate use, it often results in babies becoming extremely irritable with a high-pitched cry, and some have seizures; muscle tone may be increased and the suck, swallow, breathe sequence may be unco-ordinated, leading to significant feeding difficulties. In addition, these babies may have frequent sneezing and hiccoughing and profuse diarrhoea leading to an extremely sore bottom. Some babies will require enhanced neonatal care and treatment with a reducing regime of oral morphine, but as symptoms may not appear for several days or even weeks, others are discharged from hospital before symptoms appear and may not receive appropriate treatment. There are also variations between treatment thresholds and regimens in different maternity units. Babies withdrawing from methadone may show more severe and longer lasting symptoms than those whose mothers took heroin alone. Babies withdrawing from cocaine may be jittery and have tonal abnormalities; many neonatal units routinely scan the brain for middle cerebral artery abnormalities. Withdrawing babies present particular challenges to foster carers; symptoms are not only distressing to the baby but also to their carers, and they can be extremely difficult to feed. Carers require excellent advice and support from both health and social care staff.

It is outside the remit of this book to explain in detail the physical, cognitive and behavioural effects of exposure to each drug a child may have been exposed to before birth, especially as research on the effects of maternal drug use on the unborn child is often lacking or contradictory and also hampered by maternal multidrug use and other variables. However, children exposed to opiates before birth appear to have an increased risk of impaired cognitive functioning at three years and in adolescence, and of ADHD and disruptive behaviour at 10 years. Cocaine-exposed children may have difficulties with expressive and receptive language and arithmetic, impaired visuospatial information processing, deficits in perceptual reasoning and attention, and aggressive behaviour and oppositional defiant disorder (Singer and Minnes, 2011). Research about the effects of cannabis exposure is limited but suggests an association with impairment of some aspects of executive functioning, especially some problem-solving skills and in maintaining attention (Fried, 2011). Although the children medical advisers see most often will be street drug-exposed, it must not be forgotten that exposure to some prescribed medications, e.g. sodium valproate, can cause significant physical and developmental harm to the foetus.

The guide, *Parenting a Child Affected by Parental Substance Misuse* (Forrester, 2012), may assist prospective carers to better understand the needs of such children and assess their ability to parent them. Health professionals will find *Alcohol, Drugs and Medication in Pregnancy* helpful (Preece and Riley, 2010).

Blood-borne infections

Risk factors for hepatitis B and C, HIV and syphilis, such as intravenous street drug use, sex working, being sexually abused/exploited or coming from a country where such conditions are prevalent, are more common in looked after children and their parents; where parents are infected, there may be a risk of household or mother-to-baby transmission. These diseases frequently go undetected for many years after the initial infection in adults, and children who have contracted blood-borne infections from their birth mothers can remain well for a similarly long period. However, severe illness can follow a period of quiescence, a situation that can be avoided if the infection is identified early, monitored and treated appropriately.

It is especially important for medical advisers to be diligent in seeking information about antenatal testing for blood-borne infections; mothers who have tested negative for hepatitis B and C, HIV and syphilis in early pregnancy may continue to put themselves at risk throughout pregnancy by intravenous drug use or sex working and therefore need further testing in late pregnancy. Others may not access antenatal care at all, and in these cases, the birth mother should be tested when admitted to hospital. Occasionally, babies are abandoned with authorities having no knowledge of the mother; an abandoned baby should be tested as soon as possible after being found, and should receive hepatitis B immunsation – local policies are usually in place for this. If testing has not been completed by the time the medical adviser sees the baby, urgent arrangements for testing should be made. Developing good links with local neonatology services can be extremely helpful in accessing information and encouraging appropriate testing.

It is sometimes extremely difficult for the medical adviser to access a birth mother's test results; she may refuse consent or disappear from professional view before consent has been obtained. The medical adviser will then have to consider testing the baby. Sometimes obstetric services are unaware of a mother's intravenous drug use and therefore do not test for hepatitis C in pregnancy. Forty-three per cent of the intravenous users who access services are infected with hepatitis C and therefore if an injecting mother was not tested appropriately, it is important for the medical adviser to consider testing the baby (Health Protection Agency *et al*, 2012).

Children coming into the country from abroad through adoption or as unaccompanied asylum seekers should be tested for relevant infections; they may require other screening too. Practice Note 46, *Health Screening of Children Adopted from Abroad* (BAAF, 2004) addresses this in detail and may also be helpful when considering unaccompanied asylum-seeking children.

Although testing, particularly for HIV, still carries a stigma, this is lessening. Informed consent from someone with parental responsibility, ideally the mother, must be gained for testing children. It is important for mothers to be made aware that if their child is infected, they are likely to be too, especially if their child is young. Most families will agree to their child being tested if they are given appropriate information in a sensitive manner. It is important to address relevant matters of confidentiality and disclosure of sensitive information with families, carers and social care staff. It is also vital to ensure, as far as possible, that if children are found to be infected, the mother is made aware of this and encouraged to access testing and treatment for herself.

Further information can be found in Practice Note 53, *Guidelines for the Testing of Looked after Children at Risk of a Blood-Borne Infection* (BAAF, 2008).

Mental ill health

It is well known that looked after children have an increased incidence of mental health difficulties compared to the general population aged five to 15 years, where approximately 10 per cent have mental health disorders. A survey found that among young people aged five to 17 years looked after by local authorities, 45 per cent were assessed as having a mental health disorder. In residential care this figure increased to 72 per cent, with older children and boys more likely to be affected. A total of 37 per cent had clinically significant conduct disorders; 12 per cent were assessed as having emotional disorders (anxiety and depression); and seven per cent were rated as hyperactive (Meltzer *et al*, 2003); this confirmed the findings of earlier studies (McCann *et al*, 1996). In comparison with children from the most deprived socio-economic groups, looked after children still showed significantly higher rates of mental health disorders (Ford *et al*, 2007). Mental health is discussed in detail in Chapter 4.

However, it must be remembered that mental and physical health problems often co-exist; over three-quarters of children with a mental health disorder in the above survey also had at least one physical complaint, compared with just over one-half of children assessed as not having a mental disorder. When seeing a child for an initial health assessment, physical health needs should not be overlooked, especially in the face of the sometimes overwhelming behaviour of the child, and conversely the mental health needs of the quiet, overly compliant child should not be forgotten either. Mental and physical health services need to establish close working relationships to allow a holistic approach to the assessment and treatment of looked after children's health needs (Hill and Thompson, 2003).

Eating disorders

A review by Casey *et al* (2010) brought together evidence confirming that problematic eating patterns and food-related behavioural difficulties are more common in those who are, or have been, in foster care. Pecora *et al* (2005) found that 2.9 per cent of their study sample of 1,609 adults who had left care at least one year previously had bulimia nervosa compared to 0.4 per cent of the general population. A study conducted in Australia by Tarren-Sweeney (2006) found that 24 per cent of children aged four to 11 years who were looked after showed other abnormal eating patterns, including over-eating, stealing and storing food (food maintenance syndrome) and pica, i.e. eating non-foodstuffs such as soil or food from inappropriate places, e.g. the bin; these difficulties were present across age groups and equally in both sexes. This study found that acute stress, including maltreatment in care, predisposed children to difficult food behaviours, but most of these children also had other significantly difficult behaviours and were more likely to have developmental impairment. Although a US study found that 35 per cent of children were overweight or obese when they entered care (Steele and Buchi, 2008), most of the children with problematic eating behaviours in the Australian study were not; it is therefore important to ask carers specifically about the eating behaviour of the child, as serious difficulties with eating may not otherwise be brought to light. Many of the risk factors for eating problems in the general population are seen more commonly in those coming into care.

Disability

Disabled children are over-represented in the care system, partly because they are particularly vulnerable to abuse and neglect – the most common precipitating factors for becoming looked after – but also because of the additional demands that caring for a disabled child can have on parents. Once in care, children with disabilities remain there for longer and are more likely to have an unsuitable placement than non-disabled children; a return home is less likely for the disabled child, and when reunification does happen, it is usually later than for non-disabled children in comparable circumstances. Finding permanent, stable placements for disabled children can be problematic and choice is often restricted; some are adopted (often by their foster carers) and although long-term foster care can be successful, the risk of placement breakdown remains, particularly when the young person's behaviour is challenging. There is often anxiety about the transition from foster care into independence or adult services as the young person approaches 18 years.[*] Children with disabilities are more likely to be placed in residential care, and whilst some of this provision is excellent and specialist, for example,

---

[*] The leaving care age may be extended to 21 in some cases; however, the individual will transfer to adult health services at the age of 18.

a school catering for young people with autism, disabled children in residential care are also especially vulnerable to abuse (Baker, 2011). It is essential for young people with disabilities to have access to the same leaving care services as their peers without disabilities.

It is vital for all professionals to communicate effectively with children with disabilities; when the child has a communication disorder, health professionals may be key in facilitating this, enabling these children to express concerns and exercise choice effectively. In addition, the medical and nursing staff from the looked after children's health team may have a key role in co-ordinating care for disabled children coming into the looked after system and their new families, especially if they are placed out of their local authority's area.

Disability is discussed in detail in Chapter 9.

Common outcomes for looked after children

Failure to achieve educational potential

Many factors may compromise a child's educational attainments. Exposure to street drugs or alcohol before birth, a family history of learning disability, abuse, neglect, poverty, poor early developmental opportunities in the home, lack of early years experience, e.g. "Play and stay" and other toddler groups, multiple changes of school, and challenging behaviour that prevents the young person accessing the curriculum may all thwart a child in achieving their potential. Uncertainty about an underlying diagnosis can lead to inappropriate learning strategies being used, e.g. it can be extremely difficult to differentiate between attachment disorder, ADHD, autism and neurocognitive difficulties caused by pre-birth exposure to alcohol. Also, young people and children may not see education as a priority, being more concerned about other aspects of their lives, for example, where they are going to live or whether their parents are still alive. Furthermore, staff in the education system may have a poor appreciation of the difficulties that children in care face; low expectations by teachers also impact on their emotional well-being (Broad, 1999). Children in the care system are seven times more likely to be permanently excluded from school; those out of education completely are more vulnerable to sexual exploitation, substance misuse and other risk-taking behaviours. Positive experiences of care and education increase the likelihood of young people having good outcomes in adulthood (Dixon *et al*, 2006).

By law, looked after and adopted children have priority admission to schools; however, it may be necessary for a child's social worker or carer to be vigorous in their attempts to obtain admission for a looked after or adopted child into the school that is right for them. Also, both looked after and adopted children in England are entitled to claim the Pupil Premium, a sum of money available to purchase services to boost their educational progress.

- Sixteen per cent of children in care, compared to 10 per cent of their peers, go to the lowest-attaining primary schools.

- Ten per cent go on to secondary schools where fewer than 35 per cent of pupils get five good GCSEs including maths and English, compared to six per cent of all children.
- Forty-nine per cent of looked after teenagers fail to achieve five GCSEs, compared to seven per cent of all pupils.
- Only seven per cent of looked after young people go on to university, compared to 40 per cent of their peers.

The admissions battle may have been won on paper, but not yet in reality, says Kevin Williams, chief executive of TACT. And it won't be won until foster carers and social workers develop the aspirations of "sharp-elbowed" middle-class parents.
(Northen, 2011)

Homelessness

Housing has been identified as a critical element of the transition out of care.
(Wade and Dixon, 2006)

The research conducted by this group also found that appropriate housing was the major contributory factor for good mental health for these young people. Unfortunately, '40 per cent of care leavers experience homelessness within the first six months of leaving local authority care' (Coombes, 2004). When they became homeless, young people are often placed in very disadvantaged areas or in bed-and-breakfast or hostel accommodation where they may be vulnerable to exploitation.

After growing up moving from family to family, school to school and social worker to social worker, the most exciting thing for me was the thought of getting my own tenancy – having my own place for the first time. And if it wasn't for the support from nice people around me and many second chances, I would not have managed with the money and the forms and the cooking type of stuff. It's taken me nearly four years of living alone to get things right but I still notice that my mate's family still give him loads of emotional and financial support even though he is 22 like me.
(Young person quoted in A National Voice, 2010)

- Fifty-five per cent of care leavers felt that they had no real choice in the accommodation offered to them.
- Twenty-nine per cent did not feel safe in their accommodation.
- Thirty-two per cent felt that their accommodation did not meet their needs.
- Fifty per cent felt that housing departments were not aware of the particular needs and circumstances of young care leavers.
- Eleven per cent were staying with friends.

• Twelve per cent were living in bed-and-breakfast or hostel accommodation.
(A National Voice, 2005)

Alongside housing issues, care leavers report lacking confidence in living skills such as budgeting, shopping, accessing benefits, etc.

Involvement with the criminal justice system

Dr Di Hart, NCB's Principal Officer, Youth Justice and Welfare, suggested that the very nature of residential care was part of the problem:

> *Various people have suggested that the worst thing to do with a turbulent, troubled adolescent is to accommodate them in a residential home with lots of other turbulent, troubled adolescents.*
> (Information given to the House of Commons Children, Schools and Families Committee Looked After Children, 2009)

Children currently looked after and adults who have been in care are over-represented in the criminal justice system, probably because they are more likely to have been exposed to the risk factors associated with youth offending such as exposure to physical abuse and domestic violence, absence of parental support and poor attendance at school. Children in care often exhibit challenging behaviour as a result of their adverse experiences and this may lead to criminality. A US study found that abused and neglected children were 11 times more likely to be arrested for criminal behaviour as a juvenile, 2.7 times more likely to be arrested for violent and criminal behaviour as an adult and 3.1 times more likely to be arrested for one of many forms of violent crime (juvenile or adult) (English *et al*, 2004). A review by Gilbert *et al* (2009) noted:

> *In addition to feeling considerable pain and suffering themselves, abused and neglected children are at increased risk of becoming aggressive and inflicting pain and suffering on others, often perpetrating crime and violence.*

Information given to the Health Select Committee by the head of the Youth Justice Board indicated that in residential care, trivial incidents, which would ordinarily be dealt with by foster carers or parents within the home, may be reported to the police by inexperienced, inadequately trained staff; this may result in an offending record for the young person involved. Di Hart from the NCB suggested to the Select Committee that the difference between looked after children and others is not necessarily in their behaviour, but in institutional responses to that behaviour; magistrates, for example, may treat looked after children more harshly, such as being unwilling to give bail to a young person who lives in a children's home.

According to *Couldn't Care Less*, a policy report from the Centre for Social Justice (2008):

- There are currently 11,672 under-21-year-olds in contact with the criminal justice system, of whom 5,719 (49 per cent) have a background in care.
- There are 2,350 children in prison in England and Wales. Thirty per cent of them have been in care, and 71 per cent were classified as "children in need" before they entered custody. (They had been involved with, or were receiving support from, social services.)
- Children aged 10–17 who have been in care for more than one year are more than twice as likely to be involved with the police.

Teenage parenthood

In 1999, the Social Exclusion Unit identified several factors that predispose to becoming a teenage parent. These characteristics are largely shared with looked after children, e.g. living in poverty; not engaging with or achieving well in education, training or work both before and after age 16; having a history of sexual abuse; experiencing mental health problems; being involved in criminal activity; belonging to a minority ethnic group; and living in one of the most deprived local authority areas. This research also demonstrated that looked after children are almost 2.5 times more likely to become teenage parents, compared with those brought up by both birth parents, a conclusion confirmed by several further research studies. Dixon *et al* (2006) showed that one in seven care leavers was expecting a child or had children within two to three months of leaving care; this figure had risen to 26 per cent nine to ten months later; female care leavers were more likely to be parents than male leavers. The study also reported a correlation between teenage pregnancy and care leavers who had experienced an increased number of placement moves, been involved in criminal activity, absconded or used street drugs; furthermore, Dixon *et al* (2006) demonstrated that those care leavers who became parents within 10 months of leaving care were considerably more likely than other care leavers to have a poor career outcome and to have been economically inactive when they left care – in their study, those who became parents shortly after leaving care were approximately twice as likely to have been unemployed when they left care as those who were not.

In some cultures, planned teenage parenthood is the norm; in others, some young women may choose pregnancy or are, at least, content with it. Having a baby is seen as a means of planning a new, more purposeful and positive life course, an opportunity to create a new family and to prove themselves capable (Cater and Coleman, 2006). However, poor sex education was also prevalent in this group (Wiggins *et al*, 2007). Teenagers who are pregnant and also leaving care face similar difficulties to their peers in obtaining appropriate neutral advice, in accessing antenatal care or parenting classes, in maintaining a healthy lifestyle, finding appropriate housing, and in continuing in education. However, they are much less likely to have consistent, positive adult support, a recognised protective factor for young mothers, and are far more likely to have to move. Young parents who are care leavers report wide variations in support available to them across the country, including access to sexual health services before they became pregnant. Care leavers who are expectant parents feel that they are discriminated against and do not receive appropriate support from statutory services. For many young parents, this results in isolation and fear of asking for any help (Voice, 2009).

The adverse effects of teenage parenthood persist into adult life with an increased risk of living in poverty and poor housing, experiencing partnership breakdown, and having a partner who is unskilled and unemployed (Berrington *et al*, 2006). Babies born to mothers under 18 are at increased risk of prematurity (Jolly *et al*, 2000), are 25 per cent more likely than average to have a low birth weight, and have an infant mortality rate 60 per cent higher than the babies of older mothers (Botting *et al*, 1998). Babies of teenagers are at increased risk of hospitalisation for accidental injuries, diarrhoea and vomiting, developmental delays and poor nutrition (Peckham, 1993). Teenage mothers are more than twice as likely to smoke and half as likely to breastfeed as older mothers (DfES and Department of Health (DH), 2007). Additionally, parents who have experienced care may have attachment disorders and other difficulties which reduce their ability to provide nurturing care for their children.

Substance misuse

Substance misuse is significantly more prevalent in the looked after population; evidence cited in the *Care Matters* White Paper (DfES, 2006) indicates that looked after children are thought to be four times more likely than their peers to smoke cigarettes, drink alcohol or use street drugs. The Government requires local authorities to collect statistics about those children whom they have looked after continuously for more than 12 months who have a substance misuse problem; at the year ending 31 March 2012, 4.1 per cent of this population were deemed to have a problem and 31 per cent of these had refused intervention (DfE, 2012b). One study asked care leavers about their drug use: 73 per cent said that they had used cannabis, 34 per cent used it daily, and 10–15 per cent reported using cocaine, heroin and ecstasy monthly; nine per cent said that they drank alcohol every day and 34 per cent drank alcohol at least once a week (Ward *et al*, 2003). Recent Government statistics demonstrated a general decline in drug and alcohol use and smoking among 10 to 15-year-olds, with five per cent smoking, six per cent using drugs and 12 per cent drinking alcohol in the previous week; drinking alcohol, smoking cigarettes and drug use were positively correlated with truancy, and smoking and drug use were more common amongst pupils excluded within the last year. Both factors are more common in the looked after population (Fuller, 2012).

The care leavers interviewed by Dixon *et al* (2006) identified a number of routes into drug and alcohol use, including teenage experimentation, peer pressure and a family history of substance misuse. These factors are held in common with other young people misusing drugs and alcohol, but the vulnerability of looked after young people, part-icularly those moving to independent living, is often increased by lack of support from a consistent, trusted adult and by living in an area where drug and alcohol misuse is prevalent. Misusing drugs and alcohol may result in debt and criminal behaviour; Dixon *et al* (2006) found that care leavers with substance misuse problems were more likely to have periods of homelessness, move accommodation more often, have poor career outcomes, and have a less positive outlook on life. Accessing services can be problematic too, especially in areas where an age limit applies.

Why are the health outcomes for children in public care so poor?

The fact that longer-term outcomes for looked after children remain far worse than their peers is evidence of an important health inequality, and needs to be treated as a public health priority.
(Haywood and James, 2008)

Before care
Genetic vulnerability
Some children are at risk of inheriting conditions from their parents, e.g. learning disability, cystic fibrosis, sickle cell anaemia, which have a lifelong impact on health.

Antenatal factors
A survey completed by the BAAF Health Group in 2009 involving 357 children under six years of age with a plan for adoption demonstrated that the children had significant levels of exposure to a cocktail of street drugs, passive smoking and excessive alcohol before birth. Sixty-five per cent of the mothers had smoked in pregnancy; 12 per cent were known to have used alcohol to excess, and a further 14 per cent were suspected of doing so. Intravenous street drug use was confirmed in 10.9 per cent and suspected in 4.2 per cent; the corresponding figures for non-intravenous use were 26.3 per cent and 5.6 per cent respectively (BAAF unpublished data).

Other antenatal factors may include maternal stress and depression, poverty, poor maternal nutrition and failure to access antenatal care, leading to poorly managed complications of pregnancy such as diabetes, low birth weight, premature delivery, etc. Thus babies' health, behavioural and developmental prospects may be compromised before birth (Hoffman and Hatch, 2000; Kramer *et al*, 2000).

Unhealthy lifestyles
Children with poor adult role models often repeat their parents' behaviour and unhealthy lifestyles and in turn find it difficult to parent adequately themselves; an episode of care

makes it twice as likely that a parent will lose the right to care for their children and approximately one-third of abused and neglected children will eventually abuse or neglect their own children (Prevent Child Abuse New York, 2003). Parents may be unaware of how to promote a healthy lifestyle, or have too few resources to do so; they may smoke, lack the funds for a healthy diet, take little exercise or be dependent on drugs or alcohol.

Parental substance misuse

In 2003, the Home Office report, *Hidden Harm*, noted that in England and Wales there were between 200,000 and 300,000 children who had one or both parents with a serious drug problem; this represented between two to three per cent of all children under 16 years of age. It did not, however, mention the estimated 790,000 to 1.3 million children in the UK affected by parental alcohol problems (Cabinet Office, Prime Minister's Strategy Unit, 2004) and it is common for professionals to concentrate on parents' drug misuse and disregard the difficulties associated with excessive drinking. Parental substance misuse is a significant factor for a third of the children entering care and generally affects the child's main carer, but social workers (and other professionals) often lack training in the subject and have difficulty in assessing the risks to children of parental substance misuse (Adams, 1999). Alcohol is more damaging to the unborn child than many other substances and is more strongly associated with domestic violence and long-term neglect than street drug use. However, reflecting society's ambivalent attitude to alcohol, children whose parents drink to excess are more likely to remain at home, to be returned home by the court, and to remain at home during proceedings than those children whose parents use street drugs (Forrester and Harwin, 2005; Forrester, 2012). There is incontrovertible evidence that exposure to alcohol before birth may result in serious developmental, behavioural and physical consequences for the child and increasing evidence of similar difficulties for children so exposed to street drugs such as cocaine. Children may thus be in double jeopardy: they may have impairments caused by exposure to toxic substances before birth and therefore require better than average parenting, but receive inadequate care from parents who are physically and emotionally incapacitated by their substance misuse.

Health behaviour is strongly influenced by the role models that children and young people have; thus those raised by parents who smoke cigarettes, drink alcohol to excess or use street drugs are more likely to behave similarly. Smoking, drinking alcohol and using street drugs are inter-related behaviours in young people and all are associated with truanting. Smoking and street drug use are linked with adverse socio-economic circumstances. Truanting and poverty are characteristics of the looked after population; they are also probably more likely to smoke, drink alcohol and use street drugs.

Neglect, abuse and poverty

Children with the adverse life experiences of neglect, abuse and poverty are more vulnerable to disability and physical and mental ill-health. Studies show the prevalence of cerebral palsy, developmental delay (particularly in speech and language) and moderate learning difficulty are all increased in lower socio-economic groups (Spencer, 2008).

> If [children in poverty] survive the first year of life, they are at increased risk of dying throughout childhood and adolescence. Poor children are more likely to suffer disability and chronic illness and more likely to be admitted to hospital during childhood. They are also more susceptible to acute illnesses. Poor children are more likely to experience mental health problems and to suffer the consequences of parenting failure associated with chronic stress, debt and depression induced by economic disadvantage. Education can act as a buffer against physical and mental illness in childhood but poor children's educational chances are also adversely influenced by their social circumstances.
> (Spencer, 2008)

Exposure to abuse and neglect, particularly when this is sufficient to necessitate local authority care, may also have both short- and long-term physical, psychological and behavioural consequences. Brain imaging studies show that abuse and neglect may result in structural differences in the developing brain; these changes may affect cognitive function. A study showed that neglected children performed significantly worse on a standardised test than their peer group; they also showed poor self-control and problem-solving skills, and were less likely to form good attachment to carers. One study showed that up to 80 per cent of previously abused young adults met the diagnostic criteria for at least one psychiatric disorder at age 21; these included depression, anxiety, eating disorders, and suicide attempts. Abused and neglected children are more likely to experience problems such as delinquency, teenage pregnancy, low academic achievement, smoking, drug and problematic alcohol use and to have increased sexual risk-taking behaviour. Adults who experienced abuse or neglect during childhood are more likely to suffer from physical ailments such as allergies, arthritis, asthma, bronchitis and high blood pressure (Lazenbatt, 2010). It is important to remember, however, that children who have been abused and neglected often retain significant attachments to their birth parents.

Health screening and immunisations

Families may be too chaotic to access routine health promotion or preventative health care, e.g. immunisations and dental checks; young people not in school can be invisible to health services and health visitors do fewer (or in some areas no) routine home visits, thus increasing the risk of these children falling through the universal health services net. This not only means that established health and developmental problems may remain unidentified, but also that valuable opportunities for health promotion are missed.

Infections

Parents who inject street drugs are more likely to have blood-borne virus infections, such as hepatitis B and especially hepatitis C (Health Protection Agency *et al*, 2012); such infections can be transmitted to the child. Other infections such as syphilis or chlamydia may occur in women who work in the sex industry; they too may have profound effects on the foetus.

During care

In addition to the health inequalities present at care entry, the impact of factors inherent in the care system is huge. However, being in care is often a better option than remaining in a neglectful, abusive household.

> Colin Green told us that 'You are balancing what may not be a very satisfactory standard of life at home with what can feel like quite a risky journey in care.' Chris Callender of the Howard League for Penal Reform told us, 'I get a bit frustrated with the argument that the care system does not work so we should not bring kids into care. Is the answer to leave them on the streets? That cannot be the answer. It is to improve the care system.' Professor Jane Tunstill warned us that, 'It is awfully important not to see merely keeping children out of care as an achievement.' For many children, going into care will be a positive step, allowing them perhaps for the first time in their life to feel safe.
> (House of Commons Children, Schools and Families Committee Looked After Children, 2009)

Placement instability and quality

In England, for the year ending 31 March 2012, 11 per cent of looked after children had experienced three or more placement moves, a figure which has been relatively stable for the past five years. Biehal *et al* (2011) found significantly worse SDQ scores (the Strengths and Difficulties Questionnaire (SDQ) is a short behavioural screening questionnaire suitable for use with children between the ages of four and 16 years) in children whose foster placements had disrupted compared to those in stable foster placements, whilst there was no significant difference in scores between adopted children and those in long-term foster care. However, for a sub-sample of children who had been studied five and eight years earlier, scores on the SDQ generally showed little change over time. This illustrates that the severity of children's emotional and behavioural difficulties may be largely determined by pre-placement adversity and the length of children's exposure to these adversities.

Living far from your home district results in loss, which may include reduced frequency of contact with family members, friends and pets, a change in school, difficulties in accessing familiar leisure activities and disruption of professional support, e.g. school nurses or learning mentors. Young people may not be placed with siblings due to a paucity of suitable placements; changes of placement may be made without appropriate introductions to the new carers or without the young person having any choice in the matter. It is of concern that in Biehal *et al*'s study, at least five per cent of the children's previous long-term foster placements ended because evidence of carer abuse or neglect was found.

The revolving door of care

Rowe *et al* (1989) and Sinclair *et al* (2007) describe a "leaving care curve", which shows that the chances of leaving care shortly after entering were high, and then reduced rapidly. They use this concept to advocate for early determined activities to enable the child to return home. Sinclair (p 88) estimated that:

Of all children entering care, 89 per cent stayed at least one week.

- If they stayed one week, 90 per cent stayed four weeks.
- If they stayed four weeks, 89 per cent stayed 12 weeks.
- If they stayed 12 weeks, 91 per cent stayed 26 weeks.
- If they stayed 26 weeks, 83 per cent stayed 52 weeks.

A review conducted by Nina Biehal for the Joseph Rowntree Foundation in 2006 showed that between one-third and one-half of all children reunited with their families re-entered care; some who returned home re-entered care at least twice within a two-year period. Wade *et al* (2010) researched the consequences of decisions to reunify children and their parents where the reason the children entered care was abuse or neglect. They found that 35 per cent of this group had re-entered the care system within six months; four years later, only one-third of the children who had been rehabilitated had remained continuously at home, 59 per cent had become looked after again although some had returned home subsequently, and one-fifth had experienced more than one reunification attempt. Those children who had remained in care were deemed to be more settled than those at home, with 65 per cent in the same placement for two or more years, compared to 41 per cent of those at home. Although a similar number in each group had moved placement, most moves for those who had remained in care were considered to be 'planned moves for broadly positive reasons' (Wade *et al*, 2010), whereas virtually all the moves for those who had gone home were necessitated by placement breakdown. Biehal's review (2006) found that children in care due to behaviour problems were more likely to return home than those placed due to abuse, neglect or parental problems, and those looked after because of physical or sexual abuse were more likely to return home than those placed after neglect. She also reported: 'The limited evidence on psychosocial outcomes of reunion suggests that reunited children may have more serious emotional and behavioural problems than those who remain looked after.'

Lack of health information

- Absence of accurate detailed information about personal and family health history may be extremely detrimental to a child's current and future health. A child may have a health condition, e.g. a congenital heart defect or renal disease requiring treatment or review, or a genetic problem, e.g. a family history of cystic fibrosis or myotonic dystrophy, which may have implications for the future health of the individual or their children. "Identifying" information is also invaluable: knowing your time of birth or what caused the scar on your forehead is not essential to future health but reduces the gaps in self-knowledge that can be so detrimental to future mental health. It is therefore essential to gather as much information as possible and this is best done when the child is brought into care or shortly afterwards, i.e. for the initial health assessment. All looked after children require this service, not just those going forward for adoption as, despite the best intentions of birth families and social workers, children who remain in foster care may have limited or no contact with their families.
- Obtaining comprehensive child and family health history is often problematic. It is essential to engage the child's birth parents, if possible by inviting them to the initial health assessment, but unknown or mistaken paternity, reluctance to disclose issues such as substance misuse and mental health conditions, disengagement from or mis-trust of professionals, and threatening behaviour can all frustrate this process. Particular difficulty may be encountered in assessing the accuracy of information obtained from birth parents, extended family members and other professionals such as social workers, as some will be "hearsay" only. Review of a parent's and child's health records requires appropriate consent but provides invaluable information; community health records follow the child and often contain social as well as health information, and so are particularly useful in the case of children who have lived in several parts of the UK. However, obtaining birth parents' consent, accessing and extracting information from all relevant GP, hospital and community health records is time-consuming and problematic, particularly when a child is placed some distance from their place of origin or has rapid changes of placement. Thus serious health issues may remain unidentified or inadequately treated and screening opportunities for diseases that present later in life, e.g. glaucoma, may be missed.
- Carers require relevant accurate health (and social) information in order to parent any child adequately; those looking after children in care often parent "in the dark". How-ever, data protection legislation and lack of government guidance severely hamper effective information sharing with carers and young people. Also, significant health information coming to light after a child is permanently placed outside their birth

family is frequently not shared between them; again, this may lead to unnecessary morbidity and even mortality.

Systemic failings

- Statutory health assessments are of variable quality and may represent a missed opportunity, not only for assessing and addressing the current and future health needs of looked after children and young people (and possibly their children too), but also for health promotion, encouraging the young person to take responsibility for their own health by living healthily, engaging with health services, etc. Inadequate assessments delivered by a service that is not user-friendly will not encourage attendance by young people, who may already feel resentful and have, to their way of thinking, more important things to do. Social workers may not appreciate the valuable contribution they can make (encouraging attendance, providing relevant information) to high-quality health assessments, or the importance of health issues identified by the assessment.

- There is a general lack of understanding among health staff that services for looked after children may need to be structured differently to avoid stigma, improve engagement and access, and ensure tolerance of the difficulties encountered due to placement moves. There is often inadequate access to specialists, especially CAMHS, as these children may not meet referral thresholds despite significant problems with their mental and emotional health. The service looked after children receive may be further compromised when they are placed out of their home area, as professionals in the placing local authority may not be familiar with the services available in the receiving district. Furthermore, those in the receiving locality may wish to re-assess the child's need for a service. Too often, children in care find themselves repeatedly at the bottom of waiting lists without the benefit of a strong advocate to expedite appointments.

- Evidence given to the House of Commons Children, Schools and Families Committee Looked After Children (2009) indicated that excellent networks often exist at practitioner level, but the delivery of health services for children in care is hampered by 'the rather less excellent partnerships at commissioning level'. Champions are needed at senior strategic levels, among those 'who actually hold the money streams and can commit to services' (Dunstall, 2009). The concept of corporate parenting gave local authorities and other statutory bodies a duty to provide children in local authority care with the kind of support any good parent would provide for their own children. However, in reality, both in local government and particularly in health services, the needs of looked after children in care are subsumed by those of other, more visible, priority groups. In addition, the advocacy role for children is difficult when responsibility is shared by different agencies that fail to understand each other's roles and responsibilities or lack the skills to communicate effectively, resulting in either multiple assessments or in children slipping through the net. Also, the impact of the unique difficulties and inequalities suffered by children in the care system is poorly understood by many.

The failure of the corporate parent and the uniqueness of being in care

Many young people in care report the difficulty of not having anyone who is completely "on their side" and whom they trust implicitly. This can lead to feelings of abandonment, loneliness and worthlessness. Research (Coy, 2005) into the routes into prostitution from local authority care used life story interviews with young women, all of whom were selling sex by the age of 16. They described feeling abandoned and neglected by their corporate parents; they had little sense of being cared about; and lack of support after they left care contributed significantly to their low self-esteem. Also, some of the women entered prostitution to support themselves financially.

In a survey conducted by A National Voice, respondents described the barriers to getting the help they needed with their emotional or mental health needs. These indicated a 'barrier which could be described as "care-specific"'. Many of the responses suggest that having been in care adds a unique quality to the issue of mental health/emotional well-being. Tied to this is a perception that those without care experience, including mental health professionals, are unlikely to understand or empathise/identify with their special circumstances:

> I need someone who REALLY understands my situation . . . because I find it easier if people have been through the situation and understand it or have any idea how I'm coping or feeling as they have not been through what I have been . . . People that have a strong family background do not understand the struggles people in care go through, you are constantly judged and criticised. Furthermore, you feel that it's your problem and no one else if they have not had the same experiences because they are not in my shoes, because you feel that they misinterpret what you are trying to say or they won't understand or don't trust anybody, because they don't know what it is like to be us.
> (A National Voice, 2010)

Obviously, the introduction of mentors who have had similar experiences and survived them would be invaluable to children and young people in the care system.

Leaving care too early

Leaving care at 18 years reduces the life chances of young people. The average age for the general population, particularly males, leaving home, has increased in recent years and becoming independent usually involves a gradual separation from one's family, with several leave-takings and returns and the ready availability of ongoing moral and financial support. A study performed by the Centre for Children, University of Chicago in 2005 (DfES, 2006) tracked 608 young people in care and found outcomes for young people who stayed in care up to the age of 21 years were much better than for those leaving care earlier. Those leaving care at 17 or 18 were 50 per cent more likely to be unemployed or out of school than those leaving care at 20 or 21; those who remained in care were much more likely to access practical support about budgeting, health, education and employ- ment; and compared to young adults still in care, the group of respondents no longer in care had higher rates of alcohol dependence, alcohol abuse, substance dependence, and substance abuse (DfES, 2006).

> *You wouldn't do that with other children at that age, it's ridiculous. You can't have them leaving at 16, no matter how well prepared they are, and not expect them to struggle.*
> (Goddard, 2006)

Particularly vulnerable groups

Some groups are especially vulnerable, e.g. those from black and minority ethnic populations not only have specific health problems but are less likely than white children to be adopted (14 per cent of all adoptions). One factor in this is social workers' percep- tions that they are "hard to place"; there has been much discussion and political comment recently about what is a "good enough" match in terms of culture and ethnicity for such children. This is discussed in more detail in Chapter 10. Other vulnerable groups include disabled children and unaccompanied asylum-seeking children, as previously discussed.

What health practitioners should do

- Reassure the child that health practitioners can be trusted, are honest, are interested in their life and future, and will maintain confidentiality unless their or others' safety is compromised.
- Ensure excellent knowledge of, and competence in, the health issues of looked after children; be familiar with the relevant NICE guidance. Understand the vulnerabilities and needs of specific groups of these children, for example, those with a disability, adopted from abroad, trafficked or seeking asylum, minority ethnic groups, and adolescents, particularly those in prison, "missing from care" or out of school as they are especially vulnerable to exploitation, particularly sexual exploitation.
- Be flexible in approaches to providing services, including making them accessible by offering a choice of venue/personnel/appointment time for health assessments and other services. Transport may be required, or a crèche facility. Young people should be consulted about the design of services.

- Help to ensure that social workers and carers have good knowledge of the health issues of children in care, are able to complete consent, parental health and carer forms adequately and, when necessary, prepare children/young people for a health assessment.
- Help, through education and training, other health professionals such as GPs and midwives to contribute essential information to the initial health assessment, e.g. through providing previous health history information or completing mother and baby forms.
- Provide excellent health assessments that are useful to the child, their carers, birth parents, social workers and other health professionals both at the time of completion, and in the future. Children and young people should be consulted in an age-appropriate manner and be involved in decision making about their health whenever possible. Ensure that plans are in place for both pre-existing and newly identified health problems to be adequately addressed and followed up.
- Always take the opportunity to ask if the child has full registration with a GP and dentist.
- Help to optimise the apposite use of health information whilst maintaining necessary confidentiality. Carers should be given enough health information to enable them to care effectively for the child they have in placement; prospective adopters should have an opportunity to explore in detail health issues relating to their child. Social workers should particularly consider mental health information to help them place children appropriately; and care leavers need knowledge of their own health history.
- Help optimise the care the child receives by providing appropriate advice about healthy lifestyles to them, their carers, birth parents and social workers. This should include raising awareness of confidential services to address sexual health and substance misuse. Use of humour, social media and other user-friendly formats should be considered and young people involved in their design.
- Communicate effectively with other professionals, including carers, to help create a unified strategy to promote the child's physical and mental health and educational progress. Be prepared to promote effective multi-agency working.
- Help, through education and training, health and other professionals to prioritise and understand the complexity of the child in care. Encourage appreciation of the particular difficulties they have in accessing services so, for example, children are not automatically discharged after failing to attend an appointment or put back to the end of a waiting list for a service when they move area.
- Raise the profile of children in care in the local health economy; in particular, liaise with commissioners of health care to ensure that appropriate staff are in place, i.e. medical adviser, specialist nurse, designated doctor and nurse, as well as accessible and well-resourced services designed for looked after children.
- Work with colleagues and commissioners to ensure that specialist services required for

looked after children are in place; this particularly applies to provision of mental health services (see Chapter 4).
- Provide support to colleagues, if necessary, to ensure that any required health provision is in place before a child moves to a different locality.

Key points

- Engage with the young people in the care system, acknowledge their special circumstances, seek their views, and be prepared to provide flexible services for them and their families. Abuse and neglect are the most common reasons why children become looked after, and can have a profound impact on their health.
- The health of looked after children is affected by health inequalities present prior to care entry and these are frequently compounded by experiences within the care system.
- Health education, sensitively delivered, can help break the cycle of an unhealthy lifestyle and mitigate the effect of poor role models.
- High levels of alcohol use are evident within society, yet prenatal exposure to alcohol has serious and permanent effects on the developing brain.
- Looked after children have poor outcomes in many areas of health and social functioning; mental health is a particular issue. Comprehensive initial health assessments are absolutely key to understanding the current and future health needs of looked after children and in providing them and their carers with the information they need to keep healthy in future years.
- Remember that birth families have much information about their child's health, which they are often willing to provide, particularly in the early days of a child's placement, if they understand the importance of it to their child's well-being.
- Children and their carers appreciate all health information, even when it does not have a direct influence on their current or future health, e.g. why they have a scar, what time they were born.
- Educate local health professionals in both primary and secondary care about the particular needs and circumstances of looked after children, which may necessitate provision of "special" services.
- Advocate with local commissioners for the health needs of looked after children.

Bibliography

Adams P. (1999) 'Towards a family support approach with drug-using parents: the importance of social worker attitudes and knowledge', *Child Abuse Review*, 8, pp 15–28

Agarwal-Kozlowski K. and Agarwal D.P. (2000) 'Genetic predisposition for alcoholism', *Therapeutische Umschau*, 57:4, pp 179–84, available at: www.ncbi.nlm.nih.gov/pubmed/10804873

BAAF (2004) *Health Screening of Children Adopted from Abroad*, Practice Note 46, London: BAAF

BAAF (2006) *Genetic Testing and Adoption*, Practice Note 50, London: BAAF

BAAF (2008) *Guidelines for the Testing of Looked After Children at Risk of a Blood-Borne Infection*, Practice Note 53, London: BAAF

BAAF and British Society for Human Genetics (2014) *Statement on the Use of DNA Testing to Determine Racial Background*, London: BAAF, available at: www.baaf.org.uk/sites/default/files/uploads/res/lpp/ethnictesting.pdf

Babor T.F., Higgins-Biddle J.C., Saunders J.B. and Monteiro M.G. (2001) *AUDIT: The Alcohol Use Disorders Identification Test, Guidelines for Use in Primary Care*, Practice Note 53 (second edition), Geneva: World Health Organisation, available at: http://apps.who.int/iris/bitstream/10665/67205/1/WHO_MSD_MSB_01.6a.pdf

Baker C. (2011) *Permanence and Stability for Disabled Looked After Children*, IRISS Insights 11, available at: www.iriss.org.uk/resources/permanence-and-stability-disabled-looked-after-children

Bebbington A. and Miles J. (1989) 'The background of children who enter local authority care', *British Journal of Social Work*, 19, pp 349–68

Berrington A., Stevenson J., Ingham R. with Borgoni R. and Cobos Hernandez M.I. (2006) *Consequences of Teenage Parenthood: Pathways which minimise the long-term negative impacts of teenage childbearing*, Research Brief 8, Teenage Pregnancy Research Programme, London: DfES/DH

Biehal N. (2006) *Reuniting Looked after Children with their Families*, London: Joseph Rowntree Foundation, available at: www.jrf.org.uk/publications/reuniting-looked-after-children-with-their-families

Biehal N., Sinclair I., Baker C. and Ellison S. (2011) *Belonging and Permanence: Outcomes in long-term fostering and adoption*, Adoption Research Initiative, available at: www.york.ac.uk/inst/spru/research/pdf/ARiBelonging.pdf

Botting B., Rosato M. and Wood R. (1998) 'Teenage mothers and the health of their children', *Population Trends*, 93, pp 19–28

Bradley K.A., DeBenedetti A.F., Volk R.J., Williams E.C., Frank D. and Kivlahan D.R. (2007) 'AUDIT-C as a brief screen for alcohol misuse in primary care', *Alcohol: Clinical and Experimental Research*, 31:7, pp 1208–17, available at: www.ncbi.nlm.nih.gov/pubmed/17451397

British Society for Human Genetics (2010) *Report on the Genetic Testing of Children*, available at: www.bshg.org.uk

Broad B. (1999) 'Improving the health of children and young people leaving care', *Adoption & Fostering*, 23:1, pp 40–47

Bryant J., Farmer J., Kessler L.J., Townsend R.R. and Nathanson K.L. (2003) 'Pheochromocytoma: the expanding genetic differential diagnosis', *Journal of the National Cancer Institute*, 20, 95:16, pp 1196–204, available at: www.ncbi.nlm.nih.gov/pubmed/12928344

Cabinet Office, Prime Minister's Strategy Unit (2004) *Alcohol Harm Reduction Strategy for England*, London: Cabinet Office, Prime Minister's Strategy Unit

Casey C., Cook-Cottone C. and Beck-Joslyn M. (2010) *An Overview of Problematic Eating and Food-Related Behaviour among Foster Children: Definitions, etiology and intervention*, Buffalo, NY: University at Buffalo, State University of New York, available at www.bsc-cdhs.org/ecdsseep/collegerelations/Cooke-Cottone2010/FinalReportASId43.pdf

Cater S. and Coleman L. (2006) *'Planned' Teenage Pregnancy: Perspectives of young parents from disadvantaged backgrounds*, London: Joseph Rowntree Foundation and The Policy Press

Centre for Social Justice (2008) *Couldn't Care Less: A policy report from the children in care working group*, London: Centre for Social Justice

Chambers H. with Howell S., Madge N. and Olle H. (2002) *Healthy Care: Building an evidence base for promoting the health and well-being of looked after children and young people*, London: National Children's Bureau

Coombes R. (2004) 'Falling through the cracks', *The Guardian*, available at: www.guardian.co.uk/society/2004/oct/13/homelessness2

Coy M. (2005) *Leaving Care, Loathing Self*, available at: www.communitycare.co.uk/Articles/03/02/2005/47974/Leaving-Care-Loathing-Self.htm

Department for Children, Schools and Families (2007) *Children Accommodated in Secure Children's Homes, Year Ending 31 March 2007, England and Wales*, SFR23/2007, available at: www.education.gov.uk/rsgateway/DB/SFR/s001077/index.shtml

Department for Education (2012a) *Private Fostering Arrangements in England: Year ending 31 March 2012*, available at: www.education.gov.uk/researchandstatistics/datasets/a00211324/private-fostering-england-31-march-2012

Department for Education (2012b) *Children Looked After by Local Authorities in England, Including Adoption*, available at: www.education.gov.uk/researchandstatistics/statistics/allstatistics/a00213762/children-looked-after-las-england

Department for Education (2013) *Children Looked After in England (Including Adoption and Care Leavers)*, available at: www.gov.uk/government/uploads/system/uploads/attachment_data/file/244872/SFR36_2013.pdf

Department for Education and Skills (2006) *Care Matters: Transforming the lives of children and young people in care*, Green Paper, London: DfES

Department for Education and Skills (2007) *Care Matters: Time for change*, available at www.education.gov.uk/publications/eOrderingDownload/Cm per cent207137.pdf

Department for Education and Skills and Department of Health (2007) *Multi-Agency Working to Support Pregnant Teenagers: A midwifery guide to partnership working with Connexions and other agencies*, available at: www.education.gov.uk/publications/eOrderingDownload/DFES-0107-2007.pdf

Department of Health, Social Services and Public Safety (2013) *Children's Social Care Statistics for Northern Ireland 2012/13*, available at www.dhsspsni.gov.uk/microsoft_word_-_childrens_social_care_stats_201213.pdf

Dhalla S. and Kopec J.A. (2007) 'The CAGE questionnaire for alcohol misuse: a review of reliability and validity studies', *Clinical and Investigative Medicine*, 30:1, pp 33–4, available at: www.ncbi.nlm.nih.gov/pubmed/17716538

Dixon J., Wade J., Byford S., Weatherly H. and Lee J. (2006) *Young People Leaving Care: A study of costs and outcomes, a report for the DFES Social Work Research & Development*, York: University of York

Dunstall S. (2009) *Evidence given to the House of Commons Children, Schools and Families Committee Looked-After Children, Third Report of Session 2008–09*, London: Stationery Office

English D., Widom C. and Brandford C. (2004) 'Another look at the effects of child abuse', *National Institute of Justice Journal*, 251, pp 23–24

Ford T., Vostanis P., Meltzer H. and Goodman R. (2007) 'Psychiatric disorder among British children looked after by local authorities: comparison with children living in private households', *British Journal of Psychiatry*, 190, pp 319–325

Forrester D. (2012) *Parenting a Child Affected by Parental Substance Misuse*, London: BAAF

Forrester D. and Harwin J. (2005) 'Pathways to care for children whose parents misuse drugs or alcohol', conference presentation at 'From womb to teenage kicks', 11 October, York

Fortuna J.L. (2010) 'Sweet preference, sugar addiction and the familial history of alcohol dependence: shared neural pathways and genes', *Journal of Psychoactive Drugs*, 42:2, pp 147–51, available at: www.tandfonline.com/doi/abs/10.1080/02791072.2010.10400687

Fried P. (2011) 'Cannabis use during pregnancy: its effects on offspring from birth to young adulthood', in Preece P.M. and Riley E.P. (eds) *Alcohol, Drugs and Medication in Pregnancy: The long-term outcome for the child*, London: MacKeith Press, pp 153–68

Fuller E. (2012) *Smoking, Drinking and Drug Use among Young People in England in 2011*, London: NHS, The Information Centre, available at:www.natcen.ac.uk/media/975589/sddfull.pdf

Gilbert R., Spatz Widom C., Browne K., Fergusson D., Webb E. and Janson J. (2009) 'Burden and consequences of child maltreatment in high-income countries', *The Lancet*, 373, pp 68–81

Gimenez-Roqueplo A.P., Burnichon N., Amar L., Favier J., Jeunemaitre X. and Plouin P.F. (2008) 'Recent advances in the genetics of phaeochromocytoma and functional paraganglioma', *Clinical and Experimental Pharmacology and Physiology*, 5:4, pp 376–79, available at: www.ncbi.nlm.nih.gov/pubmed/18307724

Goddard (2006) 'Leaving care Act brings little change for care leavers', *Community Care*, available at: www.communitycare.co.uk

Haywood J. and James C. (2008) *Improving the Health of Children in Care and Care Leavers in London 2008/9*, unpublished paper, Care Services Improvement Partnership

Health Protection Agency, Health Protection Services and Microbiology Services (2012) *Unlinked Anonymous Monitoring Survey of People who Inject Drugs in Contact with Specialist Services: Data tables*, London: Health Protection Agency

Hill C. and Thompson M. (2003) 'Mental and physical health co-morbidity in looked after children', *Clinical Child Psychology and Psychiatry*, 8:3, pp 315–21, available at: http://ccp.sagepub.com/content/8/3/315.abstract

Hoffman S. and Hatch M.C. (2000) 'Depressive symptomatology during pregnancy: evidence for an association with decreased foetal growth in pregnancies of lower social class women', *Health Psychology*, 19:6, pp 535–43, available at: www.ncbi.nlm.nih.gov/pubmed/11129356

Home Office (2003) *Hidden Harm: Responding to the needs of children of problem drug users*, London: Home Office

House of Commons Children, Schools and Families Committee Looked After Children (2009) *Third Report of Session 2008–09*, London: Stationery Office

Hoyme H.E., May P.A., Kalberg W.O., Kodituwakku P., Gossage J.P., Trujillo P.M., Buckley D.G., Miller J.H., Aragon A.S., Khaole N., Viljoen D.L., Jones K.L. and Robinson L.K. (2005) 'A practical clinical approach to diagnosis of Foetal Alcohol Spectrum Disorders: clarification of the 1996 Institute of Medicine Criteria', *Pediatrics*, 115, pp 39–48, available at: www.ncbi.nlm.nih.gov/pmc/articles/PMC1380311/

Jolly M., Sebire N., Harris J., Robinson S. and Regan L. (2000) 'Obstetric risks of pregnancy in women less than 18 years old', *Obstetrics and Gynaecology*, 96, pp 962–66

Jones L., Bellis M., Wood S., Hughes K., McCoy E., Eckley L., Bates G., Mikton C., Shakespeare T. and Officer A. (2012) 'Prevalence and risk of violence against children with disabilities: a systematic review and meta-analysis of observational studies', *The Lancet*, 380:9845, pp 899–907, available at: www.thelancet.com/journals/lancet/article/PIIS0140-6736(12)60692-8/fulltext

Kramer M.S., Goulet L. and Lydon J. (2000) 'Socio-economic disparities in pregnancy outcome: why do the poor fare so poorly?', *Paediatric and Perinatal Epidemiology*, 14:3, pp 194–210, available at: www.ncbi.nlm.nih.gov/pubmed/10949211

Lazenbatt A. (2010) *The Impact of Abuse and Neglect on the Health and Mental Health of Children and Young People*, NSPCC Research Briefing, available at: www.nspcc.org.uk/Inform/research/briefings/impact_of_abuse_on_health_pdf_wdf73369.pdf

Light J.M., Irvine K.M. and Kjerulf L. (1996) 'Estimating genetic and environmental effects of alcohol use and dependence from a national survey: a "quasi-adoption" study', *Journal of Studies on Alcohol*, 57:5, pp 507–20, available at: www.ncbi.nlm.nih.gov/pubmed/8858548

McCann J., James A., Wilson S. and Dunn G. (1996) 'Prevalence of psychiatric disorders in young people in the care system', *British Medical Journal*, 313:15, pp 29–30

Melzer H., Corbin T., Gatward R., Goodman R. and Ford T. (2003) *The Mental Health of Young People Looked After by Local Authorities in England*, London: Stationery Office, available at: www.ons.gov.uk/ the-mental-health-of-young-people-looked-after

A National Voice (2005) *There's No Place Like Home*, Manchester: A National Voice, available at: www.anationalvoice.org/work/reports/no-place-like-home

A National Voice (2010) *Emotional Well-being Report*, Manchester: A National Voice, available at: www.anationalvoice.org/work/reports/emotional-well-being-report

NICE/SCIE (2010) *Promoting the Quality of Life of Looked-After Children and Young People*, PH28, London: NICE/SCIE

NICE (2013) *Looked After Children and Young People*, Public Health Guidance 28, available at www.nice.org.uk/nicemedia/live/13244/51173/51173.pdf, www.voice project.org

Northen C. (2011) 'Looked after children let down by the education system', *The Guardian*, available at: www.guardian.co.uk/education/2011/sep/19/children-in-care-education-system

Peckham S. (1993) 'Preventing unplanned teenage pregnancies', *Public Health*, 107, pp. 125–33

Pecora P., Williams J., Kessler R., Downs A., O'Brien K., Hripi E. and Morello S. (2005) *Assessing the Effects of Foster Care: Mental health outcomes from the Casey National Alumni Study*, Seattle, WA: The Casey Foundation, available at: www.casey.org/Resources/Publications/pdf/Casey NationalAlumniStudy_FullReport.pdf

Preece P.M. and Riley E.P. (eds) (2010) *Alcohol, Drugs and Medication in Pregnancy: The long-term outcome for the child*, London: MacKeith Press

Prevent Child Abuse New York (2003) *The Costs of Child Abuse and the Urgent Need for Prevention*, available at: www.preventchildabuseny.org/files/6213/0392/2130/costs.pdf

Rowe J., Hundleby M. and Garnett L. (1989) *Child Care Now: A survey of placement patterns*, London: BAAF

Sinclair I., Baker C., Lee J. and Gibbs I. (2007) *The Pursuit of Permanence: A study of the English child care system*, London: Jessica Kingsley Publishers

Singer L. and Minnes S. (2011) 'Effects of drugs of abuse on the foetus: cocaine and opiates including heroin', in Preece P.M. and Riley E.P. (eds) *Alcohol, Drugs and Medication in Pregnancy: The long-term outcome for the child*, London: MacKeith Press, pp 130–52

Skuse T., Macdonald I. and Ward H. (2001) *Looking After Children: Transforming data into management information. Report of longitudinal study at 30 September 1999, third interim report to the Department of Health*, Loughborough: Centre for Child and Family Research

Social Exclusion Unit (1999) *Teenage Pregnancy Report*, London: ODPM Publications, Cabinet Office

Spencer N. (2008) *Health Consequences of Poverty for Children*, London: End Child Poverty, available at: www.endchildpoverty.org.uk/files/Health_consequences_of_Poverty_for_children.pdf

Statistics for Wales (2012) *First Release*, available at: http://wales.gov.uk/docs/statistics/2012/12092 7sdr1622012en.pdf

Steele J. and Buchi K. (2008) 'Medical and mental health of children entering the Utah foster care system', *Pediatrics*, 122:3, pp 703–709, available at: http://pediatrics.aappublications.org/content/122/3/e703.long

Stratton K., Howe C. and Battaglia F. (eds) (1996) *Foetal Alcohol Syndrome: Diagnosis, epidemiology, prevention, and treatment*, Washington DC: Committee to Study Foetal Alcohol Syndrome Division of Biobehavioral Sciences and Mental Disorders, Institute of Medicine, National Academy Press, pp. 63–81, available at: www.nap.edu/openbook.php?record_id=4991&page=R1

Streissguth A.P., Barr H.M., Kogan J. and Bookstein F.L. (1996) *Final Report: Understanding the occurrence of secondary disabilities in children with Foetal Alcohol Syndrome (FAS) and Foetal Alcohol Effects (FAE)*, Seattle, WA: University of Washington Publication Services

Tarren-Sweeney M. (2006) 'Patterns of aberrant eating among pre-adolescent children in foster care', *Journal of Abnormal Child Psychology*, 34, pp 623–34

Voice (2009) *Care Leavers who are Expectant Parents Feel they are Discriminated Against*, available at: www.epolitix.com/fileadmin/epolitix/stakeholders/Positive_about_young_parents.pdf

Wade J., Biehal N., Farrelly N. and Sinclair I. (2010) *Maltreated Children In The Looked After System: A comparison of outcomes for those who go home and those who do not*, York: Social Policy Research Unit, University of York, available at: www.education.gov.uk/publications/standard/publicationDetail/Page1/DFE-RBX-10-06

Wade J. and Dixon J. (2006) 'Making a home, finding a job: investigating early housing and employment outcomes for young people leaving care', *Child and Family Social Work*, 11, pp 199–208

Ward J., Henderson Z. and Pearson G. (2003) *One Problem among Many: Drug use among care leavers in transition to independent living*, London: HMSO

Welsh Government (2014) *Adoptions, Outcomes and Placements for Children Looked After by Local Authorities*, available at: www.wales.gov.uk/docs/statistics/2014/140327-adoptions-outcomes-placements-children-looked-after-local-authorities-2012-13a-en.pdf

Wiggins M., Oakley A., Sawtell M., Austerberry H., Clemens F. and Elbourne D. (2007) *Teenage Pregnancy Research Programme*, Research Brief 7, London: DfES/DH

3   The child's oral health

Colin Flanagan

It is estimated that up to 40 per cent of adults in the UK do not attend a dentist regularly (Prendergast, 2001; Department of Health, 2009), meaning that they attend only when in pain or not at all. This has implications for their children, who may not receive the advice and treatment they need to establish and maintain good oral health. When these children do have pain, having teeth extracted may often be the only option, with the potential harm to self-esteem that can result from this, in addition to any possible risks if a general anaesthetic is required (Department of Health (DH), 2005).

For looked after children, this situation is heightened because they may not have a stable home life, and might even have been in abusive relationships that may also result in low self-esteem and neglect (Department for Children, Schools and Families (DCSF) and DH, 2009). The risk factors for general health, which have already been mentioned in Chapter 2 of this guide, also apply to oral health, arguably to an even greater extent. Traditionally, oral health has been of low priority within a child's overall care needs, with medical health and social care understandably deemed more urgent and important. The abuse or neglect that a child may have suffered before coming into care, and the frequent placement moves that may have occurred, may cause further impairment of their dental health and education (DCSF and DH, 2009). This can obviously be detrimental to their future dental well-being.

Statutory duties

The duties and responsibilities for looked after children are statutory under the Children Act 1989. The system aims to support rehabilitation back to birth families where this is possible, or otherwise to place children into foster or adoptive families. So we are faced with a fluid and changing group of children. In England, *Statutory Guidance on Promoting the Health and Well-being of Looked After Children* (DCSF and DH, 2009, revision expected in 2015) states that health commissioners must:

> . . . *ensure children and young people who are looked after are registered with GPs and dentists near to where they are living, even if this is a temporary placement, and that primary care teams are supported where appropriate in fulfilling their responsibilities to looked after children.*

Welsh guidance, *Towards a Stable Life and a Brighter Future* (Welsh Asssembly Government, 2007) states that:

the responsible authority should arrange for the child to receive the full range of NHS dental treatment. Regulation 8(3)(b) Placement of Children (Wales) Regulations 2007 requires the responsible authority to ensure the child is placed under the care of a dentist no later than 20 working days after the date of placement.

Regulation 8(4) requires a responsible authority to ensure that a child continues to be registered with a general practitioner and under the care of a registered dental practitioner, throughout the duration of the placement.

Regulation 7(2) of the Arrangements for Placement of Children (General) Regulations (Northern Ireland) 1996 states:

During the placement of the child the responsible authority shall ensure that arrangements are made for the child to be provided with health services, including medical and dental care and treatment.

The Foster Placement and Fostering Agencies Regulations (Northern Ireland) 2014, which are currently being consulted on, highlight the need for the foster care agreement to outline arrangements for the delegation of responsibility for consent for medical and dental care.

Barriers to oral care provision for looked after children

The main issues concerning oral health for looked after children are detailed below.

- Dentistry is something that most people don't regard with a lot of enthusiasm! It takes time to build up a rapport and develop trust with a dentist. If a looked after child is moved to varying locations, it may not be practical to attend the same dentist, due to distance. So along with the change in carers, the child has to cope with different dentists and other health personnel (DCSF and DH, 2009). Therefore, the looked after child can be even more nervous about seeking dental treatment. This may appear as a rebellious reaction.
- Frequency of changing placements means that consistency in dental care may be a problem. A dentist gets to know the patient and, over a long-term relationship, develops awareness of when decay is active and when it is static. Similarly referrals, e.g. to an orthodontist, cannot be followed through if the child is placed elsewhere. The child is then disadvantaged and their self-esteem and oral health are at risk. This can result in the child being difficult to manage or indifferent to his or her own personal and oral hygiene. This is not helped by a lack of consistency in receiving dental care.
- Consistency in home dental care may likewise be lacking. A looked after child may have a history of care in children's homes and/or foster care, with a consequent variability in emphasis on oral health from their various carers. The child therefore

receives mixed messages and mixed practices. At worst, they will not have the means to carry out basic oral hygiene. With the looked after child moving families, it may be difficult for foster carers to achieve a routine in dental care. Carers may feel that they have enough to cope with and the child's oral health is a lower priority than other issues, or they may not deem dental care to be important themselves and so do not encourage their foster child. In these ways, the child's oral health is at risk of being neglected.

- The children themselves have had huge changes to their lives and may not be used to structures or routines, thus implementing tooth brushing or a stricter diet is alien to what they have been used to. They may just dislike the taste of the minty toothpaste, or refuse to brush as a sign of rebellion to show choice in a world that doesn't offer much choice for them. Some may never have brushed their teeth before and so are wary about the reasons for it. Others may view it as an invasion of their personal space. In some cases, children may have been abused physically or sexually (including oral sexual abuse) and so anything to do with the mouth brings back horrific memories. Putting a toothbrush in the mouth may thus be very challenging for them, and gradual acclimatisation will be required to achieve tooth brushing or dental treatment.
- There is often a multidisciplinary team involved with looked after children, including social workers, health care personnel and the carers themselves. With the child having a wide range of complex issues, it can sometimes become difficult to monitor what care the child has received and what he/she needs (DCSF and DH, 2009).

All these factors can impact on oral health in looked after children.

How dental care fits in with overall health

Poor oral health can affect appetite and the ability to eat, result in malnutrition, and hence compromise general health and well-being. Oral health is vital in that it is often a window into what is occurring in the body. Systemic diseases can affect the mouth, e.g. diseases of the gastrointestinal tract and diabetes, and oral health can influence the other organs, e.g. diabetes, obesity, cardiovascular and respiratory illness. The days of reducing oral health to something with which only the dentist is concerned should be a thing of the past.

To put it simply, whatever is put in the mouth has implications for the body and oral cavity. A diet that is too high in sugar and calories can cause obesity and dental decay (Levine and Stillman-Lowe, 2009). Gum disease can affect the control of diabetes, and conversely, diabetes has adverse effects on the blood vessels and immune response, which can exacerbate severe gum disease. Research suggests a link between gum disease and heart attacks, but this is unclear (Seymour and Steele, 1998). Some respiratory illnesses such as pneumonia can arise from the inhalation of bacteria from the teeth and gums. Common factors can affect both the body and the mouth (Davies and Davies, 2005).

Smoking can increase the likelihood of gum disease and oral cancer by up to seven times (DH, 2005). The combined effects of tobacco use, heavy alcohol consumption and poor diet are thought to account for more than 90 per cent of cases of head and neck cancer. Stress and mental health can impact on the health of the gums. Regular oral examinations can enable early detection of eating disorders, as early signs include erosion of tooth enamel and swelling of the salivary glands.

Specific considerations in carrying out dental care for looked after children

Carrying out dental care for looked after children can be more challenging than for most children, due to problems with variable experience of dentistry, anxiety about dental care, lack of trust, and extent of disease. Consistency of care should be of utmost importance to engender a sense of the constant and reliable in what can be in general an unstable life. Keeping the same dentist can build up trust and enable more to be done to maintain oral health. If the child has frequent placements in different localities, then it may be better to attend a central Dental Access Centre for his or her dental care. If the placements are few in number, it may help the child to integrate into the family by attending their General Dental Practitioner (GDP). A diagram of the care pathway is shown below.

Care pathway

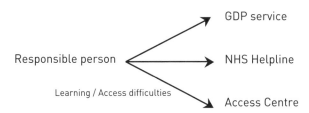

When it comes to dental care at home, if the child is not compliant, the following suggestions for the carer may help.

- Listen and talk to the child. Try and reason with him or her.
- Give the child some control. Encourage them to brush their teeth, but give them some flexibility over the choice of toothbrush and toothpaste.
- Some children do not like strong flavours so may prefer a milder flavoured toothpaste; often "own-brand" toothpastes in the supermarkets have milder tastes. OraNurse is an example of an unflavoured toothpaste.
- Start with easy steps. Don't try and accomplish everything in the first instance. Start with, for example, the front teeth and then progress to the back. It is better in the long term not to discourage the child in the initial stages.

- Brush with the child, with both of you holding the brush. In this way, they exert some control over the brushing and you can simply guide their hand.
- Try brushing your teeth at the same time as the child, so that they can copy and learn by imitation. You can be a positive role model by brushing alongside the child and demonstrating that it is straightforward.
- Reinforce the positives and not the negatives – for instance, the benefits of their personal health and hygiene which will make them more pleasant to interact with, etc.
- The dentist should be aware of the fact that the child is looked after and take into consideration the possible anxieties described.

What constitutes good oral care for looked after children?

The treatment and advice given to looked after children should at least be the same as that offered to their peers in the general population.

Good oral care should take into account the fact that teeth are important, and that includes the first/milk/baby/deciduous teeth. In the early stages of life, teeth have various roles.

- Function – teeth help a child to chew and therefore obtain the nutrients and vitamins that he or she requires for development.
- Speech – pronunciation of some syllables depends on the presence of teeth and their extraction can impair the development of speech.
- Keeping the shape and form of the face. Teeth contribute to the height and fullness of the face.
- Retaining the space for the permanent teeth. The first/milk/baby/deciduous teeth guide the second/adult/permanent teeth into position but if these teeth are removed at an early age, there may be reduced space for the rest of the permanent dentition.
- Aesthetics – self-confidence is greatly enhanced if the child has a full set of sound teeth, can speak properly and can therefore smile.
  (DH, 2005; DH/BASCD, 2007; Levine and Stillman-Lowe, 2009)

Two basic steps to maintaining oral health

The first is **brushing** with a family fluoride toothpaste containing at least 1,350 ppm (parts per million) fluoride. This will help to protect the teeth from decay and also guard the gums against gum disease. Plaque is the white substance that builds up on the teeth if they are not brushed. It contains lots of bacteria that can convert the sugar eaten into acid. This acid then attacks the teeth which, if sugar is eaten frequently (more than about four times a day), can lead to decay. The more frequent and the longer the duration of exposure, the less time the saliva has to re-harden the tooth structure, and therefore decay can occur. Brushing last thing at night and then not having anything but water to drink means that the teeth are exposed to fluoride, which strengthens the teeth and combats acid attack. The saliva flow decreases during the night so the fluoride remains around the teeth for longer; however, less saliva also means any acid (as a result of eating or drinking after brushing) does not get washed away.

Bacteria also give rise to gum disease. Plaque builds up around the teeth within 24 hours, and if this is not brushed off, the gums can become inflamed and bleed. Brushing can remove the plaque but all the surfaces of the teeth need to be cleaned, right to the gum margin.

The second factor, which is essential to oral health, is **what we eat**. An unhealthy diet, and the quantities of each category of food that a person eats, have a huge impact on the likelihood of decay. A balanced diet, as illustrated by the diagram below, consists of starchy food (pasta, rice and bread); fruit and vegetables; milk and dairy products; fish, meat and other proteins; with only a small portion of food that is high in fat and sugar. Many foods that contain added sugars also contain large numbers of calories, but often have few other nutrients. Eating these foods frequently can contribute to obesity, as well as causing decay. To maintain a healthy, balanced diet, we should eat these types of foods only occasionally, and obtain the majority of our calories from other food groups, such as starchy foods and fruits and vegetables (see the Eatwell Plate diagram below).

Sugary foods and drinks can also cause tooth decay, especially if eaten between meals. The longer the sugary food is in contact with the teeth, and the more frequently it is eaten, the more damage it can cause. The sugars that are added to a wide range of foods, such as sweets, cakes, biscuits, chocolate, and some fizzy drinks and juice drinks are harmful and their consumption should be reduced.

The Eatwell Plate

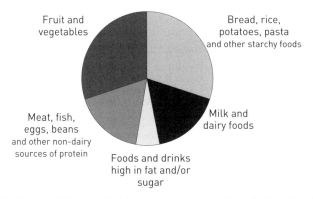

(Adapted from The Eatwell Plate, available at: www.nhs.uk/Livewell/Goodfood/Pages/eatwell-plate.aspx)

For this reason, restricting sweet or acidic food and drink to *mealtimes only*, while offering sugar-free snacks in between mealtimes, can help to prevent decay. Snacks such as fresh fruit, vegetable sticks, small quantities of cheese, wholegrain breadsticks or bread, or suitable sandwiches are good alternatives for snacks. Similarly, water or milk with no flavourings should be consumed between meals. This ensures that there is no exposure to sugar and therefore acid too frequently.

The sugars found naturally in whole fruit are less likely to cause tooth decay, because the sugars are contained within the structure of the fruit. But when fruit is juiced or blended, the sugars are released and can damage teeth, especially if fruit juice is drunk frequently. Fruit juice is still a healthy choice, and counts as one of the recommended five daily portions of fruit and vegetables, but it is best to drink it at mealtimes rather than between meals, in order to minimise damage to teeth.

These tips can help cut down on sugar intake.

- Instead of sugary fizzy and juice drinks, restrict unsweetened fruit juice to mealtimes (remember to dilute these for children, to further reduce the sugar) and have water between meals.
- Instead of cakes or biscuits, have a healthy snack like vegetable sticks. If adding sugar to hot drinks or breakfast cereal, gradually reduce the amount until it can be cut out altogether.
- Rather than spreading jam, marmalade, syrup, treacle or honey on toast, try a low-fat spread, sliced banana or low-fat cream cheese instead.
- Check nutrition labels to help pick the foods with less added sugar, or choose the low-sugar version.
- Try halving the sugar used in recipes. Choose tins of fruit in juice rather than syrup.
- Choose wholegrain breakfast cereals, but not those coated with sugar or honey. (DH/BASCD, 2007)

Nutrition labels and sugars

Nutrition labels often tell how much sugar a food contains. Comparing labels can help with choosing foods that are lower in sugar. Look for the "Carbohydrates (of which sugars)" figure in the nutrition label.

The sugars figure in the nutrition label is the total amount in the food. It includes sugars from fruit and milk, as well as those that have been added. Checking the ingredients list (see below) will show whether the food contains lots of added sugars.

Criteria for 100mg food

Text	LOW	MEDIUM	HIGH	
Colour code	Green	Amber	Red	
(Total) sugars	≤5.0g per 100g	>5.0g and ≤22.5g per 100g	>22.5g per 100g	>27g per portion

Criteria for 100ml of drink

Text	LOW	MEDIUM	HIGH	
Colour code	Green	Amber	Red	
(Total) sugars	≤2.5g per 100ml	>2.5g and ≤11.25g per 100ml	>11.25g per 100ml	>13.5g per portion

Labels on the front of packaging

Labels containing nutritional information are displayed on the front of some food packaging. This includes traffic light labelling, and displays the types of food as a proportion of the recommended daily amount, or the reference intake. The amount of sugar is expressed as a proportion of the reference intake for sugar which, in the case shown below, is low. Traffic light labelling shows at a glance if the food is high, medium or low in sugars.

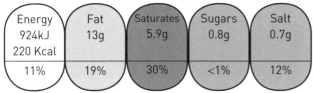

Energy 924kJ 220 Kcal	Fat 13g	Saturates 5.9g	Sugars 0.8g	Salt 0.7g
11%	19%	30%	<1%	12%

of an adult's reference intake
Typical values (as sold) per 100g: Energy 966kJ / 230kcal

Ingredients list

The ingredients list is arranged in order of the weight of ingredients contained. Added sugars must be included so if sugar is near the top of the list, then the food is likely to be high in added sugars. Watch out for other words that are used to describe added sugars, such as sucrose, glucose, fructose, maltose, hydrolysed starch and invert sugar, corn syrup and honey. The Government guidance, *Guide to Creating a Front of Pack (FoP) Nutrition Label for Pre-Packed Products Sold through Retail Outlets*, provides more information on labels and ingredients lists (available at: www.food.gov.uk/multimedia/pdfs/pdf-ni/fop-guidance.pdf).

Looked after children assessments: oral health

Doctors and nurses have a lot to find out during the assessment of a lookcd after child, but dental health is important and should be considered at every statutory health assessment (DCSF and DH, 2009). The following questions should be asked as part of a comprehensive oral health assessment.

- Has the child had a dental check in the last 12 months? If so, when?
- What is the name of the practice and dentist?
- Did the child have a regular dentist prior to the last visit?
- When does the child brush his/her teeth?
- Does the child have his/her own toothbrush?
- Does the child use adult toothpaste?
- Has the child had fillings?
- Does the child have any sign of decay?
- Does the child have medical, physical, mental or emotional health issues that could make brushing his/her teeth difficult?
- Does the carer supervise/assist with brushing if the child is under eight years of age?
- Does the child have sweet snacks or drinks in between meals?
- How often does the child consume fizzy drinks?

Health professionals should check that all looked after children are registered with a dentist (DH, 2004; DCSF and DH, 2009), and information about oral health should be made available in an integrated approach (DfES, 2004) as it is often an early sign of neglect.

Summary

Foster carers and adopters have a very important and challenging role, and often oral health is far down the list of priorities. However, four very simple practices can make a world of difference to oral health.

- Restrict sweet food and drinks to mealtimes only.
- Brush last thing at night and one other time using family fluoride toothpaste. Spit out the excess when finished but do not rinse.
- Have regular checks at the dentist.
- Offer an atmosphere and a culture of good oral health. Encourage the child to care for their teeth and watch what they eat.

What health professionals should do

- Ensure that every child is registered with a dentist.
- Record information about oral health and the child's last dental check, including details of their dentist, at every health assessment.
- Promote understanding of the importance of oral health to other professionals, carers and children.
- Signpost carers to appropriate sources of information and services for oral health and for management of difficult behaviours.
- Advocate for development of local services.

Key points

- Children's oral health has often been neglected prior to care entry and it may take time to establish good oral hygiene practices (including attending a dentist) with looked after children.
- Health professionals have an important role in ensuring that oral health is considered at every statutory health assessment and that all looked after children are registered with a dentist.
- Good oral health is important not just for healthy teeth and gums, but for its impact on general health, speech and language development, appearance and self-esteem.
- There are a number of barriers to good dental care for looked after children, including lack of familiarity with dental hygiene, anxiety about dentistry, lack of consistency in practices and routines for dental care that may be exacerbated by placement moves, and lower prioritisation of oral health when children are perceived to have more pressing health needs.
- Advice is available for carers to help them gradually establish good dental hygiene routines with children.
- Brushing teeth twice daily with a family fluoride toothpaste and eating a healthy balanced diet are two essential steps to good oral health. Children and their carers will benefit from education about the importance of mainly choosing foods low in sugar, use of food labels to assist in choices, and restricting sweet food and drinks to mealtimes only.

Bibliography

Davies R.M. and Davies G.M. (2005) 'Periodontal disease and general health', *Dental Update*, 32, pp 438–442

Department for Children, Schools and Families and Department of Health (2009) *Statutory Guidance on Promoting the Health and Well-Being of Looked After Children*, London: DCSF and DH

Department for Education and Skills (2004) *Every Child Matters: Change for children*, London: DfES

Department for Education and Skills (2009) *If this were my Child: A councillor's guide to being a good corporate parent to children in care and care leavers*, London: DfES

Department of Health (2004) *Choosing Health: Making healthy choices easier*, London: DH

Department of Health (2005) *Choosing Better Oral Health: An oral health plan for England*, London: DH

Department of Health (2009) *Adult Dental Health Survey*, London: DH

Department of Health/British Association for the Study of Community Dentistry (BASCD) (2007) *Delivering Better Oral Health: An evidence-based toolkit for prevention*, London: DH/BASCD

Department of Health (2013) *Guide to Creating a Front of Pack (FoP) Nutrition Label for Pre-Packed Products Sold through Retail Outlets*, available at: www.food.gov.uk/multimedia/pdfs/pdf-ni/fop-guidance.pdf

Levine R. and Stillman-Lowe C. (2009) *The Scientific Basis of Oral Health Education*, London: British Dental Association

Prendergast M. (2001) 'Public dental health: dental attendance, oral health and the quality of life', *British Dental Journal*, 190, p 251

Seymour R.A. and Steele J.G. (1998) 'Is there a link between periodontal disease and coronary heart disease?', *British Dental Journal*, 184, pp. 33–38

Welsh Assembly Government (2007) *Towards a Stable Life and a Brighter Future*, Cardiff: WAG

4 The child's mental health and well-being

Geraldine Casswell

Looked after children and young people are at greater risk of mental health problems, conduct disorders and emotional disorders than their non-looked after peers. This is a consistent message from outcome studies (McCann *et al*, 1996; Meltzer *et al*, 2003). A significant proportion have a serious psychiatric disorder when entering the care of the local authority (Dimigen *et al*, 1999). Many are at increased risk of poor outcomes in educational attainment, employment and criminality. Ford *et al* (2007) suggest that fewer than one in 10 of looked after children have positively good mental health. Tarren-Sweeney (2011) writes:

> Studies have consistently established that more than half of children in care, regardless of where they reside in the Western World, have mental health problems of sufficient scale and severity to warrant the provision of mental health services.

Given these poor outcomes in mental health, any health assessment should also include a consideration of the known mental health risk factors so that decision-making regarding placement or additional needs can be fully informed. This can be a complex area, as the children concerned may have problems in more than one domain, and some problems, such as attachment difficulties, are difficult to assess accurately (O'Connor and Zeanah, 2003).

Access to mental health practitioners, whether based in a Child and Adolescent Mental Health Service (CAMHS) or within a local authority looked after children (LAC) team, has been patchy in provision. A survey (Holland *et al*, 2005) about promoting placement stability for looked after children revealed a high level of concern from local authorities and independent agencies about the availability of mental health services. This same observation is noted in a Scottish study (Minnis *et al*, 2006). In Tarren-Sweeney's review (2011), the evidence suggests:

> . . . that sizeable proportions of children in public care who manifest mental health problems do not receive adequate clinical assessment or access to mental health services.

This is acknowledged within key publications, and recommendations in *Every Child Matters* (Department for Education and Skills (DfES), 2004), the Adoption and Children Act 2002, the *National Service Framework for Children* (Department of Health (DH), 2004), *Care Matters* (Department for Children, Schools and Families (DCSF), 2007),

Promoting the Health and Well-Being of Looked After Children (DCSF and DH, 2009, revision expected in 2015) and *Promoting the Quality of Life of Looked After Children and Young People* (NICE/SCIE, 2010; 2013). These documents all recognise the need for mental health assessment and therapeutic support.

> *Focusing on the mental health issues is important because with the support of the social worker, the young person and the carers (including birth parents), interventions can be made which make a difference and which reduce disturbed and disturbing behaviour, improve relationships and make the care situation manageable. These interventions are made at a number of levels. It is possible to support the network around the child by means of consultation, offering an understanding of the problem and strategies for management, so that the carers and professionals work consistently together to alleviate the difficulties. Foster carers and residential staff may also be offered group support. Therapeutic interventions may be offered to the young person individually, or together with his or her foster carers. There is a range of treatment options, including the use of cognitive and behavioural programmes, individual family and group therapy, medication and a combination of these. Rarely, hospitalisation may be required. Interventions may not necessarily relieve the symptoms entirely, but may strengthen the relationship with the child, so that family life can go on. Effective intervention may reduce the risks for the future.* (Richardson and Joughin, 2002, p 9)

What you need to know to assess the child's mental health needs

Comprehensive assessments

Statutory health assessments are required throughout a child's journey through the care system. In England, the statutory guidance on *Promoting the Health and Well-Being of Looked After Children* (DCSF and DH, 2009, revision expected in 2015) directs that local authorities, health trusts and Clinical Commissioning Groups (CCGs) need to build awareness of the high level of mental health needs among looked after children into their strategic planning and their operational delivery of CAMHS. They advise a focus of assessment for each age group.

- Health assessment of the under-fives should include consideration of attachment behaviours.
- For older children (5–18), the assessment should cover mental and emotional health, including depression and conduct disorders.

A mental health assessment involves a review of background information about the child, their birth family and significant relationships as well as their current and past placements. For a school-age child, additional information about academic achievement and conduct in school is important. Information from those who have been directly involved in providing care is essential to understand the nature of the child's relationships.

Further assessment from CAMHS, psychology or specialist LAC services will depend on the age of the child.

- For a baby or young infant, observational assessment develops an understanding of the baby's capacity to be soothed and settled, to make eye contact and to engage with the parent and carer.
- For young children, play-based sessions can provide a picture of how they relate to strangers, their current carers and parental figures, and how they make sense of their world.
- Older children can also enjoy play-based assessments (e.g. computer games), but are able to participate in discussion and complete questionnaires that explore how they view themselves, their family of origin, their experience of alternative caregivers, and their previous life events. In the event that the young person does not want to be assessed, information can be obtained from social workers, family placement and residential workers, teachers, foster carers, etc.

Many services (both health and social care) use screening tools. In England, guidance (DCSF, 2009) tasks local authorities with assessing the emotional health and well-being of all children entering care, including through completion of the Strength and Difficulties Questionnaire (SDQ). The SDQ was developed by Goodman (1997, 1999, www.sdqinfo.org/) and is designed to give a rating (compared to the general population) of difficulties in the dimensions of emotional symptoms, conduct problems, hyperactivity, peer problems and pro-social behaviour. The advantage of this tool is that any professional can access and use it and it has different questionnaires depending on the age of the child and the person completing it (e.g. young person, parent, teacher). The disadvantage is that it is not sensitive to children whose distress is expressed through more avoidant behaviours and who may appear settled but are unable to form relationships. The SDQ is perhaps best viewed as a generic mental health tool but it will help to provide a baseline measure and point the way forward for more specialised, comprehensive and qualitative assessments.

Another useful tool is the Carer's Report (Form CR–C/CR–YP) (BAAF, 2008), a form which has been developed to give a voice to the first-hand experience of carers. Observational information from those who have lived with the child offers invaluable insights into their day-to-day life and experiential data on what it is like to care for the child. The form is designed to provide behavioural evidence for how the child seeks care and manages states of distress, as well as evidence of their behaviour, emotional well-being, play, peer relationships and capacity to concentrate and learn. The reports are designed to work alongside the health assessment forms and are available for two age groups (0–9 years, 10+ years). They provide a necessary qualitative "flavour" of what it is like to care for a child. This can easily be omitted from professional reports and inadvertently mislead matching or placement considerations.

The most common mental health and emotional well-being difficulties for children and young people in care are attachment difficulties and disorders, anxiety and fears, depression and conduct problems. A smaller proportion may develop serious mental illnesses, such as schizophrenia and bipolar affective disorder. Trauma and abuse can increase the risk of post-traumatic stress disorder (PTSD) and self-harming behaviours, including suicide attempts. In some situations, the impact of traumatic conditions can exacerbate the onset of psychosis in adolescence. These young people are also at greater risk of managing their despair and distress by high-risk behaviours, such as misuse of drugs and alcohol, sexual promiscuity and prostitution, any of which may lead them into criminal acts. Comprehensive assessments can highlight known risk factors and point the way forward for early interventions.

> People shouldn't label us as problem kids just because we are adopted. We don't want to be stereotyped: people need to get to know us.
> (Sophie, aged 15, personal communication)

Hidden disabilities

We are more aware of how, even before a baby is born, the developing embryo is sensitive to the uterine environment. In particular, our understanding is growing in clarity concerning how smoking tobacco, ingesting alcohol and chemical substances during pregnancy, and exposure to maternal stress can impact on the developing brain. Early neonatal risks are associated with withdrawal from drugs of abuse (McElhatton, 2004), pre-term births and sudden infant deaths in women who smoke (Cosgrove *et al*, 2004) and Foetal Alcohol Syndrome (FAS) in babies born to mothers with confirmed excessive alcohol use (Plant, 2004).

Very often, it is difficult to separate out other factors that may be commonly associated with mental health issues and problems surrounding emotional well-being, such as poverty, depression, neglect and general deficits in socio-economic lifestyle. Whilst the physical health of the child can be improved through good nutrition and care, the behavioural, cognitive and emotional consequences may be less amenable to immediate reversal.

In a review paper on foetal alcohol spectrum disorders (FASD), Manning and Hoyme (2007) estimate the prevalence to be as high as one per cent of all live births, across all ethnic groups. They point out that primary care physicians may under-diagnose FASD and that a multidisciplinary team will be best placed to assist in the assessment, diagnosis and treatment interventions. The mental health practitioner is well placed to assess for behavioural and cognitive deficits. When there is strong evidence to suspect actual FAS, Chudley *et al* (2005) recommend that, in addition to the physical assessment, specialist assessments are necessary to ascertain speech and language delays, learning difficulties, attention deficits and hyperactivity, as well as problems with executive functions and memory difficulties. (See Chapter 2 for further discussion of FAS and FASD.)

Executive functions refer to a collection of cognitive and behavioural skills that are at the centre of learning and problem-solving. This includes skills that enable self-regulation, organising, planning and directing behaviour. These skills help a person to maintain independent and goal-directed (purposeful) behaviour within the demands and expect-ations of everyday life. The skills emerge alongside the neurological development of the pre-frontal regions of the brain. Because this development happens in a protracted manner (especially over the first five years), these skills are vulnerable to damage from accident or trauma.

Accurate information about a birth mother's alcohol or chemical substance use is often lacking and a child's difficulties may be attributed to other variables. The behavioural and emotional problems may have other aetiologies but a functional assessment can advise education staff on how to help a child, and assist care staff, birth parents, foster carers and adoptive parents in understanding that the child's struggles are more often "can't do" rather than "won't do".

Case study

An adoptive parent was both frustrated and confused that her 10-year-old daughter could not remember an instruction for long enough to go upstairs and fetch some-thing or stay on task for more than three minutes – yet she had a clear memory of autobiographical events from her birth family. At school, the girl was impulsive in her behaviour and under-performing academically. Assessment by a paediatrician, with access to social care records, revealed that her birth mother had used alcohol to excess. Psychological assessment of her executive functions showed a marked deficit in her working memory, particularly her verbal memory, but with better ability in her visual memory. A system of visual aids, such as visual timetables and picture reminders of tasks to be done to get ready for school, lessened the day-to-day struggles. In turn, the school was able to increase the level of support and develop grounds for applying for a Statement of Educational Needs as she approached secondary school.

Primary relationships and attachment

A baby's first experience of care becomes fundamental to care-seeking in future relationships; how they learn of their self-worth and importance; and how they manage to regulate their emotional lives. These core experiences are the paving stones for mental health and emotional well-being. Our understanding of child development and specifically how a child first develops a relationship has been enriched by attachment theory. John Bowlby's books and writings (1973–1998), based on his own research and clinical experience, set out the core tenets of attachment that have gone on to inspire a large and productive body of research and application.

The baby arrives in the world with a sophisticated set of communication behaviours (eye contact, smiling, facial expressions, etc) that act as signals or cues to their parent. The parent responds to these cues (also called attachment behaviours) and in meeting the baby's need, enables the child to settle and be comforted. This cycle of communication through attachment behaviours and parental response happens hundreds of times as the parent learns to make sense of the behaviours and cues. If the parent is sufficiently reliable, consistent in response and attuned to the baby's need, the baby experiences a felt sense of security. This allows the developing infant to feel safe enough to explore their environment, to learn and to enjoy other relationships.

Secure attachments

Of central importance is the concept of attachment security. When a baby experiences sensitive caregiving, he or she develops a secure attachment – secure in the experience that their parent will be available as a source of comfort and safety at times of stress. As the infant grows, these experiences will also shape their cognitive development and provide a perspective in how they learn and understand themselves, the world and other people.

Attachment theory lays emphasis on the very early experiences as being critical for later development. The type and quality of caregiving provide the first template for later experience. If a child experiences insensitive parenting, such as neglectful or rejecting care, they are at greater risk of developing insecure attachments. The child cannot rely on the parent to feel safe and secure and has to develop alternative communications or attachment behaviours to elicit care, especially when they are feeling worried or distressed.

Insecure attachments

Some children minimise their own needs and the expression of these in order to remain close to their parent and not risk further rejection. These children often appear self-reliant or compliant, sometimes passive and withdrawn, or sometimes overly helpful and attending to the needs of their caregiver. This is called an insecure–avoidant attachment security because whilst the child still needs their parent, they avoid any overt display of need, because they fear rejection. These children's problems are at a greater risk of being missed by carers and professionals because of their extreme compliance, and are often described as "too good to be true". It is important for any assessment to look further than just behavioural observations and explore how the child is able to express their emotional needs.

Children who have experienced a lot of inconsistency from parents become very uncertain about how to let them know that they need them. They therefore develop attachment behaviours that increase the volume of their communications, such as persistent whining or crying, demanding or clinging behaviour, in the hope that they will be attended to. Confusingly for carers, these children often resist being comforted, because they fear that, if they settle, they may be left alone again. This is called an ambivalent–resistant attachment security, as the child is unsure about how to obtain care and resists being soothed and comforted. In contrast to the avoidant attachments, these children are well noticed by carers and do get referred to mental health services. It is important not to focus solely on behaviour management as a method of intervention, as these children experience high levels of distress and need help in managing their internal worlds.

Disorganised/controlling attachments

In more extreme situations, a parent may be frightening or terrifying and the child does not know how to organise their behaviour in order to elicit care. They experience high levels of distress and confusion resulting in behavioural and emotional dysregulation. The child both needs and fears the parental response and develops controlling attachment behaviours. This prevents the child from intimacy with a frightening figure and allows them to attain some measure of predictability in their lives. The high levels of fear and stress lead to the development of disorganised or controlling patterns of attachment security. The child is neither able to seek out comfort or protection, nor are they able to effectively explore the world around them. Their sense of self is that they are unworthy of love, powerful and bad. These experiences remain with the child as they travel through placements and characteristically present as controlling styles of relating to new carers. These children never learn how a parent can be a reliable source of comfort and this perpetuates the child's experience of not feeling safe and compromises their emotional well-being.

Children with no selective attachment figure

The majority of children do form attachments with their primary caregivers (even if they are highly insecure or traumatised in nature), but for a small proportion there is an absence of caregiving. This may have arisen through early life in an institution when only physical care was provided or if a child has been severely neglected. These children do not learn how to elicit or receive care and protection and do not have a selective attachment figure. Consequently, they may present as very disinhibited in their behaviour, seeking attention from whoever they can, or they may be extremely withdrawn and passive, having no expectations from others at all.

The importance of attachment security for looked after children

The development of attachment happens crucially in the first months of life. The baby is responsive to the care received from the moment of birth but as they develop, they are more able to actively seek care and attention. Over the first six months, they begin to discriminate between people, showing a clear preference for some. These are usually the parental figures, although for some children this may include members of the extended family or regular carers. By the age of six to nine months, the child will have a clear preference and show selective attachments. This continues to consolidate over the first two years, with clear signs of protest from the child when they are separated from their primary attachment figure.

Children develop more than one attachment figure but will have a hierarchy of preference, usually with mothers as first choice. As the child develops language and mobility, they are more able to explore a wider world, yet still need access to their attachment figures to manage separations and distress. Children in public care often have to manage separations repeatedly and are frequently disadvantaged because of prior experiences. On arrival in a new home, they often display "honeymoon" behaviours, when they initially respond to the safety and consistency of a good placement. This can mislead professionals, who may report that the child is well settled and not displaying any significant difficulties. Careful assessment of the child's patterns of behaviour before coming into care and interactions with other adults (particularly those providing care) can help develop a fuller understanding of the child's attachment securities. Information is often used from observation of contact sessions in expert reports for care proceedings. However, it is important that the child's attachment behaviours are activated (as when the child is distressed or seeks care) to give a true reflection of their attachment patterns.

Some assessments have been developed to observe the child's reactions when their familiar caregiver leaves them temporarily and they are then reunited. The Strange Situation test (Ainsworth *et al*, 1978) is a way of observing young children under the age of two. Assessments for older children seek to understand the child's representational (internal working) models of attachment relationships; this may be done through story completion tasks using play or verbal narratives. Assessment helps to demonstrate the child's state of mind, their affective memories of being cared for, and subsequent attachment behaviours that are used to seek safety and protection from a replacement or surrogate caregiver.

Within a systemic, organismic view of development, attachment is important precisely because of its place in the initiation of these complex processes. It is an organising core in development that is always integrated with later experience and never lost. While it is not proper to think of attachment variations as directly causing certain outcomes, and while early attachment has no privileged causal status, it is nonetheless the case that nothing can be assessed that is more important.

Infant attachment is critical, both because of its place in initiating pathways of development and because of its connection with so many critical developmental functions – social relatedness, arousal modulation, emotional regulation and curiosity, to name just a few. Attachment experiences remain, even in this complex view, vital in the formation of the person. (Sroufe, 2005, p 365)

The impact of trauma and loss

The term "external foetus" has been used to describe the relative immaturity of the newborn baby's brain (Sunderland, 2006), since as much as 90 per cent of the growth and maturation of the human brain happens in the first five years of life. This relatively unfinished nature of the brain means that it is very susceptible to experience that can help to shape its potential for better or worse.

The research on normal brain development has gathered momentum and sophistication in recent years. Whilst the brain is seen as a robust structure that can withstand stress, it is not immune to severe or chronic stress. Belsky and de Haan (2011) describe brain development as a complex scaffolding of gene-driven processes, experience-expectant processes (such as critical periods), and the unique experiences of every individual. This helps to account for individual variations and why some children appear to cope better with adversity. The summary of research evidence that draws on child maltreatment populations suggests that the brain structure is altered: 'that these parenting conditions of extreme adversity, including institutionalisation, are associated with reductions in cortical grey and white matter volumes' (Belsky and de Haan, 2011, p 423). There is also evidence to show that the function of the brain is adversely affected by maltreatment and severe deprivation. In their review of EEG (electroencephalogram) studies, Belsky and de Haan (2011, p 421) write that 'this body of work suggests that maltreated children process facial emotion differently when they are required to attend to anger and that they process auditory information about anger whether or not they are required to attend to it'.

These findings accord with carers' experiences of living with children who have experienced trauma and loss. The child is often on high alert and over-reactive to minor stresses. They have difficulty in regulating their affective and behavioural responses. In these heightened states of arousal, the neurochemical messages are triggered by the amygdala in the mid-brain, which in turn sets off the hypothalamic pituitary adrenal (HPA) axis (the hypothalamus triggers the pituitary gland, which in turn activates adrenal glands). This results in extra cortisol being produced to enable the emergency response systems to function and to put bodily systems on hold while the stress is being dealt with.

For children who have experienced trauma and loss, this can become a repetitive experience and the increased levels of cortisol can affect the growth of the developing brain and shape the responses to perceived danger and threat. This provokes the child to a state of hyper-arousal, activating the brain's emergency system (largely lower brain) of aggression, avoidance or withdrawal (fight, flight or freeze).

- Fight responses include aggression, high levels of irritability or anger, trouble concentrating, constant provocation, oppositional behaviour, hyperactivity or inability to settle.
- Flight responses include withdrawal or escape behaviours, such as running off, isolating themselves in a group, avoidance of opportunity or people.
- Freeze responses include overly restricted emotional expressions that can appear as compliance or being "too good", denial of their own needs, being watchful, looking dazed, being forgetful or daydreaming.

Many of these children present as having PTSD-like symptoms of hyper-arousal, withdrawal and dissociation. However, when this type of complex trauma occurs in early childhood and is chronic in nature, many researchers now describe the cluster of difficulties as developmental trauma (van der Kolk, 2005). This more accurately reflects the breadth and impact of early adversity, and denotes that the primary stressor arises from a chronic interpersonal trauma and results in dysregulation across many domains (emotional, cognitive and social). The child develops altered attributions and expectancies about themselves (i.e. *I am bad*) and others (i.e. *I can't trust you*) as well as functional impairments.

> *It gets bigger and bigger . . . it starts in my feet and comes up to my head and I explode! Then I hurt [sister] . . . I don't think my mum wants me any more.*
> (Adopted boy, aged seven, telling his mother how he struggles to manage his feelings and behaviour, personal communication)

Carers can find themselves overwhelmed by living with a child who is frequently hyper-aroused and unable to easily accept comfort. Consequently, they can find themselves feeling traumatised. It is important to help those caring for a child to recognise these states of secondary trauma so that the carer can be safely supported and, in turn, enable the child to feel safe. A safe carer will also be able to help a child regulate their altered states far more effectively.

Coping with multiple losses

Children who enter the public care system experience a disruption and separation from their primary caregivers temporarily and sometimes permanently. Many go on to experience multiple losses as they move from one placement to another and may also be separated from siblings and their extended family. Each child has to learn how to manage these psychological and physical separations and find internal resources to self-soothe the resulting anxiety and distress. The way in which a child manages to do this will be in large part determined by how they were parented in the first years of life.

When a baby is separated from their primary attachment figure, they use their repertoire of attachment behaviours to alert the carer to stay close, as they are wholly dependent on the parental figure for their physiological needs to be met. If the parent's response is attuned to the needs of the child, the child experiences the parent as supportive, calming and understanding. This shapes the child's expectations for how a parental figure will respond to future needs. The capacity of the parent to hold the child's needs in mind and respond appropriately helps the child to learn over time how to manage or regulate these powerful feelings and how to recognise their emotions. This cycle then enables the child to later recognise the needs of others, which is an important step in the development of empathy, social understanding and conscience.

A child who does not experience attuned and sensitive care is disadvantaged and will struggle to recognise their internal states, regulate their emotions and understand or empathise with others. This disadvantage becomes very apparent when a child is faced with separation or moving placement, as they are frequently unable to manage their distress or to receive comfort from new carers. This, in turn, is hard for new carers, who may feel disempowered or rejected.

When the children move into new homes they initially behave with their new parent as they did within their original family, by signalling their emotional and attachment needs in a distorted way. This makes it difficult for the new parent to provide sensitive care. The children who have previously developed avoidant patterns of attachment may act as if they do not need nurture when feeling distressed, whilst the children who have previously developed ambivalent patterns of relating may seek nurture and comfort even when distress is low. The children are organising their behaviour around what they expect of the parent rather than around the actual availability of the parent. (Golding, 2008, p 63)

Some children may experience initial relief at being removed from a dangerous environment but there will still be a sense of loss. As the child develops, they will need to make sense of these losses if the past is not to continually interfere with the present. Many children commonly attribute their removal as being a result of their bad behaviour and this can then be re-enacted within the new home.

Resilience

The likelihood of developing a mental problem can be seen as a result of the interplay between risk and adversity factors with resilience or protective factors. Over the past 25 years, a growing field of research has developed around the factors that enable some children to succeed in spite of adversity or disadvantage. Initial research focused on the individual or intrinsic factors that develop resilient qualities and led to the idea that some children were innately more resilient than their peers. The focus then moved to looking at the extrinsic factors that can be found in the family and community, that can either enhance risk or protection. This latter emphasis has led to a more positive outlook in which the key question is: 'What needs to happen or what resources need to be put in place to improve the odds for the child where they are stacked against them?'

This focus has helped to develop mental health promotion. Dwivedi and Harper (2004) write:

> Mental health promotion includes strengthening individuals (such as through enhancing parenting, self-esteem, psychosocial competence and so on), communities (such as through social inclusion, anti-bullying school policies and so on) and reducing structural barriers to mental health (such as removing discrimination and inequalities in access to housing, education, employment and so on). (p 17)

In developing resilience, Aumann and Hart (2009) encourage parents and carers to consider five areas: basics, belonging, learning, coping and core self. In the absence of good basic care, interventions can be developed to prevent further damage or compensate for threats, e.g. nutritional programmes, early childhood education, adequate medical care, education that can promote skills in attention and thinking skills, safe housing, etc. What is core to each of these domains is that they are best achieved when there is a competent and caring adult available. Ideally this should be a parent, but the presence of a caring adult who is not a parent can still bring about lifelong changes. Through the provision of one or more supportive relationships (e.g. teacher, youth worker, mentor, family member, member of the faith community), a child can be introduced to new opportunities, helped through adverse events and empowered to develop their own voice. These experiences help the child to develop a sense of competence and positive self-esteem, a sense of belonging and security, and a sense of self-efficacy, which are the essential building blocks for managing adversity.

Resilience is not a static concept and children may display resilience in some contexts and not others, but a core meaning of resilience, as outlined by Gilligan, is that 'change is possible' (2009, p 10). In considering the mental health of a young person, it is good practice to consider the intrinsic strengths and skills that they bring (e.g. ability to learn and make friendships) but also to identify what network or team around the child can be put in place to maximise their potential.

Other issues

Contact arrangements

Care plans for looked after children must consider the frequency and nature of contact with family members. There may also be directions from the court, which aim to balance the needs and rights of both birth parents and the child. However, the Children Act (England and Wales) 1989 and the Children (Northern Ireland) Order 1995 require courts to prioritise the welfare of the child. An assessment around the needs and well-being of the child can assist the courts and those professionals involved in representing and protecting the needs of the child.

The mental health practitioner can provide both observational evidence and an informed perspective on the developmental needs of the child. Schofield and Simmonds (2011), in a paper on contact for infants subject to care proceedings, note that 'the key point here is that enabling the infant to achieve developmental goals during this critical period is of great value, whether following care proceedings the infant returns home, is placed with extended family members or is placed for adoption'.

In his guide on planning for contact in permanent placements, Adams notes that 'it is widely agreed that maintaining or developing contact must provide a developmental benefit for the child: it has no inherent value in itself' (2012, p 10). He continues that the key purposes are to enable attachment to new carers, to promote positive identity, and to enable emotional healing and promote self-esteem.

An assessment can address central questions that relate to the child's stage of development. These can include:

- Do the frequency, length and quality of contact sessions promote a positive experience with the birth parent?
- Is the child's need for consistent physical and emotional care in the alternative home severely interrupted or compromised?
- Is the child able to make a sufficient recovery from contact, especially if highly stressed?
- What are the child's wishes and feelings about contact arrangements, having regard for their age, understanding and the complexity of the issues involved?
- Does the child have any vulnerability (e.g. known abuse or trauma) that would potentially put the child at risk of re-traumatisation from contact with birth parents?
- Are the arrangements for contact robust enough to prevent undue stress due to factors such as time spent in travel, lack of familiarity with escorts who may change frequently, or unfamiliar venues?

It's really hard . . . we want her to see her mum but she gets so upset and for the next few days is out of sorts with herself. We were arranging contact every two or three weeks but are wondering if this is doing more harm than good?
(Grandparents, with a special guardianship order, caring for their four-year-old granddaughter)

Therapeutic support and specialist LAC teams

Mental health services are frequently asked to provide therapy for looked after children. Unfortunately, there has often been difficulty in accessing this help in many areas. Holland *et al* (2005) conclude that the availability of mental health services is one of the key issues affecting the stability and continuity of a placement. More specifically, Selwyn *et al*'s study (2006), which followed 130 children placed for adoption, found that a recurring theme was the need for ongoing support from CAMHS, with particular help for attachment difficulties and conduct disorders. Minnis *et al* (2006) studied a group of 182 children in "mainstream" foster care in Scotland and found that their overall mental health difficulties predicted ongoing involvement with social workers, and that those with elevated hyperactivity scores were more likely to receive community paediatric services. This study also found a low rate of access to CAMHS and that the access was unrelated to the number and severity of children's mental health problems.

The statutory guidance for England (DCSF and DH, 2009, revision expected in 2015), recognises the increased prevalence of mental or behavioural problems in children coming into care. This guidance, along with the good practice guidance issued by NICE/SCIE (2010; 2013), makes key recommendations for dedicated and specialist mental health services to be available to provide mental health assessments and therapeutic support. This can include interventions such as consultation, advice, support and training groups for both professionals and parents or carers.

In Northern Ireland, the report *Healthy Child, Healthy Future* (Department of Health, Social Services and Public Safety (DHSSPS), 2010) recognises looked after children as having acute physical and emotional health care needs for which more targeted services are required.

Services need to be targeted yet flexible in their delivery. The statutory guidance recognises that, when young people are consulted, their priorities are more often around their feelings about life, housing issues, having close personal relationships, their care experience and depression. Incidents of self-harm and the prevalence of depression are high and young people are sensitive to the stigma they perceive as being associated with mental health services. This worry about being stigmatised is shared by some professionals and has sometimes acted as a barrier to seeking mental health support. However, mental health services that are multidisciplinary, and which practise effective multi-agency collaboration, enable interventions that may be directed to the child, carer and birth family and thus broaden the traditional understanding of "therapy". Interventions may initially take the form of advice given to the care team, or work with the carer and child together, and may only later consist of providing direct work to the child or young person.

Specialist and dedicated LAC teams (whether sitting organisationally within the local authority or health services) that are jointly commissioned are in a better position to develop comprehensive services. This can facilitate more effective multidisciplinary working, communication and planning. They can be more flexible, and include:

- access to mental health services that are not dependent on diagnosis or tight referral criteria;
- informal and community-based services;
- a choice for young people about whether they participate in counselling or therapy;
- a range of therapeutic approaches that are tailored to the needs of the child and carer;
- consultation around specific issues and specialist training for carers and professionals in promoting emotional well-being, and the early identification of mental health difficulties at different developmental stages;
- capacity and expertise to work with groups such as black and minority ethnic groups or unaccompanied asylum seekers;
- high quality assessments that assist with planning around placement moves and sibling contact issues;
- supporting transfer to adult mental health services.

Post-adoption support

The Adoption Support Services Regulations 2005 in England and the Adoption Support Services (Local Authorities) (Wales) Regulations 2005 in Wales require the local authority to assess need in relation to adoption support, including therapeutic support. It would be sensible for any assessment and plan for adoption and support to build on the work already undertaken to ensure that there is a seamless transition to adoption support services and to avoid duplication of assessments.

In Northern Ireland, the Adoption (Northern Ireland) Order 1987 requires Trusts to establish and maintain a service to meet the needs of children who have been adopted, their birth parents or guardians and adoptive parents. Adoption Regional Policy and Procedures (Northern Ireland) 2010 outline the key elements of a comprehensive post-adoption support service.

As the child ceases to be looked after at this point, some CAMHS do not extend their looked after children provisions. However, the child's needs are no different to when they were in care and often the problems can intensify as the child experiences new carers. Adoptive parents may have had no parenting experience and yet are caring for some of the most damaged children. It is important therefore that children being placed for permanency have adequate mental health assessments that can inform social workers and adoption panels so that the post-adoption support plan is well informed about the likely level of the child's future needs.

> *It was such a relief when the worker from CAMHS "got it". We have seen so many professionals who didn't know what we were on about. People kept telling us it was just normal adolescence but she rejected all our help, fell out with every person in her class and seemed to hate us but could be nice to people she had never met.*
> (Adoptive mother talking about access to services)

Common dilemmas

Whose responsibility is it to provide mental health services when a child has moved out of area?

Mental health teams in different areas may provide different services, as well as having varying referral criteria and thresholds for intervention. These variations may be a barrier for looked after children, for example, continuing to receive Theraplay services available in a previous placement.

It is the responsibility of health services from the placing authority to commission appropriate mental health provision for individual children placed out of area. Health services in the authority where the child is placed are required to provide the service. Arrangements should be agreed prior to the placement. Further information is available on out of area placements in Chapter 17.

How long can CAMHS continue seeing a young person who is looked after?

CAMHS are tasked with the provision of mental health services until a young person's 18th birthday (National Service Framework for Children, Young People and Maternity Services 2004, Standard 9). Young people leaving care may well require long-term support, and accessing adult mental health services can be difficult as the threshold for severity is generally higher for referral to adult services. Multi-agency LAC teams or networks are generally more able to extend the age range for help or to develop a pathway of access to adult services. The NICE/SCIE guidelines (2010, Recommendation 49; 2013) propose that case management and treatment of young people receiving mental health services continue until an assessment and completed care plan with relevant adult services are in place.

Mental disorder versus emotional and behavioural difficulties

Children and young people entering care frequently present with a wide variety of emotional and behavioural problems. Professionals and carers who are not trained in mental health are often concerned that the problems indicate a mental disorder or syndrome which requires diagnosis. Common queries are about ADHD, autism or mental illnesses, such as schizophrenia and bipolar affective disorder. These are understandable concerns as the initial presentations can appear very similar, and mental health assessment is important in determining the aetiology of the presenting behaviour as the treatment plan will be shaped by the formulation.

Case study

Jack was moved into foster care when he was five years old. His foster carer was very concerned that after three months, Jack was unable to sit still for long, he didn't listen to instructions, kept taking food and talked inappropriately to complete strangers; she therefore wondered if he had ADHD. Jack had grown up in a household with high levels of domestic violence and had been severely neglected and often gone without food. He had become sensitised to high levels of danger and was constantly on the alert. He had also had to take control of his own welfare on many occasions and had little expectation that adults could meet his needs. Assessment suggested that these experiences accounted for his behaviour and strategies were put in place to help Jack experience safety and to have ready access to food. His concentration improved and his need to accost strangers diminished as his reliance on his carer developed.

Case study

Sarah arrived in her adoptive home aged four and displayed no upset on leaving her foster home. She appeared uninterested in her new home and sat for long stretches fiddling with her clothes. She did not get upset or seek comfort when she fell over. She liked to spin herself around a lot and seemed unaware of others around her. Her adoptive parents were concerned that she had some autistic traits. Sarah had previously lived with her birth mother who had been a heroin addict and had been involved in the sex trade to fund her habit. She had been known to leave Sarah on her own at night whilst she was out. Sarah's birth mother had physically cared for her child but had not been attuned to her daughter's emotional and psychological needs for safety, interaction, fun and play. As Sarah's needs and wishes had not been recognised or noticed by her mother, she had no experience of being held in mind. Consequently, she had not developed an awareness of other people's states of mind (i.e. their wishes, desires and intentions) and had become used to self-soothing through rhythmic movement. Sarah's adoptive parents were helped to use principles associated with baby bonding (keeping Sarah close, noticing her unique qualities, developing sensory experiences) which enabled her to experience emotional and psychological nurture, and experience herself through new eyes.

In practice, the process of clarifying whether a child's presenting difficulties are part of an organic condition such as autism can be challenging, particularly as detailed developmental information may be absent. Using information from as wide a source as possible helps to build a baseline assessment that can then be matched against the child's progress in placement.

An associated dilemma for referrers is when to make a referral for specialist mental health input. Some services have high referral thresholds; some have specific criteria such as not providing therapy until a child is in a settled or long-term placement. Golding (2010) makes the point that creative solutions are needed to address this issue and services will have to provide a broad range of mental health interventions, working with the child, family and wider system as appropriate. Increasingly, evidence points to the benefits of early interventions as a way of preventing severe mental health problems.

Providing an assessment for emotional and behavioural problems can itself be controversial as social workers are often concerned that by naming current or potential difficulties (such as foetal alcohol spectrum disorder) that the child may have, people can be put off considering the child for adoption. However, a common criticism from adopters is, 'We weren't given a clear understanding of what to expect'. Providing a well-informed assessment can be used constructively to forward plan what help may be needed, and should not be compromised. Sharing of all information is essential so that prospective carers can consider their ability to meet the needs of the child. This will also reduce the risk of placement breakdown.

'I'm not mad, I don't want to see a shrink'

Young people are often wary about seeing a mental health professional for fear of being stigmatised, yet those caring for the child are often worried by the child's behaviour, particularly if the young person self-harms. Deliberate self-harm needs to be taken seriously, as it does demonstrate the young person's level of distress and may be indicative of a more serious psychiatric disorder. Referrers generally identify externalising problems more readily but many looked after children have hidden emotional distress and are at greater risk of their difficulties not being picked up by services (Golding, 2010). Inter-agency meetings where mental health professionals can share knowledge with social care staff and carers can help to highlight these concerns but also assist in decision-making and recommend more timely interventions. In the event that a young person refuses to see a mental health professional, it is important that those caring for the child have access to consultation and advice. Specialist LAC teams are more able to be flexible regarding who is seen (i.e. social worker, foster carer, residential worker, school support staff) and also offer alternative ways of engaging with and seeing the young person (e.g. in an alternative venue). In some localities there are good services provided by the voluntary sector, which are often more acceptable to the young person because they are not statutory.

In the event that a young person still refuses to be seen, those caring for the child can be supported and given advice on how to deal with emergency situations. Use of the Mental Health Act 1983 (England and Wales) and the Mental Health (Northern Ireland) Order 1986 is reserved for very acute situations when the young person's mental health is so poor that they are at serious risk to themselves or others. In these situations, if the young person is over 16, use may be made of the Mental Capacity Act 2005 (England and Wales) as this provides a statutory framework for those who lack capacity to make decisions for themselves. In Northern Ireland, a new Mental Capacity Bill, which will combine mental incapacity and mental health provision, is currently being drafted and at the time of writing (December 2014), timescales for its introduction are unclear. Similarly, admission to an in-patient mental health unit is only for serious cases of mental illness. For young people who have been through multiple placements, it is advisable, if at all possible, to try to provide interventions in the community.

What health professionals should do

- Ensure that mental, emotional and behavioural health needs are considered at the time of every health assessment.
- Be aware of any changes in regulations and guidance in this area.
- Keep abreast of developments in understanding mental and emotional health issues in this population.
- Be aware of the range of mental health services available locally and the referral criteria.
- Advocate for the development of specialist services designed to meet the needs of looked after and adopted children.
- Ensure that all available information is shared with prospective adopters and long-term carers at matching.
- Promote understanding that adopted children and their families may require ongoing or intermittent support from mental health professionals.

Key points

- Children and young people entering care are at greater risk of having or developing a mental health problem or having difficulties with emotional well-being that require specialised advice and interventions.
- Access to mental health services for looked after children is now a statutory requirement and works best when there are dedicated resources that have been jointly commissioned by health services and the local authority.
- Mental health services meet children's needs most effectively when they are multi-disciplinary and work in partnership with other agencies so that they can be accessible to all who support the child and flexible in how and when they see them.

- Comprehensive mental health assessments can assist in the early detection of mental health issues, in provision of advice to carers and social workers and in recommending appropriate treatment interventions.
- Mental health assessments can help ascertain if a child's presenting difficulties are a result of early adversity (which may begin in utero), insecure attachment relationships or the impact of trauma and loss.
- Young people and children, including babies, have needs and rights to have contact with birth families but consideration of how this is best achieved can be assisted by a mental health assessment.
- Therapeutic services need to be flexible in their delivery and offer a wide range of interventions that can support the child and adults who care for them.
- Adopted children and their families often have as much need for support as looked after children, and well informed assessment can assist the adoption support plan in obtaining necessary services.

Bibliography

Adams P. (2012) *Planning for Contact in Permanent Placements*, London: BAAF

Ainsworth M.D.S., Blehar M.C., Waters E. and Wall S. (1978) *Patterns of Attachment: A psychological study of the Strange Situation*, Hiilsdale, NJ: Erlbaum

Aumann K and Hart A (2009) *Helping Children with Complex Needs Bounce Back*, London: Jessica Kingsley Publishers

BAAF (2008) *Carers' Report: Profile of behavioural and emotional well-being of a child or young person*, London: BAAF

Belsky J. and de Haan M. (2011) 'Parenting and children's brain development: the end of the beginning', *Journal of Child Psychology and Psychiatry*, 52:4, pp 409–428

Bowlby J. (1973) *Attachment and Loss, Vol.11 Separation: Anxiety and anger*, New York, NY: Basic Books

Bowlby J. (1980) *Attachment and Loss, Vol.111 Loss: Sadness and depression*, New York, NY: Basic Books

Bowlby J. (1982) *Attachment and Loss, Vol.1 Attachment*, New York, NY: Basic Books

Bowlby J. (1998) *A Secure Base: Clinical applications of attachment theory*, London: Routledge

Chudley A.E., Conry J., Cook J.L., Loock C., Rosales T. and LeBlanc N. (2005) 'Foetal alcohol spectrum disorder: Canadian guidelines for diagnosis', *Canadian Medical Association Journal*, 172, pp S1–S21

Cosgrove C, Hill C and Charles T (2004) 'The effects of smoking tobacco', in Phillips R (ed) *Children Exposed to Parental Substance Misuse*, London: BAAF

Department for Children, Schools and Families (2007) *Care Matters: Time for change*, London: Stationery Office

Department for Children, Schools and Families and Department of Health (2009) *Statutory Guidance on Promoting the Health and Well-Being of Looked After Children:* London: Stationery Office

Department for Education and Skills (2004) *Every Child Matters: Change for children*, London: Stationery Office

Department of Health (2004) *National Service Framework for Children, Young People and Families*, London: DH

Department of Health (2007) *Who Pays? Establishing the responsible commissioner*, London: DH

Department of Health, Social Services and Public Safety (2010) *Healthy Child, Healthy Future: A framework for the universal child health promotion*, Belfast: DHSSPS

Dimigen G., Del Priore C., Butler S., Evans S., Ferguson L. and Swan M. (1999) 'Psychiatric disorder among children at time of entering local authority care: questionnaire survey', *British Medical Journal*, 319, p 675

Dwivedi K.N. and Harper P.B. (2004) *Promoting the Emotional Well-Being of Children and Adolescents and Preventing Their Mental Ill Health*, London: Jessica Kingsley Publishers

Ford T., Vostanis P., Meltzer H. and Goodman R. (2007) 'Psychiatric disorder among British children looked after by local authorities: comparison with children living in private households', *British Journal of Psychiatry*, 198, pp 319–325

Gilligan R. (2009) *Promoting Resilience*, London: BAAF

Golding K.S. (2008) *Nurturing Attachments*, London: Jessica Kingsley Publishers

Golding K.S. (2010) 'Multi-agency and specialist working to meet the mental health needs of children in care and adopted', *Clinical Child Psychology and Psychiatry*, 15:4, pp 573–587

Goodman R. (1997) 'The Strengths and Difficulties Questionnaire: a research note', *Journal of Child Psychology and Psychiatry*, 38, pp 581–586

Goodman R. (1999) 'The extended version of the Strengths and Difficulties Questionnaire as a guide to child psychiatric caseness and consequent burden', *Journal of Child Psychology and Psychiatry*, 40, pp 791–801

Holland S., Faulkner A. and Perez-del-Aguila R. (2005) 'Promoting stability and continuity of care for looked after children: a survey and critical review', *Child and Family Social Work*, 10, pp 29–41

Manning M.A. and Hoyme H.E. (2007) 'Foetal alcohol spectrum disorders: a practical clinical approach to diagnosis', *Neuroscience and Biobehavioural Reviews*, 31, pp 230–238

McCann J., James A., Wilson S. and Dunn G. (1996) 'Prevalence of psychiatric disorders in young people in the care system', *British Medical Journal*, 313, pp 1529–1530

McElhatton P (2004) 'The effects of drug misuse in pregnancy', in Phillips R (ed) *Children Exposed to Parental Substance Misuse*, London: BAAF

Meltzer M., Corbin T., Gatward R., Goodman R. and Ford T. (2003) *The Mental Health of Young People Looked After by Local Authorities in England*, London: Stationery Office

Minnis H., Everett K., Pelosi J., Dunn J. and Knapp M. (2006) 'Children in foster care: mental health, service use and costs', *European Child Adolescent Psychiatry*, 15:63, pp 63–70

NICE/SCIE (2010) *Promoting the Quality of Life of Looked-After Children and Young People*, PH28, London: NICE

NICE/SCIE (2013) *Looked After Children and Young People*, London: NICE/SCIE

O'Connor T.G. and Zeanah C.H. (2003) 'Attachment disorders: assessment strategies and treatment approaches', *Attachment and Human Development*, 5, pp 233–244

Office of the First Minister and Deputy First Minister (2006) *Our Children and Young People – Our Pledge: A ten year strategy for children and young people in Northern Ireland, 2006–2016*, Belfast: Office of the First Minister and Deputy First Minister

Plant M. (2004) 'Parental alcohol misuse: implications for child placements', in Phillips R (ed) *Children Exposed to Parental Substance Misuse*, London: BAAF

Richardson J. and Joughin C. (2002) *The Mental Health Needs of Looked After Children*, London: Gaskell

Schofield G. and Simmonds J. (2011) 'Contact for infants subject to care proceedings', *Family Law*, June, pp 617–622

Selwyn J., Sturgess W., Quinton D. and Baxter C. (2006) *Costs and Outcomes of Non-Infant Adoptions*, London: BAAF

Sroufe A.L. (2005) 'Attachment and development: a prospective longitudinal study from birth to adulthood', *Attachment and Human Development*, 7, pp 349–367

Sunderland M. (2006) *What Every Parent Needs to Know*, London: Dorling Kindersley

Tarren-Sweeney M. (2011) 'Concordance of mental health impairment and service utilisation among children in care', *Clinical Child Psychology and Psychiatry*, 15:4, pp 481–495

van der Kolk B. (2005) 'Developmental trauma disorder', *Psychiatric Annals*, 33:5, pp 401–408

5 Health provision through pathways of care

Carolyn Sampeys

Looked after children should be considered as part of a continuum. The majority of children enter the care of a local authority because of abuse or neglect. Prior to becoming looked after, many are likely to have been considered as "children in need" by the local authority's children's services. Many will have been the subject of safeguarding concerns and child protection conferences, family group conferencing and additional support. They may have been subject to a child protection plan.

In England, statistics released by the Department for Education (DfE) contain figures on the numbers of children referred to and assessed by children's services, the characteristics of children in need and children who were the subject of a child protection plan. There were 378,600 children in need at 31 March 2013 and a total of 736,100 episodes of need throughout the year. A total of 43,100 children were the subject of a child protection plan at 31 March 2013 (DfE, 2013). The statistics can be accessed on the DfE website (see Bibliography for details).

In Northern Ireland, figures published jointly by the Department of Health, Social Services and Public Safety (DHSSPS), and Northern Ireland Statistics and Research Agency indicated that 29,508 children were referred to Health and Social Care Trusts during 2012/13. On 31 March 2013, the names of 1,961 children were on child protection registers in Northern Ireland, and 2,807 children were looked after (DHSSPS, 2013). These figures can be accessed via the DHSSPS website (see Bibliography for details).

In Wales, there were 20,240 children in need included in the Children in Need (CIN) census, and 2,295 children on the Child Protection Register at 31 March 2012 (Welsh Government, 2014). The statistics can be accessed on the Welsh Government website (see Bibliography for details).

Whether the child is deemed to be "in need", "subject to a child protection plan" or looked after, this is still the same child with the same historic concerns and the same adverse life events.

Raising awareness of the needs of looked after children in health care settings is an important part of the role of health professionals for looked after children. Training of paediatricians, nurses, GPs, therapists, CAMHS and colleagues in all fields who may come into contact with looked after children is important, to ensure an awareness of their vulnerability and additional needs, as well as the complexity of consent issues and statutory requirements. This is particularly important in Accident and Emergency departments, Ear, Nose and Throat (ENT), paediatric surgery, etc. Training of colleagues within

Figure 1
Pathway of a looked after child

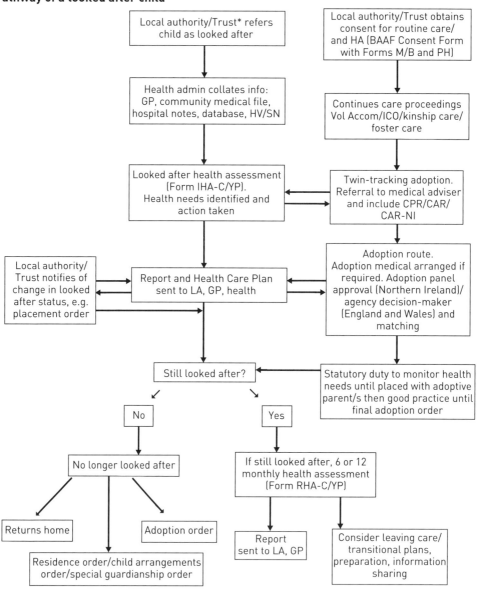

* Trust refers to Health and Social Care Trust in Northern Ireland

Key: GP: general practitioner; HV: health visitor; SN: school nurse; HA: health assessment; ICO: interim care order; Vol accom: voluntary accommodation; CPR: child's permenance report (England); CAR: child's adoption report (Wales); CAR-NI: child's adoption report (Northern Ireland).

local authorities and education departments is also important to ensure effective multi-agency working.

Pathways in the care system

There are, by necessity, different pathways for children within the care system. Over half will return home with or without continued intervention by children's services. For children whose care plan does not include rehabilitation home, there are a range of options for achieving permanency. These include kinship care, special guardianship orders (England and Wales), residence orders (Northern Ireland), child arrangements orders (England and Wales, formerly residence orders till April 2014), long-term foster care and adoption.

Figure 1 details the pathway of a looked after child. The guidance below outlines various steps along the pathway and includes reference to a range of BAAF health forms that have been developed and revised by the BAAF Health Group over the years. This guidance will be helpful for health professionals to share with multi-agency colleagues to ensure an understanding of processes within health and between agencies. It can provide the basis for drawing up local multi–agency pathways and procedures.

Health guidance for pathway of looked after child: procedure where child/young person is accommodated

BAAF publishes integrated health forms, which are referenced below.

- When a child is accommodated by the local authority/Trust, consent should be obtained from the child's birth parent/s for routine care, including immunisations, emergency treatment and also health assessment under the Care Planning, Placement and Case Review (England) Regulations 2010, the Children (Northern Ireland) Order 1986, *Guidance and Regulations Volume 3, Family Placements and Private Fostering* and the Placement of Children (Wales) Regulations 2007. Looked after children essential information documentation can be used.
- The local authority/Trust meets with the birth parent/s to explain the statutory health assessment and stresses that the birth parent/s make an important contribution to this. The social worker explains the need to obtain child and family health history and asks the birth parent/s to sign BAAF Consent Forms (one for each parent for each child). The social worker also asks the birth parent/s to complete BAAF Form PH (parental health, one for each parent for each child), and provides assistance if needed. Engagement with the child's birth parent/s is important. Every effort should be made to continue to engage with them at every stage in the process.
- The local authority or Trust/Health Board, depending on local arrangements, sends Form M/B and a copy of the Consent Form to the hospital of the child's birth with a

covering letter requesting completion (or locally agreed procedure).

- The local authority/Trust refers each child/young person to a responsible professional within the Trust/Health Board. The referral *must* contain essential information and enclosures, e.g. Part A of BAAF Form IHA–C or IHA–YP (initial health assessment for a child or young person), with consent to carry out the health assessment, and a Consent Form to gather health information on the child and birth parent/s. This should be carried out in a timely manner to ensure timescales specified in regulations can be met.
- The Trust/Health Board requires a comprehensive social history from the local authority, e.g. core assessment, minutes of child protection conference. Children's services should advise in advance if there are any issues regarding personal safety.
- If any information is not available, reasons for non-enclosure should be identified. This is likely to delay compilation of the health report.
- The Trust/Health Board arranges the LAC health assessment in or out of county. A form such as BAAF Form IHA–C or YP (initial health assessment of a child or young person) is recommended. The child's foster carer, and ideally the social worker who is familiar with the child, should be present and the birth parent/s are invited to the appointment so that the health professional can discuss the health history of the child and birth parent/s in such a way that the child's health is promoted, whatever the final care plan may be. In certain circumstances, it may be necessary for the health professional to meet with the birth parent/s at a different time or place.
- The local authority/Trust arranges for the child's foster carer to complete a profile on the child, using BAAF Form CR–C or CR–YP (carer's report on a child or young person). This should be completed once the child has settled into the placement and the foster carer has come to know the child, and in time to inform the initial health assessment.
- The health professional carries out a LAC health assessment, completing Part B of Form IHA–C or IHA–YP, using information from various sources, e.g. Form M/B, Form PH, Form CR–C or CR–YP, child health database, health visitor, GP, specialists, health records of child and birth parents, and examination of the child. The health professional completes a summary and health recommendations (Part C), which is then forwarded to the child's social worker to inform the health care plan. A copy of Part C is also sent to the GP who holds the lead record. It is essential that a copy of the full report is kept in the child's community medical record which will follow them should they move out of area. NB: In adoption cases, the whole report should be sent to the adoption agency to comply with adoption agency regulations.
- The local authority/Trust notifies the nominated health professional when the review or update health assessment is due. This is completed using BAAF Form RHA-C or RHA-YP (review health assessment of a child or young person). The Trust/Health Board may have a process for flagging health reviews.

- In England and Wales, when adoption is considered as an option for a child following review, the child's social worker refers the child to the adoption team within the local authority. Local procedures should be drawn up to ensure continuity and that the child's record follows them. In Northern Ireland, practice varies but where adoption is proposed as the child's care plan, the child is normally referred to the adoption or family placement team for matching. While social workers from this team will not usually assume statutory responsibility for the case, they will retain involvement with the child and the adoptive family until adoption has been achieved.
- The adoption agency/Trust notifies the medical adviser that adoption is being considered and ensures that any new or outstanding or updated information on the child or birth parents, including Form CPR (in England)/CAR (in Wales)/CAR–NI (in Northern Ireland) and any reports prepared for court by experts, such as by psychiatrists and psychologists, are provided to the medical adviser for consideration in the adoption health report. The Adoption Agencies Regulations 2005, Regulation 15(2), and Adoption Agencies (Wales) Regulations 2005, Regulation 15(2), require the adoption agency to arrange an examination and obtain a health report, unless the agency's medical adviser advises that it is unnecessary. The Adoption Agencies Regulations (Northern Ireland) 1989, Regulation 7(c), requires the Trust to obtain a written report from a medical practitioner unless such a report has been obtained in the six months before opening the child's file. *Provided all the required information is available from comprehensive LAC health assessment/s*, then a separate health assessment for adoption should not be necessary. If the child has had multiple review health assessments, the medical adviser may prefer to write an updated report including this information.
- The adoption agency/Trust arranges for the case to be referred for a decision that the child should be placed for adoption following a Looked After Review where adoption is identified as the child's permanence plan. If the child is the subject of ongoing care proceedings in England or Wales, this decision will be taken by the agency decision-maker on the submitted paperwork. In all other cases, the agency decision-maker must take the recommendation of the adoption panel into account before making a decision. The medical adviser provides a written summary of the child's health history, current state of health and future health needs to the adoption agency, and attends the panel to interpret and advise on health issues, as well as acting as a full panel member. Where the child's case is referred straight to the agency decision-maker (in England and Wales), the medical adviser will need to be available to provide any further advice that the decision-maker may require.
- In England and Wales, the local authority notifies the Health Board of any changes in placement or status for the looked after child/young person, including movement home, placement order, adoption order, special guardianship order or child

arrangements order (formerly residence order till April 2014). In Northern Ireland, the Trust ensures that all records in relation to the child are updated.

- Relevant health information is shared as appropriate to provide health care, e.g. with the child's birth parent/s, foster carers, GP, consultants, and to assist with care planning, e.g. for adoption or special guardianship, and for planning when young people leave care.

Bibliography

Department for Education (2013) *Characteristics of Children in Need in England: 2012 to 2013*, available at: www.gov.uk/government/publications/characteristics-of-children-in-need-in-england-2012-to-2013

Department of Health, Social Services and Public Safety (2013) *Children's Social Care Statistics for Northern Ireland 2012/13*, available at: www.dhsspsni.gov.uk/childrenssocialcarestatisticsfor northernireland201213.pdf

Welsh Government (2014) *Wales Children in Need Census*, available at: www.wales.gov.uk/statistics-and-research/wales-children-need-census/?lang=en

6 Consent and legal provision

Alexandra Conroy Harris and Melanie Bracewell

Health provision for looked after children will require consent for:

- medical treatment;
- accessing health records of children and their birth families;
- carrying out health assessments; and
- sharing of health information with relevant parties/partners.

Consent for medical treatment

Consent for medical treatment needs to be obtained in all circumstances except for emergency life-threatening situations or where a court has ordered treatment to be administered. Treatment without consent could result in legal action against the practitioner in both civil and criminal courts. A young person may be able to give consent themselves, or there may be more than one adult who is able to give consent to the treatment of a child. An adult may only give valid consent to the treatment of a child if they have parental responsibility for that child. It is only necessary to obtain consent from one source, although it is good practice to consult all parties with parental responsibility for a child.

Parental responsibility

A woman who gives birth to a child automatically has parental responsibility for her child, which cannot be removed except by the child's adoption or, in the case of a surrogate mother, by parental order.

A father has parental responsibility if:

- he was married to the child's mother at the time of the child's birth, or has subsequently married her;
- he is named on the child's birth certificate (but only if the birth was registered after 1 December 2003);
- he has entered into a parental responsibility agreement with the child's mother; or
- a court has made a parental responsibility order in his favour.

Parental responsibility granted by a court may be removed by court order.

Adoptive parents of a child have parental responsibility for that child. Prospective adopters in England and Wales will have parental responsibility for a child placed with them for adoption, but such responsibility is subject to any restrictions imposed by the placing authority. In Northern Ireland, adoptive parents acquire parental responsibility only on the granting of an adoption order.

Where a child is conceived in a surrogacy arrangement, the commissioning parents will obtain parental responsibility through a parental order, which allows for the re-registration of the child's birth, naming them as the child's parents.

The female partner of a woman conceiving by artificial insemination will be able to register as a child's second female parent and so acquire parental responsibility.

A step-parent (a person married to, or the civil partner of, a child's parent) may acquire parental responsibility by court order, parental responsibility agreement or adoption.

A person who is named in a court order as a special guardian for a child, or in whose favour a residence order or child arrangements order (formerly a residence order in England and Wales till April 2014) has been made, has parental responsibility for that child for so long as the order remains in force. In England and Wales, a court must give a parent, and may give any other person named in a child arrangements order, parental responsibility.

A local authority in England and Wales or a Health and Social Care Trust in Northern Ireland will have parental responsibility for a child under an emergency protection order or a care order (interim or final). In England and Wales, it may also have parental responsibility through a placement order or, in Northern Ireland, a freeing order. The local authority/Trust will not have parental responsibility for a child who:

- is being cared for by it under a child assessment order;
- is under police protection;
- has been remanded into its care by a criminal court; or
- is being looked after in England and Wales under s.20 of the Children Act 1989 (with parental consent), or in Northern Ireland under s.21 of the Children (Northern Ireland) Order 1995.

Local authorities/Trusts, foster carers, private foster carers, relatives, child-minders and others will not have parental responsibility for a child but may be able to exercise another's parental responsibility on their behalf. This is likely to be evidenced by written agreement (for instance, a placement agreement for foster carers). This is called "delegated authority" and may be given for a particular event or arrangement, e.g. a medical appointment. In the absence of such authority, the person who has care of the child is able to do what is reasonable in the circumstances of the case for the purposes of safeguarding or promoting the child's welfare. Statutory guidance states that what is reasonable will depend on the urgency of the situation and how practical it is to consult a person with parental responsibility. So, for example, a teacher or foster carer may take a child in their care to hospital for urgent treatment for a minor injury without the parents' consent. Where there is time to discuss the need for treatment with a parent, this should be done wherever possible, and the parents be given the opportunity to consent or object to the proposed course of treatment.

A medical professional will only require consent from one person with parental responsibility; however, it is best practice to seek consent from all parties with parental responsibility for that child, wherever feasible. If others oppose the treatment, they may apply to court for a specific issues order, for directions under an interim care order or to the High Court for wardship. These orders have been used where one parent opposes immunisations, as well as in extreme cases where one party wishes to give or withhold lifesaving treatment.

Child consenting to their own treatment

A child may consent to their own treatment if they are thought to be competent to do so. A child of 16 is assumed to be competent, but the assumption could be rebutted if the child has learning difficulties or is otherwise unable to understand the implications of consenting or refusing treatment. The tests for deciding a child's competence were laid down in *Gillick v West Norfolk & Wisbech Area Health Authority* [1985] UKHL 7, as a result of which a child is now referred to as being "Gillick competent" or not. The case was brought by a mother who wanted assurances that her daughter would not be given contraception without the mother's knowledge and consent. The judgement of Lord Fraser gave specific guidelines on the prescribing of contraception to under-age girls without parental consent; these are known as the Fraser Guidelines. The principles set out have implications for all treatment of children, not just for the provision of contraception.

Gillick competence

Parental right yields to the child's right to make his own decisions when he reaches a sufficient understanding and intelligence to be capable of making up his own mind on the matter requiring decision.

. . . it is not enough that she should understand the nature of the advice which is being given: she must also have a sufficient maturity to understand what is involved.
Lord Scarman

Consent to access child and family health records

Health records contain sensitive personal information that is protected by the Data Protection Act 1998. It should usually only be disclosed when the subject of that information has consented to it being shared with others. In the same way in which consent for treatment of a child can be provided on a child's behalf by a person with parental responsibility for him or her, consent for disclosure of a child's health records can be given by any person with parental responsibility. A child may also give consent for disclosure of health information if he or she is competent to do so. The age at which a child is assumed to have capacity to consent to information sharing is 12, and the Department for Education (2011a) has published guidance: *How to Judge a Child or Young Person's Capacity to Give Consent to Sharing of Personal Information.*

If a parent refuses to consent to sharing their own medical records, it may still be possible to obtain relevant information. Information held on the mother's records may also be the child's information, to which they would be entitled under Data Protection Act principles, so, for example, a mother may refuse to allow disclosure about her substance use during pregnancy, but information that the foetus failed to gain an appropriate birth weight because of maternal smoking is the child's information and so can be shared. It will be for the data controller of the hospital or practice that holds the mother's notes to separate out the child's information from the mother's and decide what can be disclosed. Information about genetic conditions, conditions that could have been transmitted from mother to child during pregnancy and infectious diseases to which the child could have been exposed while living with that parent may be disclosed if it is in the public interest to do so. Government guidance, *Information Sharing: Guidance for practitioners and managers* (Department for Children, Schools and Families (DCSF), 2008) sets out helpful principles. It may be in the public interest to disclose such information to enable testing or treatment that would protect the child from serious harm, notwithstanding the parent's refusal to consent. Legal advice or advice from your organisation's Caldicott Guardian* should be sought before disclosing material in the public interest.

If a parent has died, access to their medical records is governed in England and Wales by the Access to Health Records Act 1990, and in Northern Ireland by the Access to Health Records (Northern Ireland) Order 1993. This allows access to records by the personal representative (the executor of their will or the person to whom a grant of letters of administration has been made if the deceased died intestate) of the deceased person, who may not necessarily be their next of kin, or any person who may have a claim as a

---

* Organisations that access patient records are required to have a Caldicott Guardian, who is a senior person responsible for protecting the confidentiality of patients and service user information, and enabling appropriate information sharing.

result of their death (which their child may have) to any information that would support their claim. Disclosure of a deceased person's records may also be made in the public interest in the same circumstance as where consent to disclosure is refused.

For adopted children, the NHS runs an Adoption Registration Service, which allows adopted people to discover whether their birth parents have died, and also allows the sharing of information about hereditary diseases between the GPs of adopted children and their birth parents. This service is subject to strict criteria that can be found at: www. hscic.gov.uk/article./1801/Hereditary-Medical-Conditions.

Consent to carry out health assessments

As a general rule, the requirements for consent to carry out health assessments are the same as the consent to treatment, subject to the exceptions listed below.

Section 43 of the Children Act 1989 and Article 62 of the Children (Northern Ireland) Order 1995

If a local authority/Trust has reasonable cause to suspect that the child is suffering, or is likely to suffer, significant harm, they may apply for a child assessment order under s.43 of the Children Act 1989 or Article 62 of the Children (Northern Ireland) Order 1995, which compels a person having care of a child to produce the child for examination as directed, and gives the medical practitioner authority to carry out the assessment ordered, notwithstanding the lack of parental consent. A fully informed and competent child may refuse such an assessment.

Section 38 of the Children Act 1989 and Article 57 of the Children (Northern Ireland) Order 1995

Where a court makes an interim care order or interim supervision order, it may make an order for medical, psychiatric or other assessment of the child, which will not require parental consent, although the child may refuse the assessment if of sufficient under-standing to make an informed decision. A court may also make an order that no, or no particular type of, assessment of a child shall take place. This provision was introduced as a result of the Cleveland Inquiry, where 125 children were subjected to testing for sexual abuse by one paediatrician.

Duty to arrange a health assessment

Consent is not required where a local authority has a duty to arrange a health assessment of a child, for example, a looked after child's medical under Regulation 7 of the Care Planning, Placement and Case Review (England) Regulations 2010, Regulation 8 of the Placement of Children (Wales) Regulations 2007 or Regulation 7 of the Arrangements for Placement of Children (General) Regulations (Northern Ireland) 1996. A medical practitioner's authority to carry out an assessment is derived from the local authority's request each time a health assessment is undertaken, and the local authority can document this on BAAF Forms IHA–C/IHA–YP and RHA–C/RHA–YP. It is important to note that although this duty does not provide consent to access health records, the report of the assessment must be submitted to the review and considered, so will be shared with the child, social worker, Independent Reviewing Officer, foster carer, adoptive parents, etc, as part of the review. However, the provisions which impose the duty to carry out an assessment also provide an exception to the duty if the child refuses to consent, 'being of sufficient age and understanding to do so' (Regulation 7(4) in England, Regulation 8(6) in Wales and Regulation 7(B) in Northern Ireland). However, it is still good practice for local authorities to seek parental consent for health assessment, particularly when children are admitted to voluntary accommodation.

Testing for blood-borne infections

Testing for blood-borne infections can be particularly sensitive, as testing on a young child who can only have contracted a blood-borne infection through maternal transmission could provide information about the mother's state of health, which she may not wish to know or share. BAAF, together with the National Children's Bureau and the Children's HIV Association, produced *Guidelines for the Testing of Looked After Children who are at risk of a Blood-Borne Infection* (BAAF, 2008a). For children in care proceedings where the parents are opposed to testing, the President of the Family Division has published the *President's Direction – HIV Testing of Children* [2003] 1 FLR 1299, requiring reference to the court.

Consent to share health information

As a general rule, the requirements for consent to share a looked after child's health information for the purpose of health provision or care planning are the same as for the consent to treatment. Only information that is relevant for the purpose should be shared and only with those who need to know. Information sharing is discussed further in Chapter 16.

Documentation

Consent to access child and family health history

The BAAF Consent Form is used to obtain:

- consent to access health information on the child, from someone with parental responsibility or the child with capacity to consent;
- consent from a birth parent to access their own health history;
- consent to share the child's and relevant family's health histories with relevant parties.

Consent for health assessments

Consent from someone with parental authority is required each time a health assessment is undertaken; or, within their duty under the regulations, the local authority may authorise a doctor to carry out the health assessment on their behalf. This can be documented on BAAF Forms IHA–C/IHA–YP and RHA–C/RHA–YP. See Chapter 7 for full details concerning use of BAAF's health assessment forms.

Legal provisions

The following text explains the various legal provisions that may apply to a looked after child or young person.

Children looked after under s.20 (Children Act 1989) and Article 21 (Children (Northern Ireland) Order 1995)

This is a voluntary arrangement between the local authority/Trust and the parents, commonly referred to as "voluntary accommodation". Strictly speaking, accommodation is provided by the local authority/Trust, without objection from somebody with parental responsibility who is able and willing to arrange accommodation. Anybody with parental responsibility retains it throughout the child's time in accommodation.

Asylum-seeking young people

These young people are usually looked after under s.20 (England and Wales) and Article 21 (Northern Ireland), and a young person may give consent if they are deemed competent to do so. If an unaccompanied asylum-seeking child is not "Gillick competent", the local authority/Trust should consider whether it is necessary to apply for a care order to allow them to consent to treatment on the child's behalf. This may be necessary when it appears that the child may need non-routine medical treatment.

Care order (s.31 Children Act 1989 and Article 50 Children (Northern Ireland) Order 1995)

A care order gives the local authority/Trust parental responsibility; this is shared with any person who had parental responsibility at the time at which the care order was granted, but the local authority/Trust decides to what extent others are able to exercise their responsibility. Children can live at home when they are subject to a care order but they remain subject to the Care Planning, Placement and Case Review (England) Regulations 2010, the Placement of Children (Wales) Regulations 2007 or the Arrangements for Placement of Children (General) Regulations (Northern Ireland) 1996.

The court may only make a care order if it is satisfied:

(a) that the child concerned is suffering or is likely to suffer, significant harm; and

(b) that the harm, or likelihood of harm, is attributable to:
   (i) the care given to the child, or likely to be given to him if the order were not made, not being what it would be reasonable to expect a parent to give him; or
   (ii) the child's being beyond parental control
(s.31(2) Children Act 1989)

Even if these "threshold criteria" are established, before the court makes an order it must satisfy itself that making an order would be better for the child than making no order at all. Before making an order, the court will expect the local authority/Trust to state what the long-term plans are to meet the child/young person's needs. A Children's Guardian (Guardian ad Litem in Northern Ireland), whose role is to protect the interests of the child, will be appointed during care proceedings. The Children's Guardian may appoint a solicitor to act for the child, and another solicitor will act for the local authority/Trust. The child's parents are also likely to be represented. It is up to the local authority/Trust to prove that a case has been made to justify the making of a care order.

Interim care order (s.38 Children Act 1989 and Article 57 Children (Northern Ireland) Order 1995)

Where an application has been made for a care order, there will be a period of time (which can be up to six months) before a full hearing takes place. The court can make an interim care order, providing that it has reasonable grounds for believing that the threshold criteria (mentioned previously under the section *Care order*) are met. In Northern Ireland, an interim care order can be made for up to eight weeks initially; this is renewed every four weeks until the final hearing.

Emergency situations (ss.44–46 Children Act 1989 and Articles 63-65 Children (Northern Ireland) Order 1995)

In an emergency, the police have the power to remove a child from the care of their parents or any other person and place him or her in local authority/Trust accommodation for up to 72 hours. Neither the police nor the local authority/Trust acquires parental responsibility for the child, but may do whatever is necessary to safeguard the child's welfare.

   If a child has to be removed from home in an urgent situation, the local authority/Trust can obtain an emergency protection order (EPO). Just one magistrate agrees these orders, which last for up to eight days, but may be renewed for a further seven days. At the end of this time, the order lapses or the local authority/Trust department concerned has to apply for an interim care order. An EPO gives the local authority/Trust limited parental responsibility for the child.

Child placed for adoption in England and Wales

In order for a child to be placed for adoption, one of the following will have been obtained by the agency:

(a) Birth parent/s with parental responsibility can agree for the child to be placed for adoption (s.19 Adoption and Children Act 2002)

Maternal consent must be witnessed by a CAFCASS officer (Children and Family Court Advisory and Support Services) and the child must be over six weeks of age. The birth mother retains parental responsibility at this point but this is shared with the local authority. The consent can be withdrawn at any time until an adoption order is made. If a child younger than six weeks old is placed with an adoption agency, the agency will have to look after the child under s.20 (voluntary accommodation) until he or she is six weeks old, and then ask for parental consent or apply for a placement order. A father with parental responsibility will have to consent as well, but his consent can be given before the child is six weeks old.

When the child is placed with prospective adopters, on placement parental responsibility is granted to the prospective adopters. However, the agency may restrict the exercise of this, so it is important to check for restrictions on the prospective adopter's parental responsibility before accepting their consent.

(b) Placement order (s.21 Adoption and Children Act 2002)

This is an order authorising a local authority to place a child for adoption. Only local authorities can apply for a placement order. They must do so if a child is the subject of a care order and there is no parental consent, or where they consider that the child is at risk of significant harm. When a court has granted a placement order for a child, parental responsibility is shared between the birth parent/s, the local authority and any prospective adopters with whom the child is placed for adoption. The local authority has the power to decide to what extent the birth parents and prospective adopters may exercise their parental responsibility.

The consent of a parent or guardian may not be necessary if:

- the parent or guardian cannot be found or they are incapable of giving their agreement, e.g. because they are mentally ill;
- the court is satisfied that the welfare of the child requires that consent be dispensed with. The welfare of the child outweighs the rights of the birth parents. However, the courts must still consider the impact on the child of ceasing to be a member of his or her birth family and the change in his or her relationship with the family that adoption would bring.

A court cannot make a placement order unless an appropriate effort has been made to notify the parents or guardians who have parental responsibility for the child that an application for a placement order is being made.

Child placed for adoption in Northern Ireland
In order for a child to be placed for adoption, one of the following will need to have been obtained by the agency:

(a) Birth parent/s with parental responsibility can agree for the child to be placed for adoption (Article 21, Children (Northern Ireland) Order 1995)
The agreement of birth parent/s must be witnessed by a Lay Magistrate. The birth parent/s retain sole parental responsibility until an adoption or freeing order is granted. Parental agreement can be withdrawn at any stage until this point. A birth father without parental responsibility is required to sign Form 3D from the Adoption Regional Policy and Procedures 2010, indicating whether he accepts paternity of the child and whether he objects to the plan for adoption. If a child younger than six weeks old is placed with an adoption agency, the agency will have to look after the child under s.21 (voluntary accommodation) until he or she is six weeks old, and then ask for parental consent. A father with parental responsibility will have to consent as well, but his consent can be given before the child is six weeks old.

The birth parents will retain sole parental responsibility until an adoption order is made, whereupon it will be transferred to the adopters.

(b) Freeing order (Article 18, Adoption (Northern Ireland) Order 1997)
Where a child is the subject of a care order (Article 50 of the Children (Northern Ireland) Order 1995), the Trust will usually apply for an order freeing the child for adoption under Article 17 (if the parents consent) or 18 of the Adoption (Northern Ireland) Order 1997. A freeing order removes all parental responsibility from the birth parents and vests it in the Trust. Prospective adopters will not have any parental responsibility for the child until an adoption order is made.

Special guardianship order (England and Wales)
This is a legal option in England and Wales, introduced into the Children Act 1989 by the Adoption and Children Act 2002, which came into force on 30 December 2005. It is intended to provide permanence for children for whom adoption is not appropriate. It is most likely to be used for older children who do not wish to make an absolute legal break with their birth family. Special guardianship is a way of building a legal relationship between the carer and the child or young person throughout childhood, the effects of which will hopefully continue into adulthood.

Unlike adoption, under a special guardianship order the birth parents remain the child's parents and retain parental responsibility, although an SGO gives the special guardian overriding parental responsibility, and the special guardian can exercise their parental responsibility to the exclusion of any other person with parental responsibility.

A special guardian can make all the day-to-day decisions about the child, *apart from*:

- consenting to the child being adopted;
- letting the child be known by another surname (unless the special guardian has the parents' written consent or the court's permission to do so);
- removing the child from the UK for more than three months (unless with the court's permission).

Common dilemmas

Birth parents not contactable

If no one with parental responsibility is available, consent cannot be obtained for medical treatment or assessment. This could arise where a child is not subject to a care order; where the parents are not contactable (for example, in the case of unaccompanied asylum-seeking children); where the parent does not have capacity to consent; or where the parent is refusing to co-operate with the local authority accommodating their child.

The local authority/Trust will be under a duty to arrange for the health assessments required under the Care Planning, Placement and Case Review Regulations 2010, Placement of Children (Wales) Regulations 2007, or the Arrangements for Placement of Children (General) Regulations (Northern Ireland) 1996, or alternatively the Adoption Agencies Regulations 2005, Adoption Agencies (Wales) Regulations 2005, or Adoption Agencies Regulations (Northern Ireland) 1989, despite the lack of consent. Each local authority/Trust will have a scheme of delegation that will identify the appropriate person (social worker, team manager or other) who has the authority to request a medical practitioner to carry out such an assessment. Authority may be provided by signing a consent form on behalf of the local authority/Trust, or by other written request. A Gillick competent child may consent to, or refuse, a medical assessment on their own account.

If treatment is necessary, a Gillick competent child will be able to provide consent for their own treatment, or a person having care of the child may do whatever is necessary to protect the child's welfare. If anything other than emergency or first aid treatment is required (for example, immunisations or blood tests), the local authority/Trust should consider whether they need to apply to court for an order giving them parental responsibility.

Reliability of third party information (without consent to obtain further health information)

In situations where consent to obtain parental health information is lacking, some health information may be available from social care documents, but health professionals must be aware that this information has not been verified. Every effort should be made to obtain consent to document the information, but when this is not possible, such information should be clearly recorded in children's records and reports as 'reported by X but not verified'.

Disclosure of third party information in adoption

Health assessments for adoption will require the consideration of information about the genetic background of the child's birth parents and any issues during pregnancy that may have had an impact on the child. If the parents refuse or are unable to consent to the disclosure of such information, the medical practitioner holding that information will have to decide what information is the child's, and what is the parent's (and so protected). A GP may not, without consent, disclose that a mother is an alcoholic who drinks a bottle of vodka every day, but he can disclose that the child was very probably exposed to significant levels of alcohol in utero.

In situations where the birth parents have not given consent to share their health information, medical advisers frequently have the responsibility of deciding whether to share this important information with prospective adopters at the time of matching. There is no doubt that it is in the best interests of the child for prospective adopters or carers to have this information, and it can be argued that it is also (either through a direct meeting to discuss the child or through written reports) in the public interest. (Categories that fall into the public interest include protecting children from significant harm and promoting the welfare of children.) In making a decision, they must weigh up what might happen if the information is shared against what might happen if it is not, and make a decision based on their professional judgement. Government guidance, *Information Sharing: Guidance for practitioners and managers* (DCSF, 2008) sets out helpful principles.

At times, it may be possible to convey family health information anonymously; however, anonymising information may not protect a family member's identity (e.g. in the case of antenatal substance misuse) and may lead to adopters declining matches on the basis of insufficient information. This may make "hard to place" children more difficult to place, or may lead to an increase in placement breakdown as a result of insufficient information. It could be argued that if prospective adopters lose confidence in the process of matching, they would become less likely to adopt, which would diminish this important national resource (Hill *et al*, 2010).

In 2003, the High Court ruled that a local authority fell below the reasonable standard of care when it failed to provide sufficient information about a child's potential behavioural difficulties to adoptive parents (*A & Anor v Essex County Council* [2003] EWCA Civ 1848, www.bailii.org/ew/cases/EWCA/Civ/2003/1848.html). The adoption regulations in England were updated in 2011 and raise expectations about the nature of specialist support to be offered to a prospective adopter, including medical information and counselling to enable them to develop an informed view of the proposed match prior to any consideration by the panel (Department for Education (DfE), 2011b).

The BAAF Health Group recommends as best practice that prospective adopters meet with the medical adviser to discuss the child's health needs, and then the medical adviser sends a follow-up written report, ensuring that the child is not identified by their full name, outlining what was discussed at the meeting. In the meeting, the adopter/s are asked to maintain confidentiality and to return all paper-work about the child if the match does not proceed. The report to the adopter/s following this meeting would reinforce this message with a statement such as:

I would be grateful if you would respect the confidentiality of this information and should you not proceed with this match, please return this information to [name of social worker].

This practice addresses several concerns:

- The prospective adopter/s hear the child's health information and its interpretation directly from the medical adviser and have a chance to ask questions.
- The medical adviser's report provides written information for the adopter/s' further use and reflection, documents what they have been told, and provides the basis of informed consent if they proceed.
- The confidentiality of third party information is protected.
- Verbal and written requests are made to return all information about the child if the match does not proceed.

In practice, the realities of many demands on limited resources mean that not all children are matched with adopters who have received this service from the agency medical adviser. Each agency must decide on the most appropriate way for adopters to receive the relevant health information whilst maintaining confidentiality.

What health professionals should do

- Ensure that you are familiar with the law regarding consent and parental responsibility.
- Keep abreast of changes in regulations with regards to looked after children and adoption.
- Assist health and social care colleagues to understand the issues and best practice concerning consent for looked after children, through training and discussion of cases where relevant.
- Be available at maching to discuss individual children's health needs with prospective adoptive parents or long-term carers.
- Ensure that those commissioning local health services for children in care are aware of the importance of the medical adviser's role in meeting prospective adopters and that this translates into an appropriate job plan.

Key points

- It is essential to obtain consent to access child and family health histories and to enable statutory health assessments to take place. It is good practice to involve all parties who have parental responsibility and to consider whether the child/young person is competent to be involved in the process.
- Adoption law encourages information sharing about family health history with prospective adopters, but professional practice guidelines and legislation governing information sharing prohibit disclosure without consent unless it is in the public interest. Further guidance is needed regarding the sharing of medical information in this unique situation to promote the welfare of the child and maintain public confidence in the confidentiality of medical records.

Bibliography

BAAF (2008a) *Guidelines for the Testing of Looked After Children who are at Risk of a Blood-Borne Infection*, Practice Note 53, London: BAAF

BAAF (2008b) *Model Job Descriptions and Competencies for Medical Advisers in Adoption and Fostering*, London: BAAF

Department for Children, Schools and Families (2008) *Information Sharing: Guidance for practitioners and managers*, available at: www.education.gov.uk/childrenandyoungpeople/strategy/integratedworking/a0072915/information-sharing

Department for Education (2011a) *How to Judge a Child or Young Person's Capacity to Give Consent to Sharing of Personal Information*, available at: http://media.education.gov.uk/assets/files/pdf/h/how%20to%20judge%20capacity%20to%20give%20consent.pdf

Department for Education (2011b) *Adoption and Children Act 2002 Adoption Guidance 2011 (England)*, London: DfE

General Medical Council (2008) *Consent: Patients and doctors making decisions together*, London: General Medical Council

General Medical Council (2013) *Confidentiality Guidance*, available at: www.gmc-uk.org/guidance/ethical_guidance/confidentiality_contents.asp

Health and Social Care Information Centre (2014) *Hereditary Medical Conditions*, available at: www.hscic.gov.uk/article/1801/Hereditary-Medical-Conditions

Hill C., Wheeler R., Merredew F. and Lucassen A. (2010) 'Family history and adoption in the UK: conflicts of interest in medical disclosure', *Archives of Disease in Childhood*, 95, pp 7–11

7 Health assessments and service provision

Florence Merredew and Kamni Anand

This chapter describes in detail the process and requirements for statutory health assessments for looked after children, including those with a plan for adoption. It includes recommendations for best practice, and use of the integrated system of forms developed by the BAAF Health Group is outlined, to set best practice standards. The roles and responsibilities of a range of health professionals and teams commonly involved with delivering health services to this vulnerable group are described, with a focus on the roles and competencies of medical advisers and specialist nurses for looked after children who have the primary responsibility.

Legal issues and statutory duties for health assessments

There are various legal and statutory duties for health assessments of looked after children in the different UK countries.

Health assessment upon becoming looked after

Regulations throughout the UK require the local authority to ensure that arrangements are made for a child to have a comprehensive health assessment carried out prior to or shortly after placement. The local authority must obtain from the practitioner a written assessment of the child's state of health and health care needs. In England and Northern Ireland, this assessment must be carried out by a registered medical practitioner, whereas in Wales a registered nurse with appropriate skills can carry out the assessment if this is considered by the LAC health team to best meet the needs of the child or children.

 In England, the statutory guidance, *Promoting the Health and Well-Being of Looked After Children* (Department for Children, Schools and Families (DCSF) and Department of Health (DH), 2009, revision expected in 2015), states that:

> The first health assessment should result in a health plan by the time of the first review of the child's care plan, four weeks after becoming looked after.

In Wales, the guidance, *Towards a Stable Life and a Brighter Future* (Welsh Assembly Government, 2007), states that:

> To avoid delay, arrangements for health assessments must be made prior to placement and no later than 14 working days after the placement, unless an assessment has been carried out within the last three months.

It further states that:

A health assessment should be in place in time for a written report and health plan to be available for discussion at the child's first review, four weeks after the child starts to be looked after.

In Northern Ireland, the Arrangements for Placement of Children (General) Regulations (Northern Ireland) require Trusts to arrange for a child to be medically examined by a doctor, who is required to compile a written report on the child's health, prior to a placement being made, or, where this is not possible, as soon as practical after placement.

This examination and assessment are not required if they have already been carried out in the three months immediately preceding the date on which the child began to be looked after by the local authority. However, even when this is the case, there may well be circumstances in which the child's history or current presentation warrant further comprehensive examination or assessment. This will be a matter for individual clinical judgment.

Review health assessment

Regulations and guidance require a review health assessment every six months until the child's fifth birthday, and then every 12 months thereafter (Care Planning, Placement and Case Review (England) Regulations 2010; Children (Northern Ireland) Order 1986 Guidance and Regulations Volume 3, Family Placements and Private Fostering; Review of Children's Cases (Wales) Regulations 2007).

Health assessment for adoption

Adoption regulations recognise the importance of medical contribution in the context of adoption, and every adoption agency is required to make arrangements for the appointment of at least one medical practitioner to be the agency's medical adviser. Details of this role are described later in this chapter.

Regulations in all three countries require that the agency medical adviser provide a summary of the child's health, including health history, and any need for future health care, to be included in the Child's Permanence Report (Form CPR) in England, Child's Adoption Report (Form CAR) in Wales and Child's Adoption Report NI (Form CAR–NI) in Northern Ireland. The matters to be included in the health report are specified in regulations (Adoption Agencies Regulations 2005, Adoption Agencies (Wales) Regulations 2005 and Adoption Agencies (Northern Ireland) Regulations 1989. If the child is looked after, then this report may be based on the statutory health assessments that have already been undertaken.

When the agency is considering adoption for a looked after child, they should consult with the medical adviser to determine whether the information obtained from statutory health assessments that have already been undertaken is sufficiently comprehensive and up to date to provide the information needed by the agency decision-maker, matching panel and prospective adopters. If not, then timely arrangements for a new health assessment should be made to avoid unnecessary delay.

In England and Wales, when a plan for adoption emerges from court proceedings for a child who is not looked after, the agency will need to arrange for the medical adviser to undertake a timely comprehensive health assessment and provide a report.

Health provision once placed for adoption

In England and Wales, a child remains a looked after child after the making of a placement order until an adoption order is made. They will continue to be subject to the Care Planning Regulations (England) or Review of Children's Cases (Wales) Regulations until they are placed for adoption.

Where a local authority is authorised to place a child for adoption (i.e. has parental consent or a placement order), the child will also be subject to case reviews required by the Adoption Agencies Regulations (Regulation 36 in England, Regulation 37 in Wales). These reviews must take place within three months of the agency being given authority to place the child and at least every six months thereafter until the child is placed for adoption. These reviews may be combined with the Care Planning or Review of Children's Cases reviews. The Adoption Regulations reviews do not require an additional health assessment and report, but must consider the arrangements made for assessing and meeting the child's health needs.

Once a child is placed for adoption, the Care Planning Regulations and Review of Children's Cases Regulations cease to apply and the agency must carry out reviews in accordance with the Adoption Agencies Regulations only. The first review must take place within four weeks of the date of placement, the second review must be held within three months of the first, and subsequent reviews at least every six months until the adoption order is made. The arrangements for further health assessments will be set at those reviews and will depend on the circumstances of the child's case.

While the duty to provide review health assessments does not apply once a child has been placed for adoption but the adoption order has not yet been made, it is good practice to continue to review and provide placement support until the adoption order is granted.

In Northern Ireland, under the Adoption (Northern Ireland) Order 1987, a child becomes a "protected child" when an application is made to adopt him or her. The Adoption Agencies Regulations (1989) require the placement to be reviewed after three months if an adoption order has not yet been made. The child's health is required to be monitored during this period in accordance with guidance provided by the Trust's medical adviser.

Health assessments for looked after children

The initial health assessment

To promote consistent practice and quality assurance throughout the UK, we recommend use of the BAAF health assessment forms. Detailed information on the use of these forms is given later in this chapter.

The social care agency has an important role to play in facilitating the child's initial health assessment. The agency should ensure that there is an effective system in place to notify the LAC health team immediately when a child comes into care, so that an appointment can be made for a timely initial assessment resulting in a health care plan by 20 working days, as specified in regulations and guidance in **England and Wales**. Information regarding any concerns about personal safety must be shared at this point. The social worker should also help prepare the child for this initial health assessment, by explaining the purpose and what will happen at the appointment; some agencies produce a leaflet that can be given to the child. Arrangements should be made for the social worker, foster carer and birth parents to attend the health assessment, unless this is contraindicated due to safeguarding issues. This is particularly helpful for obtaining the complete health history of the child and his or her parents, as well as building a co-operative working relationship with the family to address health inequalities and to promote the child's health and well-being.

It is the responsibility of the social worker to either obtain the birth parent's consent to undertake a health assessment (documented on BAAF Form IHA) or to document that such consent has been given as part of the paperwork arranging for the child to become looked after. It is also the responsibility of the social worker to ask the birth parents to sign the BAAF Consent Form so that health histories of the child and family may be accessed. (For further details, see the section on use of the BAAF Consent Form later in this chapter, and Chapter 6). The social worker should also ask each birth parent to provide their health history by completing BAAF Form PH (parental health), offering assistance if needed. **In Northern Ireland**, the birth parents are also asked to consent to their GP completing the Adopt 3B Birth Family History Information (Adoption Regional Policy and Procedures, 2010). Additionally, by completing Part A of Form IHA, which provides information on the child's social history, legal status and reason for coming into care, the social worker ensures that the health practitioner has important details about the child.

Practice surrounding the health assessment of looked after children varies across the UK. In light of the significant health inequalities described in other chapters of this book and experienced by most looked after children, we believe health assessment is essential for best practice, and government guidance supports the principle that all looked after children should have a comprehensive health assessment carried out shortly after entering care. Regardless of their ultimate pathway through care, all looked after children deserve a comprehensive assessment of their health and development, as appropriate for their age. The following should all be undertaken:

- antenatal and birth history and early developmental history;
- family history;
- past medical history, including experiences of abuse and neglect and a chronological list of health events, including injuries and common illnesses;
- current physical health;
- sexual health and lifestyle issues, as appropriate for the child's age;
- mental health and behaviour, including experiences of trauma and loss;
- due to the high prevalence of mental health problems, a Carers' Report and Strengths and Difficulties Questionnaire (SDQ) should be obtained;
- physical examination;
- developmental and functional assessment;
- health promotion, as appropriate for the child's age.

The initial health assessment creates an opportunity to get to know the child and, for older children and young people, to discuss their health concerns. The emphasis should be on engaging the young person in the assessment, as an initial step towards working in partnership and assisting them over time to assume responsibility for their own health. To the extent that it is age-appropriate, the issues raised in the initial health assessment should be discussed with the child.

Arrangements for the assessment of children placed outside of local authority boundaries will vary and are discussed in Chapter 17.

Obtaining initial information

We cannot emphasise too strongly the importance of obtaining as much information as possible when it first appears probable that a child will be looked after. This may be the *only* chance to obtain early health information and a family history, as it is impossible to foretell how long children will be in care or accommodation, or how firm contact with birth relatives will remain. Early knowledge is essential to the provision of current health care, as well as in planning long-term placements for children, and in helping carers and adoptive parents to deal with health problems that may occur later. We also know that adults who were separated from their birth families in early childhood often become anxious about their own or their children's health when they do not have access to their early health history. It is therefore extremely important to engage effectively with the child's birth parents at the time of the initial health assessment, as this may be the only opportunity to access crucial child and family health information. It also serves to raise awareness of health inequalities and issues with the birth parents, which will need to be addressed if the child returns home.

At times, it may be necessary to obtain further health information about a sibling who is not looked after, for example, one with a genetic condition. It will be important to identify who can give consent to access such information.

Social care records, including psychology and independent expert reports, may at times reveal potentially important but undocumented information about the health of family members. It is important to record such information as "hearsay" and, wherever possible, obtain consent to access accurate data.

The high incidence of mental health needs in the looked after children population is well recognised (Meltzer *et al*, 2003). In addition to the significant trauma experienced by many children before becoming looked after, the care system presents further challenges, with changes in living arrangements, frequent moves and placement breakdown. The importance of gathering information and reports to help identify emotional and behavioural difficulties and other mental health problems cannot be underestimated. The BAAF Carers' Report, which provides the carer's perspective of the child or young person (Forms CR–C and CR–YP), can be a useful tool, particularly for younger children. Many professionals have included screening tools like the SDQ (Goodman, 1997) to help with assessment of children from four to 16 years of age. For more details, see Chapter 4.

It is also important to obtain information about the ethnic and cultural background, language and religion of the child's birth family, as these will have relevance to the health and well-being of the child. Knowledge of a child's ethnic background can assist with appropriate screening for certain hereditary conditions that are prevalent in particular ethnic groups, for example, sickle cell anaemia, thalassaemia and Tay-Sachs disease.

Additionally, there is evidence that it is usually in the child's best interests to be in a placement that can reflect as fully as possible their ethnic and cultural background, language and religion. This becomes especially important for children who remain in care in the long term, or for whom a permanent placement is sought, who may experience confusion about their identity with adverse effects on their self-esteem and emotional health and well-being. However, in England the Department for Education (DfE) has made it clear in statutory guidance for adoption (July 2013 revision, Chapter 4), that delay in permanent placements while waiting for a "perfect match" regarding ethnicity, language and culture is unacceptable (DfE, 2013). The statutory requirement for adoption agencies to give due consideration to religion, race and cultural background was abolished for placements in England by the Children and Families Act 2014.

There may at times be uncertainty about the ethnic and cultural background of a child, particularly when the identity or details of the birth father are lacking. However, the use of DNA testing to determine ethnicity is not recommended as these tests have not been adequately evaluated or validated as being accurate for use in such situations. For details, see the joint BAAF and British Society for Human Genetics *Statement on the Use of DNA Testing to Determine Racial Background* (2011; see Appendix A).

Regardless of whether the child quickly returns to their birth family, remains in care for some time while plans are being made, or has a plan for permanence, the information above is needed to provide current care for the child as well as to complete a high quality health assessment, and to contribute to a comprehensive individual health care plan. This is an opportunity to catch up on missed immunisations, screening and health promotion, to ensure that known health problems are being effectively managed, to identify previously undiagnosed illnesses and conditions, to assess developmental, social, emotional and mental health needs, and to contribute to a placement that will adequately safeguard the child's cultural, religious and linguistic background.

Collating health information from various sources, including, for instance, the child's GP, community and hospital records, health visitor, school health service and other specialist services prior to assessment, and organising the transfer of records is a time-consuming activity and some services have developed an administrative post to ensure access to relevant information and cost-effective use of health professional time.

Understanding the child in their social context

Children and young people want:

- to be treated holistically and as "normal children";
- recognition of the central role of family in their lives, so that families get the support needed to adequately care for and parent their children, or if this is not possible, to prioritise placement in the care of family or friends;
- respect for their cultural and religious identities, and services which take these into account.

(Mainey *et al*, 2009)

Engagement and accessibility

Older children and young people may be reluctant to engage with health practitioners as they may feel stigmatised by the requirement for statutory health assessments and concerned that sensitive personal information may not be kept confidential. Taking their views and wishes into consideration in planning and delivering services can help overcome these barriers.

Who undertakes the initial health assessment?

There is variation across the UK concerning who carries out the initial health assessment. While in many areas (particularly those where the local authority and Trust/Health Board cover a large geographical area) GPs carry out initial health assessments, in other areas this is largely done by the community paediatrician (or specialist nurse in Wales), who is part of a health team for looked after children. Having the initial health assessment completed by their usual GP with whom they are already familiar can provide reassurance to the child at a difficult time, as well as facilitate ready access to the child's own and their family's social and health history, which are key to a comprehensive understanding of the child's health needs. In practice, the child is usually moved to a new GP who will not have ready access to important health information and may lack both the required expertise in the needs of looked after children and the time to carry out a comprehensive statutory initial health assessment.

Many areas offer secondary care for looked after children through development of a specialised and expertly trained health team that includes designated doctors and nurses, medical advisers who are community paediatricians, specialist nurses for looked after children, health visitors, school nurses and midwives. The team may also include GPs with a special interest, who wish to develop their expertise on looked after children. Some children may be well known to particular services because of an ongoing condition or disability and it may be most appropriate for a health professional from this team to carry out statutory assessments. This skills-based team approach allows the most appropriate professional to engage with individual children and young people with a range of needs, with the added benefit of quality assurance provided by a small team with expertise in the health issues of looked after children, working closely together.

Regardless of the professional designation, it is important that the health professional is trained to a high standard and can demonstrate the competencies appropriate to their role, as outlined in *Model Job Descriptions and Competencies for Medical Advisers in Adoption and Fostering* (BAAF, 2008); available in the members' area at www.baaf.org.uk; and *Looked After Children: Knowledge, skills and competences of health care staff* (Royal College of Nursing and Royal College of Paediatrics and Child Health, 2012; available at www.rcpch.ac.uk).

Review health assessments

The frequency of review health assessments is specified in regulations or guidance for each UK country, but may be carried out more frequently if there is a particular concern about a child.

The request for a review health assessment is usually initiated by the child's social worker. The review health assessment is often nurse-led, and provides an opportunity to follow up on earlier issues raised and recommendations made in the previous Health

Care Plans (HCP), and to monitor access to specialised services, as well as to offer health promotion that is appropriate to the child's age and stage of development. Each health assessment provides further opportunities to develop knowledge, skills and attitudes to assist the young person in becoming responsible for their own health.

Documentation for health assessments

The use of the system of integrated BAAF health forms is recommended as best practice, as they collate important health information about children and their families in a standardised format. The use of standardised forms throughout the UK sets the same standard of practice and facilitates placement across borders. They are designed to meet statutory requirements throughout the UK.

The complete system of integrated BAAF health forms includes:

- **Consent Form**: To access health history of child and parent, and share information as appropriate
- **Form M**: Obstetric report on mother
- **Form B**: Neonatal report on child
- **Form PH**: Health report on a birth parent
- **Form IHA–C**: Initial health assessment for the child from birth to nine years
- **Form IHA–YP**: Initial health assessment for the young person aged 10 and older
- **Form RHA–C**: Review health assessment for the child from birth to nine years
- **Form RHA–YP**: Review health assessment for the young person aged 10 and older
- **Form CR–C**: Carer's report on the child from birth to nine years
- **Form CR–YP**: Carer's report on the young person aged 10 and older

Completion of the forms will ensure that all necessary health and social information is obtained for the initial health assessment and care plan.

The agency's medical adviser should sign any letters from the agency to doctors requesting information or health assessments, as a doctor's signature may encourage a prompt and open response.

A signed Consent Form should accompany a request to a health professional to complete Forms M, B, PH, IHA–C, IHA–YP, RHA–C and RHA–YP, to facilitate access to health information about the child or family. The issues of consent and confidentiality are potentially complex and are dealt with in greater detail below, and in Chapter 6.

Consent Form

The Consent Form has been developed in accordance with the principles outlined in Chapter 6. It is not used to obtain consent for health assessment, which must be obtained at the time of each health assessment and documented on the relevant form. It also does not address consent for medical treatment (see Chapter 6). Rather, it is used to secure consent to obtain the child's health information that is needed to complete a comprehensive health assessment and health care plan. It is also used to obtain consent from the birth parent(s) to access their health information from various sources. Additionally, consent can be given to share the information with other health professionals, social workers and others planning the child's care, and with carers. Finally, the signed Consent Form allows the child or young person to receive relevant family health information at suitable times in the future.

The Consent Form should be signed when birth parents are usually most available – when the child or young person first becomes looked after – so as to avoid problems obtaining consent at a later date, which is a major contributor to delay. The form has different sections to complete depending on whether child or parental health information is being accessed, and who has parental responsibility.

The Consent Form should accompany Forms M, B, PH, IHA–C, IHA–YP, RHA–C and RHA–YP to access information held by physicians and their records, and to permit the sharing of health information, as detailed above. When the child or young person becomes looked after, the social care agency *must* ensure, so far as possible, that the Consent Form is completed by the appropriate individuals.

Agencies must ensure that social workers are adequately trained to undertake the task of obtaining parental consent and have a clear understanding of what health information is needed, why it is important, and how it will be used. They must have the ability to effectively communicate this information and answer any questions that arise, in accordance with the parent's level of ability. Agency policies and procedures must make it clear that each case requires proper assessment and the exercise of judgement concerning the young person's understanding and capacity to consent.

A child or young person should not be asked to consent unless they have the capacity, i.e. that they understand the implications of consenting. In England, Northern Ireland and Wales, the principles of "Gillick" competency (*Gillick v West Norfolk and Wisbech Area Health Authority* [1985] 3 All ER 402) will apply. For the initial sharing of information, the young person's informed consent to disclosure, witnessed by the social worker, should suffice.

If there is a question of an examination by a medical practitioner where clinically indicated, it will be for that practitioner to determine whether the young person has the capacity to consent. Although parental consent is not required if the child or young person has the capacity to consent, it is best practice in most circumstances to involve the birth parent(s) in the process and seek their agreement as well.

Part A of the form should be completed by the social care agency.

Part B should be completed by the birth parent, who may give consent for two different purposes:

- Comprehensive health information is needed about the birth parent and his or her family, and consent to access this can only be given by the birth parent;

- Comprehensive health information is needed about the child or young person, and consent is needed from the birth parent or other person with parental responsibility only if the child or young person does not have the capacity to consent on his or her own behalf.

Part C should be completed by the child or young person with capacity to consent, to allow access to his or her health information, and to share information as appropriate.

Part D should be completed by another adult with parental responsibility, or if the local authority holds parental responsibility, by a representative authorised to give consent on behalf of the local authority.

Note: A single BAAF Consent Form may be used to obtain consent to access health information for the child and one birth parent. The other birth parent must sign a second Consent Form to allow access to his or her health information.

Since it is important for the child's current and future health and well-being to have comprehensive health information about both birth parents and their respective families, every effort should be made to contact both birth parents, so that each can complete a Consent Form. If more than one child in the family becomes looked after at the same time, a separate Consent Form should be completed by each parent for each child, so that information can be accessed and shared on behalf of each child.

When signing Part B at the time that the child or young person becomes looked after, the birth parent with parental responsibility for a child or young person who does not have capacity to consent gives consent for ongoing and continuous assessment and planning for the child, unless the consent is specifically withdrawn at a future date. While this is useful in situations where the agency is unable to maintain contact with a birth parent, it would be considered best practice to involve the birth parent(s) in ongoing health assessment and planning. All relevant health history should be accessed in time for the initial health assessment, so it should not be necessary to repeat this, unless new information comes to light, in which case it would be best practice to obtain specific consent to access this.

The Consent Form should be sent to the agency medical adviser, who will ensure that it accompanies requests for completion of Forms M, B, IHA–C, IHA–YP, RHA–C and RHA–YP. The Consent Form must also accompany letters to physicians and hospitals requesting further health information on looked after children and their birth parents.

Form M: Obstetric report on mother

This form should be completed for all children who are becoming looked after. It provides health information on the mother before, during and after delivery, which will be relevant for immediate placement, care planning and future health. It also provides information for the new GP and prospective carers. A copy of the signed Consent Form should accompany a request for the completion of Form M.

Part A is completed by the social care agency, indicating the name and contact details of the agency medical adviser to whom the form should be returned.

Part B is completed by a doctor or midwife. It may be helpful to ask the social worker at the hospital where the child was born to arrange for the completion of the form.

Form B: Neonatal report on child

This form should be completed for all children who are becoming looked after. It provides basic information for current and future health care and for decisions regarding future placements, for prospective adopters or foster carers and for the new GP, and about a child's earliest days, which may be relevant to health care later and which will be greatly valued by the child in later life. A copy of the signed Consent Form should accompany a request for the completion of Form B.

Part A is completed by the social care agency, indicating the name and contact details of the agency medical adviser to whom the form should be returned.

Part B is completed by a doctor or senior nurse who has access to the child's birth records. It may be helpful to ask the social worker at the hospital where the child was born to arrange for the completion of the form.

Form PH: Health report on a birth parent

This form provides a family health history, which will assist in planning for the child's placement, contribute to his or her current and future health care, and provides evidence of the birth parent's consideration of the child's future welfare, which may be of importance to the young person in later life. This form is completed by the birth parent together with the social worker, each parent completing a separate form.

The completed form is passed to the medical adviser, who may wish to contact the birth parent's GP or specialist to obtain further information or confirm data provided by the birth parent. A copy of the signed BAAF Consent Form must accompany any request for further information. Clinical judgement will be required to determine when further information or confirmation is required. Form PH should be available to the doctor examining the child.

Form IHA–C: Initial health assessment for the child from birth to nine years

This form is designed to record a comprehensive and holistic health and developmental assessment, and will incorporate the health information obtained on Forms M/B and PH. Such a thorough assessment will form the baseline for all later reviews and it is important that it is comprehensive and completed to a high standard. The form should be used for infants, young children (up to approximately nine years) and older children with developmental delay. In England, the assessment is carried out by a physician; in Northern Ireland, by a paediatrician; and in Wales, by either a physician or a registered nurse; and should be completed by the child's first review, which should be held within 20 working days of becoming looked after. Reports prepared by hospital specialists or other health professionals on children with disabilities or serious medical conditions may be attached to the form. The assessing doctor should always be provided with a social work report on the child. A copy of the signed Consent Form should accompany a request for the completion of Form IHA–C.

Part A is completed by the social care agency, indicating the name and contact details of the medical adviser to whom the form should be returned. The legal status and holder of parental responsibility must also be indicated. Unless the child has capacity to consent to the health assessment, consent is needed from the birth parent, or another adult with parental responsibility, or an authorised representative of the agency holding parental responsibility.

Part B should be completed by the examining doctor, or in Wales by a specialist nurse, experienced in paediatrics and the health needs of looked after children. The examining health professional will need to determine whether the child or young person has the capacity to consent. The child with capacity to consent to the health assessment should indicate his or her consent by signing the consent at the start of Part B. Although parental consent is not required if the child or young person has the capacity to consent, it is best practice in most circumstances to involve the birth parent(s) in the process and seek their agreement as well. If someone outside of the LAC health team is carrying out the assessment, a letter should accompany the form, drawing the doctor's attention to the child's and family's health history. The people present at the assessment (e.g. the social worker, birth parent(s) and carer) should be listed at the beginning of Part B.

Note: Since Part B contains personal and possibly sensitive information about other family members, as well as the child, it should be retained in the child's health record, and treated with the utmost care with respect to confidentiality. For *adoption only*, the entire report should be returned to the adoption agency for retention in the adoption file (Adoption Agencies Regulations 2005; Adoption Agencies Regulations (Northern Ireland) 1989; Adoption Agencies (Wales) Regulations 2005).

Part C is completed by the examining health professional, but where this individual has limited experience of looked after children, it may be necessary for a health professional from the LAC health team to review the report to ensure that all relevant information is included and issues addressed. It is a summary report and outlines health recommendations that contribute to the child's health care plan. The responsible health professional must ensure that it contains all of the detailed information needed to create and monitor compliance with the health care plan (HCP), such as required health promotion and immunisations, dates of dental checks, and details of future appointments and referrals. Part C can be used as the basis for a discussion with current and future carers, provided consent has been obtained to disclose the information. It can also be used to report to adoption and fostering panels.

Form IHA–YP: Initial health assessment for the young person aged 10 and older

This form has the same purposes as Form IHA–C. In addition, however, it creates an opportunity to discuss their health with the young person – including physical and emotional development, relationships, sexual health and the use of tobacco, drugs and alcohol – and to encourage the young person to begin taking responsibility for his or her own health. It should be completed by the examining doctor or, in Wales, a specialist nurse, experienced in paediatrics and in the assessment of adolescent development. A copy of the signed Consent Form should accompany a request for the completion of Form IHA–YP.

Forms RHA–C and RHA–YP: Review health assessment for the child from birth to nine years and the young person aged 10 and older

The purpose of these forms is to provide a holistic review of the health and development of looked after children and young people, to determine if previous health care plans have been carried out, to identify new issues, and to integrate into the child's overall care plan. The health assessment offers carers, children and young people an opportunity to discuss with a health professional any concerns and encourages young people to take responsibility for their own health and to adopt a healthy lifestyle. A copy of the signed Consent Form should accompany a request for the completion of Form RHA–C or RHA–YP.

Part A is completed by the social care agency, giving the name and contact details of the agency medical adviser to whom the form should be returned.

Part B will be completed by the health professional undertaking the assessment. This will usually be the nurse for looked after children, subject to local arrangements, and there may be a request for the involvement of a doctor for individual children or young people as needed. The health professional will need to ensure that they have the appropriate consent to undertake the assessment. Regardless of who completes the form, it is essential that previous health assessments, health recommendations and any updated health information are made available.

Note: Since Part B contains personal and possibly sensitive information about other family members, as well as the child or young person, it should be retained in the child or young person's health record, and treated with the utmost care with respect to confidentiality. For *adoption only*, the entire report should be returned to the adoption agency for retention in the adoption file (Adoption Agencies Regulations 2005; Adoption Agencies Regulations (Northern Ireland), 1989; Adoption Agencies (Wales) Regulations, 2005).

Part C should be completed by the health professional undertaking the assessment and returned to the child's social worker. It contains a summary report and health recommendations that contribute to the child's care plan, and should note whether all action points from the last assessment have been addressed. All relevant information needed to inform and carry out the health recommendations, such as dates of dental or other appointments, should be included. Part C can be used as the basis for a discussion with current and future carers, provided consent has been obtained to disclose the information. It can also be used to report to adoption and fostering panels, although if a significant interval has elapsed between completion of the assessment and discussion at panel, the agency medical adviser may need to write an updating letter.

Carers' report forms: Form CR–C – Carers' report on the child from birth to nine years

This form should be completed by the main carer, and is designed to provide a description, in the carer's own words, of the child's emotional and behavioural well-being. The form should be completed once the child has settled into the placement and is known by the carer. While some carers may need help from their social worker to complete the form, the responses should reflect the carer's views. It should be completed every time the child has a statutory health assessment, or when they change placement, and can thus help to indicate change over time. It should be used for infants, young children (up to approximately nine years) and older children with developmental delay.

Form CR–C allows recognition of positives and flags up possible problems to assist health professionals in determining whether worrying behaviour or symptoms are present. It is not a diagnostic tool for mental health problems – such tools already exist. It is to be used to guide the need for further assessment and support.

This form can assist adults involved with the child or can help to organise their way of thinking about the child. It provides information for the social worker that will give a clear and realistic picture of the child, inform important stages of their journey in care, e.g. planning meetings, review meetings and placement panels, and promote stability in placements. It also provides an opportunity for children to be involved, as appropriate for their age and stage, in addition to receiving information from the carer.

The form has been designed to integrate with other reports, e.g. the Child's Permanence Report (England), and will become part of the child's permanent social care record, thus providing a "voice" for the carer/s in the child's assessment.

Form CR–YP – Carers' report on the young person aged 10 and older

This form has the same purposes as Form CR–C. In addition, however, it creates an opportunity to discuss concerns about social or emotional health and well-being with the young person, and to encourage the young person to begin taking responsibility for his or her own health.

Strengths and Difficulties Questionnaire (SDQ)

The SDQ is a short behavioural screening questionnaire suitable for use with children between the ages of four and 16. It has five sections covering details of emotional difficulties, conduct problems, hyperactivity or inattention, friendships and peer groups, and positive behaviour, plus an impact supplement to assist in predicting emotional health problems. It is usually completed by the parent or carer; there is a version for a teacher to complete, as well as a version for the young person to complete if desired. The tool has been internationally validated and is appropriate for all ethnic groups.

Some local authorities use the SDQ to assist in identification of children who may have difficulties with mental and emotional health and who may benefit from interventions.

In Northern Ireland, while there is a regional requirement to undertake screening, SDQs are not routinely used. Health and social care trusts have developed their own methods of emotional health and well-being screening.

Health promotion

Health promotion needs should be addressed at every health assessment and contact, as appropriate for the age and understanding of the individual child. Chapter 8 covers a range of topics and signposts to relevant resources.

Health care plan

It is the responsibility of the social worker to develop the child's health care plan, using information provided from statutory assessment.

The health professional undertaking the health assessment should utilise all of the information about the child or young person obtained using the forms described above, to provide a summary and health recommendations on Part C of whichever Form IHA or RHA is required and appropriate for the age and development of the child or young person.

This report should include comments on birth history, family history, past medical history, current physical and mental health and behaviour, and a developmental assessment. Some children may already be under the care of specialists or be linked to other services such as physiotherapy, speech therapy or psychological services. The examining health professional must ensure that the summary contains all of the detailed information needed to create and monitor compliance with the health care plan, such as required health promotion and immunisations, dates of dental checks, and details of future appointments and referrals.

If the child needs screening, tests or referral for a specialist opinion, the health professional should ascertain the local protocol and decide whether to make a direct referral or to suggest it is made by the child's own GP. The health professional may well be the most appropriate individual to assume the responsibility for ensuring that the child receives treatment or that a referral is made, especially if the child has recently had to register with a new GP.

The health care plan should include clear strategies for health promotion, surveillance and ongoing assessment of progress. The medical adviser should be clear about his or her role in each of these areas.

Part C should be returned to the child's social worker to contribute to the health care plan developed by the social worker.

What looked after children and young people want from health services

- Health professionals who are interested in their concerns and wishes.
- To be treated as a partner in their own care and involved in decisions concerning their care.
- To be consulted on the planning, implementation, delivery and evaluation of services.
- To be invited to health assessments.
- Services which don't stigmatise them.
- Accessible venues and times, e.g. leisure centre, evening drop-in.
- Health concerns must be confidential and information should be shared sensitively and on a "need to know" basis.
- Greater professional awareness of cultural issues, interpreters and resources for non-English speakers.
- Appropriate staff for gender-specific problems.
- Locally available services, particularly for young asylum seekers with less knowledge of the area and more limited transport options.

(Mainey *et al*, 2009)

Services and roles of health professionals involved with looked after children

There are many universal and specialist services that may be involved with looked after children and their families for short or longer periods of time. All children and families have ongoing input from their GPs, midwives, health visitors, school nursing service, and hopefully dental care. It is essential that all health professionals who may come into contact with looked after children should be aware of their particular needs and vulnerabilities and the local services available. The LAC specialist team can facilitate training of these professionals.

Looked after children may well have been the subject of safeguarding procedures, and monitoring by community paediatricians and health visitors for failure to thrive, neglect, developmental delay, or antenatal substance exposure. They may have had input from the wider multidisciplinary team, such as physiotherapy, occupational therapy, speech and language therapy, clinical psychology, portage or audiology. School-age children are likely to be known by their school nurses. Some looked after children receive specialist paediatric services such as neurology, endocrinology, ophthalmology, for infectious diseases, and from ear, nose and throat specialists.

The "team around the child" approach, information sharing and effective multi-disciplinary working are crucial for looked after children, helping to ensure that there is no duplication and that concerns about unmet health needs and barriers to progress in improving health and well-being are shared in the best interests of the children.

Universal services
The primary health care team
The primary health care team working with a range of community services delivers health care in a wide variety of settings to local populations. Primary care, including the GP and practice nurse, is often the first point of access for the majority of health care services for families and children who can subsequently be directed to a wide range of community/hospital services depending on individual needs.

The majority of community services will respond to a direct contact from parents/carers/young people. However, specialist services, for example, paediatrics, physiotherapy, occupational therapy and speech and language therapy, require a referral from another health professional.

General Practitioners
GPs will provide primary care services for looked after children, and the lead health record for the looked after child should be the GP-held record. It is therefore essential that copies of the summary and recommendations from health assessments as well as a copy of the health care plan are sent promptly to the child's GP, with relevant consent to do so. It is important for GPs to understand that this vulnerable group of children has considerable needs for secondary and tertiary paediatric care, including mental health services.

Health visitors, school nurses and midwives
These mainstream community nurses work closely with primary care, education and social care to promote the physical, emotional and mental health of pre-school and school-age children within the context of family, school and community. School nurses work on a geographical school pyramid basis and health visitors are aligned to GP practice populations or to a geographical area.

Roles include health surveillance at specific ages, health promotion services to children in need (which includes looked after children and children with disabilities), child protection, immunisation, and individual support for young people, parents and carers. Various programmes offering a range of services to enhance early years experiences are also available for families with the greatest need.

In many areas around the UK, health visitors, school nurses and midwives will undertake health assessments for looked after children and provide individual help, advice and counselling. It is important that they receive appropriate specialised training on the health needs of looked after children in order to develop expertise in working with this group, and that they work closely with the LAC health team.

Specialist services for looked after children
Specialist LAC health teams

The gold standard for a service for looked after children is a multidisciplinary specialist service described below, including paediatricians and nurses with a special interest and expertise in the needs of looked after children, with sufficient administrative and secretarial support. The specialist LAC team should work closely with colleagues within community paediatrics and the wider NHS, and also with colleagues within education and social care.

There are generally three roles for doctors involved with looked after children, and what follows is a summary based on the model job descriptions and competencies published by BAAF in 2008. The roles of nurses are also included where applicable. The job descriptions have, as far as possible, been drafted to reflect the variations in nomenclature and regulations in the different countries and to encompass the different roles, both strategic and service delivery. While there is local variation in both the scope and scale of these posts, they generally reflect the range of health services required to provide an integrated service for this very vulnerable group of looked after children.

Designated doctor* and nurse for looked after children

Posts for the designated doctor and nurse are statutory in England. Although Northern Ireland does not have designated doctors, the role of designated nurse for looked after children is statutory. In Wales, the Designated Doctors for Safeguarding, including looked after children, are strategic all-Wales posts appointed by Public Health Wales NHS Trust. The strategic overview of health services for looked after children within each Health Board is fulfilled by the Named Doctors for looked after children with additional responsibility (Named Doctor for looked after children, strategic role).

Designated doctors and nurses (Named doctor, strategic role, Wales) are experienced

---

* Named doctor for looked after children is a strategic role in Wales.

senior practitioners who take a strategic overview of health services for looked after children, including those with an adoption plan. Their key responsibilities are to:

- assist commissioners of health services to fulfill their responsibilities to meet the needs of looked after children and young people;
- advise the Trusts/Health Boards on, and contribute to, planning, strategy and audit of quality standards for health services for looked after children;
- provide expert advice;
- take a strategic overview of the service, and monitor the quality;
- ensure robust clinical governance arrangements within NHS services;
- develop and ensure awareness of relevant policies, procedures and roles;
- maintain regular contact with health staff undertaking health assessments;
- liaise with social care and other Trusts/health boards for out-of-area placements;
- produce an annual report on the service, including a statutory safeguarding report that includes looked after children and those with a plan for adoption; and
- ensure all staff are appropriately trained.

Medical adviser/named doctor and nurse for looked after children

LAC nurses (nurses with specialist training and experience of the holistic health needs of looked after children, including health visitors and school nurses) and LAC doctors (generally community paediatricians, but may also be GPs with a special interest in looked after children) provide health services for looked after children and young people and their parents/carers, taking account of the views of the child as appropriate to their age and stage of development.

Their key responsibilities are to:

- take a lead role in arranging and undertaking health assessments/reviews and to provide a comprehensive written report on the child's health, development and well-being that will address the future implications for the child of their health history, and previous family and social situation, including their experiences in the care system;
- develop and review health care recommendations to meet identified health needs;
- work with children/parents/carers, taking account of the views of the child;
- provide liaison, training and education on promoting the health of looked after children, with social care services, health, education, carers and voluntary agencies;
- advise on particular health matters that arise in connection with looked after children and the permanence process, as well as other relevant issues such as consent, confidentiality and information sharing;
- maintain contact and work closely with local paediatricians, local child and adolescent mental health services (CAMHS), primary care, and other relevant health professionals and specialists, to address the health needs of looked after children;

- work closely with the local safeguarding and health professionals working with all looked after and accommodated children to ensure delivery of high quality clinical services through monitoring and audit; and
- advise on the health of prospective carers, which will include interpretation of health and lifestyle information provided by the applicant and their GP, and if necessary, to liaise, with consent, with specialists about details of health problems identified.

In England, the Fostering Services (England) Regulations 2011 do not require a medical adviser to be a member of the panel; however, they provide that the panel may request medical advice.

Health and social care trusts in Northern Ireland are required to appoint a LAC nurse whose role is to support the heath needs of looked after children.

Medical adviser to the adoption agency

Adoption is the legal process by which parental responsibility for a child or young person is vested in a new parent or parents. It is a permanent and lifelong commitment to the child.

The Adoption Agencies Regulations 2005, the Adoption Agencies Regulations (Northern Ireland) 1989 and the Adoption Agencies (Wales) Regulations 2005 recognise the importance of medical contribution in the context of adoption, and every adoption agency is required to make arrangements for the appointment of at least one medical practitioner to be the agency's medical adviser. In Northern Ireland and Wales, the medical adviser is appointed to an adoption panel. In England, the Adoption Agencies Regulations 2005, as amended by the Adoption Agencies and Independent Review of Determinations (Amendment) Regulations 2011, require an adoption agency to maintain a central list of persons suitable to be members of an adoption panel. This list must include the medical adviser to the agency (or at least one of the medical advisers if there is more than one).

The medical adviser will act in the best interests of the child or young person by providing a high quality service to meet their needs, to enable them to achieve lifelong optimum health and well-being. The whole service encompasses close multi-agency working, which is essential to effective delivery. The medical adviser will:

- Undertake pre-adoption health assessments of the child with an adoption plan. In England and Wales, where panels no longer consider whether a child should be placed for adoption, the medical adviser may need to access required health information available through court proceedings. Provided the statutory health assessment/s for looked after children are sufficiently comprehensive and up to date, they may be used to prepare the statutory medical report required for adoption.

- Prepare a statutory comprehensive health report that should address the future implications for the child of their health history, and previous family and social situation, including their experiences in the care system, and address adoption support needs. This should be provided to the adoption agency, which will ensure that it is available for the adoption panel and/or the agency decision-maker as appropriate.
- Provide expert advice to the child's social work team, adoption team and panel in relation to the child's identified present and lifelong health needs.
- Counsel prospective adoptive parents about the health needs of the child.
- Collate health information and provide a written report to the adoption panel on the health of prospective adopters, which will include interpretation of health and lifestyle information provided by the applicant, their GP and, if necessary and with specific consent, by specialists.
- In England, may attend as a full member of the adoption panel when required and respond to any requests by panel members for further medical advice. In Northern Ireland and Wales, the medical adviser is required to be a full panel member (Adoption Agencies Regulations (Northern Ireland) 1989; Adoption Agencies (Wales) Regulations 2005).
- Create policies and procedures within the healthcare setting to enhance the health provision to looked after children and those moving to adoption.
- Monitor policies and procedures, ensuring that timescales are adhered to within the adoption framework.
- Provide teaching, training and updates to professionals from all agencies on health issues related to adoption.
- Work closely with medical advisers/named doctors and specialist nurses, as well as designated professionals in strategic roles.
- Ensure effective teamwork and liaison with colleagues in health/social care/education for the benefit of the child.
- Maintain lines of communication for and with the child/young person moving to adoption, taking their views into account.

Competencies in adoption and fostering
Over the last decade, there has been increasing recognition that health provision for looked after and adopted children and their carers is a specialised area for which health professionals require specific knowledge, abilities and skills. This has resulted in the following developments.

- Higher specialist training competencies for paediatricians in training, published by the Royal College of Paediatrics and Child Health, now include several specific aspects of working with looked after children and those with an adoption plan.

- Competencies and three model job descriptions (including a table suggesting time required for different tasks) encompassing the following areas of work are available in the members' section of the BAAF website (BAAF, 2008):
  - designated doctor for looked after children, i.e. a strategic role;
  - medical adviser to adoption panels, as required in adoption agency regulations;
  - medical adviser/named doctor for looked after children.
- In 2012, the Royal College of Nursing and Royal College of Paediatrics and Child Health published the Intercollegiate Role Framework, *Looked After Children: Knowledge, skills and competences of health care staff* (revision expected in 2015). This sets out levels of competencies required from health professionals providing universal and specialist services for looked after children.

The competencies and model job descriptions are intended to assist commissioners and managers in the development of high quality services for looked after children. In addition, they provide a framework for health professionals in negotiating appropriate resources and a programme of training for their posts. The Trust has the responsibility to set service specifications for health and decide what level of service to provide.

Qualities that children and young people want in health professionals

- The ability to empathise and understand the child and young person's situation and experiences.
- Seeking their views and feedback.
- Being a good listener/having good communication skills.
- Friendliness, warmth, kindness and a caring attitude.
- Being honest, straightforward and genuine.
- A young, positive and informal approach, balanced with professionalism.
- Showing interest, praising and encouraging.
- Being committed, following through, showing that they see their work with the young person as being more than just a job, that they genuinely care.
- Being respectful, fair, unprejudiced, non-discriminatory and not making judgments or assumptions.
- Being reliable and dependable.

(Mainey *et al*, 2009)

Mental health services for looked after children

There is a high incidence of emotional and behavioural disorder in looked after and adopted children. The overall conclusion that can be reached is that around 45–70 per cent of looked after children in the UK have a mental or behavioural problem (DCSF and DH, 2009; NICE/SCIE, 2010; 2013). In addition to the significant trauma experienced by many looked after children, the care system itself can present some of these children and young people with further challenges, including coping with placement breakdown and frequent moves.

National policy drivers have recognised the need for provision of mental health assessment and therapeutic work for looked after children (Department for Education and Skills (DfES), 2006; DH, 2004; DCSF and DH, 2009; NICE/SCIE, 2010; 2013). Mental health service provision tends to be targeted with specialised teams/services dedicated to meeting the needs of looked after and adopted children. A variety of organisations may provide these services, including children's services, mental health trusts, health trusts and voluntary sector agencies. Services may sit separately from other locally-based Child and Adolescent Mental Health Services (CAMHS) provision, sit within the mental health provision but function as a separate team, or form an integrated part of more general CAMHS.

In whatever way services are configured, young people, their carers and professionals should have access to a targeted and specific resource that is able to ensure that young people can smoothly access the full range of CAMHS when needed.

All professionals and carers working with looked after children have a contributing role in meeting their emotional and mental health needs. Mental health services will work with this "system" around each child, in addition to assessing and treating the children/young people themselves.

Locally-based mental health services are likely to provide the following (NICE/SCIE, 2010; 2013):

- partnership working with other key agencies to create a more integrated approach to care that will:
  - promote the psychological, physical, emotional, social and spiritual health of looked after and adopted children;
  - promote stability of placement;
- consultation, specialist training and therapeutic input to carers and professionals working within other agencies involved with children who are in the care of the local authority or adopted;
- provision of streamlined access to direct assessment and treatment of mental health difficulties, including direct therapy when appropriate.

Child protection/safeguarding team

All those who come into contact with children and families in their everyday work, including practitioners who do not have a specific role in relation to child protection/safeguarding, have a duty to safeguard and promote the welfare of children. The child protection/safeguarding team is a specialist team that monitors the structure and processes of risk management that contribute to the safety of children. The team acts as a conduit between health trusts and allied organisations that provide childcare and the child protection process. The child protection process involves children who may become looked after by social care services. Therefore, the child protection and looked after children teams will work closely, sharing information, guidance and support to improve the lives of children in the care system.

Specialist paediatric services, multidisciplinary and interagency working

In addition to specialist looked after children services, safeguarding and child protection services, and CAMHS, there are several other specialist services that may be involved with looked after children. These include community and hospital paediatrics, audiology, children's community nursing, special school nursing, paediatric occupational therapy, speech and language, physiotherapy, learning disabilities nursing, communication aids, dentist, orthoptist and development centres. The specialists work with children and families, and multidisciplinary, interagency working is an important part of the service to achieve optimal quality of service for all children, particularly those in special circumstances.

These services are delivered to children and families from a number of locations,

The team around the child

including clinics, schools, special schools, GP surgeries, health centres, acute hospitals and family homes.

As can be clearly seen in the description of different roles outlined above, there are many health professionals involved in optimising health services and care for looked after children. In addition, a variety of other individuals, such as teachers, sports coaches, leaders of music, theatre and other leisure activities may play an important role in promoting health in the broadest sense. The social worker has overall responsibility for the looked after child, and must ensure that statutory health assessments are carried out, develop health care plans and make sure that the resultant actions are taken. Central to attaining good health and outcomes is a committed carer who will act as advocate, encourage healthy lifestyles and choices, and ensure attendance at various appointments and events. Given the diversity of professionals involved, developing a shared language, goals and understanding of professional roles and responsibilities will optimise the chances of attaining the best possible health outcomes for looked after children.

What health professionals should do

- Advocate for high quality, child-centred services that address the diverse needs of looked after children.
- Ensure familiarity with legal requirements for health assessments and health service provision for looked after children.
- Develop competency to carry out responsibilities to a high standard, and participate in ongoing learning.
- Develop good working relationships with multiagency colleagues in various teams around the child.
- Participate in training within agencies and multidisciplinary teams to promote understanding of various roles in providing high quality health assessments and services.
- Audit quality and outcomes of health assessments and compliance with regulations.

Key points

- It is essential to obtain consent to access child and family health histories (on the BAAF Consent Form) and to undertake statutory health assessments (on Forms IHA and RHA).
- There is a statutory requirement for an initial comprehensive health assessment of the child on becoming looked after, and for health reviews at specified intervals.
- Use of BAAF health assessment forms promotes consistent practice and quality assurance throughout the UK, and facilitates placements across boundaries.
- Social workers have a statutory duty to contribute to the health assessment process,

including prompt notification, ensuring completion of the Consent Form and Form PH (parental health) as well as preparing the child and birth parents for the statutory health assessment.

- Given the high level of health inequalities on entry to care, *all* children should have a comprehensive health and developmental assessment shortly after becoming looked after, to be documented on appropriate forms, including mental, emotional and behavioural health, and health promotion.
- Mental health difficulties are prevalent in looked after children and must be considered by all health professionals who work with them.
- All health professionals involved with looked after children should meet, or be working towards, published competencies. Services should be commissioned to support the health standards described in statutory regulations and guidance for looked after children and those with an adoption plan.
- Given the large number of health and social care professionals involved with looked after children, it is essential to develop effective multi-agency working with shared language, goals, training and understanding of roles and responsibilities.

Bibliography

BAAF (2004) *Using BAAF Health Assessment Forms: Setting standards of health practice across all agencies*, Practice Note 47, London: BAAF

BAAF (2008) *Model Job Descriptions and Competencies for Medical Advisers in Adoption and Fostering*, London: BAAF

BAAF and British Society for Human Genetics (2014) *Statement on the Use of DNA Testing to Determine Racial Background*, London: BAAF, available at: www.baaf.org.uk/sites/default/files/uploads/res/lpp/ethnictesting.pdf

Department for Children, Schools and Families and Department of Health (2009) *Statutory Guidance on Promoting the Health and Well-Being of Looked After Children*, London: DCSF and DH

Department for Education (2013) *Adoption Statutory Guidance: July 2013 revision*, London: DfE

Department for Education and Skills (2006) *Care Matters: Time for change*, London: HMSO

Department of Health (2004) *The National Service Framework for Children, Young People and Maternity Services*, London: DH

Goodman R. (1997) 'The Strengths and Difficulties Questionnaire: a research note', *Journal of Child Psychology and Psychiatry*, 38, pp 581–586

Mainey A., Ellis A. and Lewis J. (2009) *Children's Views of Services: A rapid review*, London: NCB

McCauley C. and Young C. (2006) 'The mental health of looked after children: challenges for CAMHS provision', *Journal of Social Work Practice*, 20:1, pp 91–10

Melzer H., Corbin T., Gatward R., Goodman R. and Ford T. (2003) *The Mental Health of Young People Looked After by Local Authorities in England*, London: Stationery Office, available at: www.ons.gov.uk/ the-mental-health-of-young-people-looked-after

NICE/SCIE (2010) *Promoting the Quality of Life of Looked After Children and Young People*, PH28, London: NICE/SCIE

NICE/SCIE (2013) *Looked After Children and Young People*, London: NICE/SCIE

Royal College of Nursing and Royal College of Paediatrics and Child Health (2012) *Looked After Children: Knowledge, skills and competences of health care staff*, Intercollegiate Role Framework, London: RCN and RCPCH

Welsh Assembly Government (2007) *Towards a Stable Life and a Brighter Future*, Cardiff: WAG

8   Health promotion

Emma Hedley

Health promotion is an essential part of the health assessment process; nurses and doctors should be aware of and enthusiastic about addressing health promotion whenever the opportunity arises. The Department of Health (DH) (2011a) highlights the need for health promotion to be both age and developmentally appropriate, and for it to occur in a setting that puts the child at ease and encourages engagement. Research states that looked after children are four times more likely to misuse drugs, become a teenage parent, and have emotional and mental health issues. These statistics emphasise the importance of effective health education, health protection and prevention of health issues. The joint DH/Department for Children, Schools and Families (DCSF) *Statutory Guidance on Promoting the Health and Well-Being of Looked After Children* (2009, revision expected in 2015) and the Welsh Assembly Government's *Towards a Stable Life and a Brighter Future* (2007) identify the health promotion needs of looked after children and care leavers, and should also be referred to when considering health promotion for this vulnerable group.

Health promotion is a lifelong process – initially aimed at parents and carers, but over time the child should become increasingly involved as appropriate to their age and developmental stage. Parents, carers, schools, sports coaches, music and arts instructors and youth leaders, as well as health professionals, play a role in educating children and young people about health issues and lifestyle choices, and in demonstrating that they should take responsibility for promoting their own health and well-being. What follows in this chapter is a very practical approach to topics that should be addressed in health promotion, but it is important to remember that this is a process that occurs gradually over time. It provides prompts or "things to think about", generally starting in infancy and progressing throughout childhood, but it is not intended to be an exhaustive list. Additionally, practitioners will need to keep in mind that adaptations in delivery, access or programmes may need to be made so that disabled children may fully benefit from universal services and health promotion, e.g. children with learning or behavioural difficulties may be less involved in team sports if they have difficulties working together or following rules, so other games may be needed to encourage physical exercise. Information on various topics is available through NHS Choices, and other useful resources are noted, although these may not be available in all areas and practitioners will need to be familiar with their local resources.

Healthy lifestyle: diet

- Discuss what is healthy, and explain what the body needs to work well.
- Talk about infant feeding, including encouraging breastfeeding; weaning, including the timing of weaning; favourite foods; and encourage trying new foods.
- Use resources such as the "healthy plate" (see the Eatwell Plate diagram in Chapter 3) and explain how to make healthy food swaps.
- Discuss eating together as a family at the dinner table, and encouraging young children to be involved in food preparation as a fun activity, then progressively building on this to enable the child to develop practical skills and knowledge of healthy eating.
- Recommend avoiding using food as a reward, which can result in mealtimes becoming stress points.
- Explain body mass index (BMI) and how obesity is a major threat to the health and well-being of children.
- Discuss eating on a budget.
- Educate staff supervising contact to encourage birth families to provide healthy food at contact visits.
- Encourage access to culturally relevant foods, e.g. vegetarian, halal, kosher.

Useful resources
- Health visitors.
- School nurses.
- Dieticians.
- Children's centre healthy eating courses.
- Food technology teachers in secondary schools.
- *Healthy Lives, Healthy People: A call to action on obesity in England* (HM Government, 2011).
- NHS Choices 5 A Day, available at www.nhs.uk/LiveWell/5ADAY/Pages/5ADAYhome.aspx.
- British Heart Foundation resources, including *Eating Well: Healthy eating for you and your heart*, and www.cbhf.net (website for 7–11-year-olds) and www.yheart.net and yoobot.co.uk (websites for 12–19-year-olds).
- Caroline Walker Trust (nutritional information), available at: www.cwt.org.uk/.
- The Change4Life campaign promotes a healthy lifestyle through exercise and a healthy diet (available at: www.nhs.uk/Change4Life).
- MEND – a national programme run by health visitors and school nurses to promote healthy eating and exercise for families, available at: www.mendcentral.org/.

Exercise, hobbies and interests

- Encourage exercise for physical, emotional and social benefits.
- Explain how exercise improves balance, strength and co-ordination, as well as increasing self-esteem and building relationships, for example, by being part of a team.
- Promote at least 60 minutes of exercise daily for over-five-year-olds and three hours per day for under-five-year-olds (DH, 2011b, 2011c)
- Make clear that there are many different ways to introduce reluctant participants to beneficial exercise and explain that it is important to find something that the child likes to do, either individually or as part of a team. Walking, playing in the park, feeding the ducks, scooting, cycling, swimming, etc, are all good exercise.
- Discuss access to appropriate exercise and leisure activities for disabled children.
- Discuss the importance of hobbies and interests, such as music, films, books, arts, drama, out-of-school activities.
- Recognise achievements.

Useful resources
- *Physical Activity Guidelines for Children and Young People (5–18)* (DH, 2011b).
- *Physical Activity Guidelines for Early Years (under 5s): Children who are capable of walking* (DH, 2011c).
- British Heart Foundation resources, available at: www.bhf.org.uk/heart-health/prevention/tips-for-parents/keeping-children-active.aspx.
- The Change4Life campaign promotes a healthy lifestyle through exercise and a healthy diet, available at: www.nhs.uk/Change4Life.
- MEND – programmes to promote healthy eating and exercise for families, available at: www.mendcentral.org/.
- Activate is a school-based physical education programme for various ages, available at: www.valsabinpublications.com/index.php.
- In many areas, looked after children have free or discounted access to leisure and fitness activities, including arts, music, sport and clubs.
- *Healthy Child, Healthy Future: A framework for the universal child health promotion programme in Northern Ireland* (Department of Health, Social Services and Public Safety (DHSSPS), 2010).

Physical health

Carers should be good role models in their appropriate use of health services, including attending for regular universal screening for themselves and for appointments to monitor any specific conditions that they may have. They should ensure that the children in their care attend for universal screening appointments, regular dental checks, and vision, hearing, and sexual health screening when necessary and appropriate.

Immunisations

Stress the importance of looked after children remaining fully immunised and up to date, including having immunisations not included in the usual national programme, e.g. hepatitis B and BCG, where necessary.

Useful resources
- Public Health England covers various aspects of immunisation, available at: www.hpa. org.uk/Topics/InfectiousDiseases/InfectionsAZ/VaccinationImmunisation/.
- WHO and UNICEF provide country-specific estimates of immunisation coverage, available at: www.who.int/immunization_monitoring/routine/immunization_ coverage/en/index4.html.
- *Vaccination of Individuals with Uncertain or Incomplete Immunisation Status* (Public Health England, 2013), available at: www.hpa.org.uk/webc/HPAwebFile/HPAweb_C /1194947406156.
- BCG clinic/TB/new entrant screening.

Dental care

(See also Chapter 3)
- Explain why oral and dental health are important.
- Advise twice daily brushing with a family fluoride toothpaste once the child's teeth appear, use of mouthwash, dental floss/tape and interdental brushes.
- Advise registering with a dentist once the child's teeth appear, then attending regular appointments.
- Discuss the effects of dummies and bottles on growing teeth, and promote moving from bottles to cups as soon as possible.
- Encourage minimal consumption of sweet food and sugary, acidic drinks, e.g. fruit juice and fizzy drinks, and encourage consumption only as part of a meal.

Useful resources
- Information on dental care for children is available at NHS Choices, at www.nhs.uk/ livewell/dentalhealth/pages/careofkidsteeth.aspx.
- List of local NHS dentists.

Development

- Encourage awareness of normal developmental milestones in infancy and childhood.
- Promote activities to maximise developmental progress:
  - tummy time for babies;
  - local toddler groups;
  - reading and looking at books together;
  - registration and activities at local library;
  - children's centres –"play and stay", music groups, gymnastics, "time to talk";
  - outdoor play, use of local parks;
  - promotion of activities to encourage speech, e.g. chatting about everyday activities.
- Suggest preschool activities such as nursery.
- For school-age children, encourage use of after-school clubs, Brownies/Cubs, sports, dance, music and arts.

Useful resources

- Health visitor.
- Staff in pre-school settings, including children's centre programmes and play specialists.
- Contact supervisors.
- Promote use of the *Personal Child Health Record*/"red book" or *Carer Held Record Record* (BAAF, 2008) for looked after children to keep a record of development.

Behavioural and emotional well-being

Behavioural changes in looked after children are frequently a response to a felt lack of safety (e.g. moving placement, loss of original parental figure) or the long-term effects of not having experienced rewarding and sustaining primary relationships. Consequently, it is important that behaviour is seen as the outward expression of internal distress. Children who are looked after are much more at risk of having disorganised attachment patterns, which means that their functioning, be it behavioural, cognitive or emotional, is likely to be dysregulated, impulsive, non-reflective and tending to the extremes of control or chaos. Assessments, interventions and health promotions need to take a comprehensive view of the child, as using the more familiar behavioural and cognitive strategies will have limited impact. Therefore, in thinking about how to promote health education and prevent further deterioration, it is important to help carers (and in some instances other professionals, e.g. teachers, social workers, general practitioners and paediatricians) understand:

- that looked after children often require different behaviour management strategies for common difficulties, such as tantrums, fighting, failure to recognise bodily sensations like hunger, satiation and pain, self-harm and approaching unknown adults indiscriminately;

- that standard behaviour management programmes, e.g. Triple P, are not always appropriate;
- the internal world of the child, and how to develop trusting relationships with a child who finds it hard to trust;
- how the child's previous experiences may impact on their reactions to everyday events, e.g. bathing;
- ways to develop safety by using a higher level of structure and supervision, e.g. regular routines, and keeping the child close when distressed;
- the child's emotional regulation and that it may be helpful to reduce over-stimulation e.g. regulated periods on the computer or TV;
- how the child comforts self, copes with frustration and disappointment, and how to help them to develop a safe place or "chill-out" zone;
- how to help the child develop healthy ways to manage stress, such as physical activity;
- the importance of creating opportunities for success, such as friendship groups, new interests and hobbies, which will also help develop self-esteem and resilience, and encouraging use of locally-run self-esteem groups, where available;
- that discovering the strengths the child has and communicating this to them is more helpful than overusing generic praise that the child finds hard to believe;
- the importance of being attuned to whether the child is being bullied, or engaged in bullying, and liaising with the school if needed;
- the need to liaise with school staff, including the school nurse, to ensure that they understand that the child's difficulties are more to do with "can't do" rather than "won't do";
- the benefit of having an identified member of staff in school to whom the child can relate on a regular basis;
- the value of having mentors for older children, both in school and in the community;
- that contact with birth family members may affect the emotional well-being of children and also influence their views of health, for example, different ideas about diet or smoking, e.g. 'Granddad smoked and lived to be 90'.

Useful resources
- Resources on managing difficult behaviour in children who have not experienced safe care (e.g. BAAF publications).
- Specialist training for carers in managing behaviour, delivered by practitioners with expertise in the field.
- Peer support groups for looked after children and carers.
- Courses in management of anger and emotional regulation.

- Dedicated CAMHS/looked after children teams.
- Educational psychologist for behaviour difficulties in school.
- Specialist advice for schools (e.g. www.theyellowkite.co.uk).
- Programmes in schools that develop emotional literacy, peer relationships and help with bullying.
- School- and community-based loss and bereavement programmes.
- Mentoring schemes.
- Local directories of services for children and young people, often online, including those supported by local authorities, health and the voluntary sector.

Sleep

- Discuss the importance of sleep to encourage growth, repair and development.
- Provide strategies to reduce the risk of cot death.
- Discuss the effects of poor sleep on mood, behaviour and concentration.
- Outline the role of sleep routines, e.g. the importance of quiet time, bath, milk, tooth brushing, story, then bed.
- Discuss the advisability of avoiding TV/video game machines/DVDs/computers in children's bedrooms.
- Talk through the use of dummies for infants and toddlers.
- Discuss the use of night lights.
- Dicuss common sleep problems, e.g. difficulty falling asleep, bedwetting, waking up for the toilet, vivid dreams or nightmares.

Promoting independence

- Urge carers to encourage younger children to feed themselves, brush their teeth, wash, choose what clothes to wear, dress and put on their shoes.
- Discuss hygiene, toilet training and bedwetting, and explain that toilet training may be delayed due to neglect or emotional issues, and that emotional difficulties may manifest as bedwetting.
- Remind carers about safety in the home and teaching this and road safety, when age and developmentally appropriate, including allowing children to walk to school on their own and to use public transport.
- Enquire about the child's attitude to strangers; discuss "stranger danger".
- Discuss with carers and older children appropriate, safe use of mobile phones and social networking websites, and ensure awareness of cyber-bullying.
- Discuss the risks of absconding and of making inappropriate friendships or relationships that may lead to sexual exploitation, substance misuse or criminal activity.
- Make young people more aware of the way in which they may be groomed for sexual exploitation, and the risks of child trafficking.

- Encourage children and young people to make their own choice of clothing, including consideration of what type of clothing is appropriate to wear in particular settings.
- Discuss with carers, and in an age-appropriate way with children and young people, ways of progressing towards independent living, e.g. learning to shop for food, cook healthy meals, budget, clean and do laundry.
- Ask if the young person knows how to access health services, including registering and making an appointment with the GP and practice nurse, using walk-in centres, pharmacies, NHS information and advice by phone or online, and when (and when not) to attend A & E/casualty departments or to dial 999.
- Encourage children and young people to ask questions and be involved in decisions about their health.
- Emphasise the importance of attending for routine health screening and for disease prevention, e.g. immunisations.
- Make carers and young people aware of local voluntary services, e.g. Young Minds.

Useful resources
- Local groups for care leavers to learn independence skills.
- School nurses and health visitors.
- School staff, e.g. food technology teachers.
- Leaflets on road safety, healthy eating on a budget, health screening, etc.
- Leaflets on managing enuresis.
- Enuresis clinics with specialist knowledge of issues common in looked after children.

Gender, relationships and sexual health

- Explore awareness of sex and gender with young children, e.g. ask if they know the difference between boys and girls.
- Promote access to a range of toys, not just gender-specific toys, e.g. cars for boys, dolls for girls, and encourage play with both boys and girls.
- Ask if the child has friends with whom they feel safe, and who they can go to when they feel angry, upset or when something amazing happens.
- Check whether they have positive male and female role models in their life, and encourage development of both.
- Clarify what knowledge they have about body changes and growing up, and their understanding of the reproductive functions of males and females.
- Encourage use of language that is friendly towards LGBTQ (lesbian, gay, bisexual, transgender and queer/questioning sexuality) people.
- Enquire whether they have a partner, how the partner treats them and whether they are happy in the relationship, feel equal and valued and are able to say "no" when necessary. Talk about issues of domestic violence, grooming and control.

- Ask if they are in a sexual relationship and, if so, how comfortable they feel with this.
- Consider the need for contraception and what form this may take; ensure that the young person is aware of all the available local services and how to access them.
- Verify that the young person is aware of the modes of transmission of sexually transmitted infections (STIs) and how to prevent them; ensure that they know where the local genito-urinary services are and encourage the young person to be screened and treated if necessary.
- Ask if they are aware of female genital mutilation (FGM) and, where necessary, help them access specialist services.

Useful resources
- Leaflets on various methods of contraception and sexually transmitted infections.
- Young people's sexual health services.
- Sexual health outreach worker.
- Maps, phone numbers, websites for local services for contraception and STIs.
- Organisations for LGBTQ young people.
- Organisations for young people infected with HIV.
- Support groups/services for young people who have been abused.
- Brook provides free and confidential information on sexual health for under 25s, available at: www.brook.org.uk.

Substance use

Smoking
- Ask about exposure to tobacco smoke, both active and passive smoking.
- Ask carers and social workers if they smoke and if this ever occurs with the child present.
- Make clear to carers and social workers that cigarettes should never be used as a reward or as a way of establishing rapport with a child or young person.
- If the child/young person smokes, establish how much and in what circumstances they are more likely to smoke, and what first started them smoking. Discuss the ways in which tobacco harms physical health and its highly addictive nature.
- Remind carers and children that smoking is expensive, smelly and becoming less socially acceptable.
- Try to use empathy and humour during discussions.
- Never think that children are too young to be asked about smoking and its effects. When a five-year-old was asked if she smoked, she laughed and then said, 'Oh no, that's disgusting and it makes you smelly'. Children are also often anxious about the effect of smoking on their loved ones.

Alcohol and drugs

- Ask about the child's previous exposure to carers' excessive alcohol use and/or street drug use, and the effects of this on themselves and the user(s).
- Ask if the child or young person is using alcohol and/or street drugs themselves and if so, what and how much they are consuming, and how this affects their behaviour, relationships, finances and enjoyment of life.
- Ask in what circumstances they are most likely to misuse substances and if they drink/ use drugs whilst with friends or when alone. Enquire about using alcohol or street drugs to party and to manage anxiety and stress, and discuss safer ways to manage these.
- Discuss ways in which alcohol and drugs harm physical health, and their addictive properties.
- Discuss the impact of being disinhibited through drinking or drug use, e.g. unawareness of danger, having unrealistic expectations of your abilities, such as thinking you can fly, being vulnerable to exploitation, including sexual exploitation, and being more prone to aggressive or criminal behaviour.
- Make carers and young people aware of what a unit of alcohol is, and use examples of their favourite drink to work out how many units they are consuming. Advise about combining alcohol consumption with food.
- Explain to young people the short- and long-term effects on babies of exposure to substances in utero.

Useful resources

- Leaflets on the effects of tobacco, alcohol and drugs.
- "Stop smoking" outreach worker for young people.
- Tools to screen for problem use, e.g. DUST (Drug Use Screening Tool), SUST (Substance Use Screening Tool).
- The Drinkaware website for information and accurate calculation of alcohol consumption, available at: www.drinkaware.co.uk/.
- The Drug Education Forum is a group of national organisations committed to improving the practice and profile of drug education in England, available at: www. drugeducationforum.com/.
- Directory of local intervention services for young people.
- Websites, e.g. Alcohol Concern, FASD Trust, NoFAS.

Culture and religion

- Consider the potential impact of culture, ethnicity and religion on health perspectives and practices. For example, during the month of Ramadan, Muslims have restrictions in place between sunrise and sunset regarding eating, drinking and taking medications.

- Ask whether the child/young person has access to relevant cultural centres, the religion of their choice and their preferred place of worship.
- Some African, Middle Eastern and Asian communities practise female genital mutilation (FGM), which is illegal in the UK. See www.nhs.uk/Pages/HomePage.aspx.
- Encourage carers to access relevant advice on skin and hair care, as appropriate.
- Access training on cultural awareness.
- Discuss the harmful impact of discrimination, signpost to resources, and assist children and carers to develop coping strategies.
- Be prepared to find acceptable ways of discussing sensitive issues with young people, for example, accessing sexual health services for young people whose religion or culture prohibits sex before marriage.
- Consider sensitive and appropriate use of interpreters.

Ending health assessments

Always end the health assessment on a positive note. Be positive about the child, praise them for the good things they have achieved and tell them that they can continue to achieve. Ask the child about their dreams and aspirations – what would they like to be when they grow up? Encouragement will speak volumes and increase self-esteem, and hopefully they will agree to see you again.

Bibliography

BAAF (2008) *Carer-Held Health Record*, London: BAAF

British Heart Foundation (2013) *Eating Well: Healthy eating for you and your heart*, London: BHF

Department for Children, Schools and Families and Department of Health (2009) *Statutory Guidance on Promoting the Health and Well-being of Looked After Children*, London: DCSF/DH

Department of Health (2011a) *You're Welcome: Quality Criteria for young people frindly health services*, London: DH

Department of Health (2011b) *Physical Activity Guidelines for Children and Young People (5–18)*, available at: www.gov.uk/government/publications/uk-physical-activity-guidelines

Department of Health (2011c) *Physical Activity Guidelines for Early Years (Under 5s): Children who are capable of walking*, available at: www.gov.uk/government/publications/uk-physical-activity-guidelines

Department of Health, Social Services and Public Safety (2010) *Healthy Child, Healthy Future: A Framework for the universal child health promotion programme in Northern Ireland*, Belfast: DHSSPS

Growing Kids, available at: www.growingkids.co.uk

HM Government (2011) *Healthy Lives, Healthy People: A call to action on obesity in England*, London: HM Government

NICE/SCIE (2010) *The Physical and Emotional Health and Well-being of Looked After Children and Young People*, London: NICE/SCIE

NICE/SCIE (2013) *Looked After Children and Young People*, London: NICE/SCIE

Need to Know books, available at: www.need2know.co.uk

Public Health England (2013) *Vaccination of Individuals with Uncertain or Incomplete Immunisation Status*, London: Public Health England

Welsh Assembly Government (2007) *Towards a Stable Life and a Brighter Future*, Cardiff: WAG

World Health Organisation (WHO) (2013) *Immunisation Surveillance, Assessment and Monitoring*, available at: www.who.int/immunization_monitoring/routine/immunization_coverage/en/index4.html

Yellow Kite (resources for schools), available at: www.theyellowkite.co.uk

Young London Matters (YLM) (2008) *The London Pledge for Children and Young People in Care*, London: HMSO

9　Disabled children

Efun Johnson

Children with disabilities are over-represented in the looked after children population, although it is difficult to obtain accurate data due to differences in definition and reporting. However, a large number of children in care have at least one disability, which creates additional needs (Marchant, 2011).

The legal framework

Under the Children Act 1989:

> *A child is disabled if he is blind, deaf or dumb or suffers from mental disorder of any kind or is substantially and permanently handicapped by illness, injury or congenital deformity or such other disability as may be prescribed (s.17(11) Children Act 1989). Disability can be considered to be a continuum from impairment to disability to handicap, with social and environmental conditions determining the degree of disability arising from the initial impairment.*

The Disability and Discrimination Act 2005 defines a disabled person as a person with 'a physical or mental impairment that has a substantial and long-term adverse effect on his ability to carry out normal day-to-day activities'. The Act suggests that, for compliance with this definition, the individual should meet the following criteria:

- have an impairment that is either physical or mental;
- the impairment must have adverse effects that are substantial;
- the substantial adverse effects must be long-term.

In Wales, the Social Services and Well-Being (Wales) Act 2014 repeals s.17 of the Children Act 1989 and replaces it with a new framework for the assessment for and provision of services to children, including those with disabilities. This new provision will come into force in April 2016.

Who are disabled looked after children?

While most disabled children become looked after for the same reasons as their non-disabled peers, most frequently due to abuse and neglect, some children become looked after because of their disability. There are no reliable national figures for looked after children with disabilities because of the way in which disability is defined and recorded. Annual statistics for looked after children in England and Wales record disability only if this is the principal reason for becoming looked after, yet many disabled children are also present within other categories of need. In England, being disabled was the main reason for three per cent of children becoming looked after for the past several years (Department for Education (DfE), 2013), while in Wales, for 2013 this figure was 1.7 per cent (Welsh Government, 2013).

In Northern Ireland, where such statistics are collected, figures for the year ending 30 September 2013 show that 14 per cent of children looked for more than 12 months were disabled, using the definition: 'The child has a physical or mental impairment which has a substantial and long-term adverse effect on his/her ability to carry out normal day-to-day activities'. A higher proportion of boys (17%) than girls (12%) were disabled. Although not directly comparable, the Northern Ireland Census found that five per cent of children in Northern Ireland had a long-term illness or disability that limited their day-to-day activity, which suggests that having a disability is more prevalent among looked after children than the general population. Furthermore, 22 per cent had multiple disabilities; these were described as:

- learning disability: 71 per cent
- autism: 16 per cent
- physical disability: 12 per cent
- visually disabled: five per cent
- mental health problem: four per cent
- hearing impaired: three per cent
- other disabilities: 17 per cent

(Rodgers and Waugh, 2014a)

Similarly, 14 per cent of young people aged 16–18 who left care in Northern Ireland during the year ending 31 March 2013 were disabled, with 61 per cent of these having a learning disability, 21 per cent a mental health disorder and 13 per cent classified as being on the autism spectrum (Rodgers and Waugh, 2014b).

Short break care

Children with complex needs require sophisticated parenting and impose enormous demands on the most competent of families. Therefore, families may need short breaks for their children, and those children with the most complex disabilities may require specialist residential schooling.

If a child is provided with accommodation by children's social care services for a continuous period of more than 24 hours, they will become a looked after child under s.20 of the Children Act 1989 and s.21 of the Children (Northern Ireland) Order 1995.

Short break care should be routinely considered for foster carers who care for children with complex needs.

Residential placements

Children may be placed in residential schools for purely educational reasons pursuant to their statement of special educational needs. If this is the case, they will not be classed as looked after children as their accommodation will be provided by education services rather than children's social care. Children may also be placed in residential schools for a mixture of social care and educational reasons, and for these children it will be a matter of interpretation as to whether they are looked after by the local authority or not.

Case study

R (RO) v East Riding of Yorkshire Council **[2011] EWCA Civ 196**

RO was a severely autistic teenager with ADHD whose parents were unable to look after him at home full-time because of the stresses his behaviour placed on the other members of the family. Originally, he was placed at a day school and had some weekend respite foster care, during which the local authority treated him as a looked after child. When his parents successfully obtained a Statement of Special Educational Needs, naming their preferred placement at a residential school, the local authority ceased to provide respite care, as the parents were able to manage RO during weekends and holidays. The local authority decided that RO was no longer a looked after child. The Court of Appeal held that as RO was a child in need (disabled) and that his parents were prevented from providing him with suitable accommodation (because they could not manage his behaviour full-time), RO was entitled to s.20 accommodation and should be treated as a looked after child.

Despite the legal definitions of who should be considered looked after, in practice there is variation in how local authorities decide this. Criteria for allocation to "children with disability" or "looked after children" teams within local authority children's services may vary from authority to authority and clinicians need to be aware of this, as these children often cross placement boundaries and clarification is needed to ensure that services are put in place. Marchant (2011) argues that disabled children in long-term residential placements should be accorded "looked after" status so that they benefit from more rigorous case planning, provision and review set out in the Children Act 1989 and associated regulations.

Why do disabled children come into care?

As stated above, most disabled children come into care for the same reasons as their non-disabled peers. However, there are additional factors that make this group of children more vulnerable.

- Children with complex needs place additional demands on even the most competent of parents, including physical mobility difficulties, emotional and behavioural difficulties, and juggling frequent health appointments. This may be even more difficult for single parents.
- Some disabilities are poorly understood or unrecognised by professionals, which can lead to inadequate support. Some disabilities may be hidden or "invisible", such as autism and foetal alcohol spectrum disorder, which means that others do not understand the issues or make any adjustment for behaviour that is difficult or outside of social norms.
- Families with disabled children report high levels of unmet need and stress. Not only may care demands occur 24 hours a day, but the need for care may last throughout the individual's life (Dobson *et al*, 2001).
- Parental learning disability and mental health difficulties may lead to neglect and poor stimulation of the child, as well as increasing safeguarding risk. It can also mean that the parents are less able to cope with the needs of a disabled child.
- The child's early attachment may have been disrupted due to separation in hospital, parental ill health or substance misuse. This may have a greater impact on disabled children who are not able to understand the experiences. Disrupted attachment and parental bonding may be an added factor in poor parenting, abuse and neglect.
- A review of the literature published from 1989 to 2005 revealed that the economic burden incurred by families as a result of caring for a child with disabilities can be substantial (Anderson *et al*, 2007). It has been estimated that the annual costs of bringing up a disabled child are three times greater than those for a child who is not disabled (Bebbington and Miles, 1989; Dobson and Middleton, 1998). Over half of families with disabled children have a low income (Gordon *et al*, 2000). Poverty can mean poor access to resources coupled with increased strain on finances from needing specialised equipment, increased transportation needs and costs, and extra assistance with child care.
- Children and parents often experience isolation if they are unable to join in ordinary child and family activities, are busy attending appointments, and have a smaller peer group (Dobson *et al*, 2001).
- Discrimination is commonly experienced by families with disabled children (Dobson *et al*, 2001).
- For a variety of reasons, children with disabilities face an increased risk of abuse and

neglect. Communication difficulties as well as isolation and dependency on their carer can affect a disabled child's ability to recognise and understand that they are being abused, as well as their ability to access help and support (NSPCC, 2003).

- The increased demands on parents of disabled children can increase safeguarding risks. Sometimes indicators of abuse are mistakenly attributed to the child's disability. Studies into the prevalence of maltreatment among children with disabilities in the US have found that these children are over three times more likely to experience abuse and neglect than non-disabled children. Disabled children in a large-scale US study were found to be 3.4 times more likely overall to be abused or neglected than non-disabled children. They were:
  - 3.8 times more likely to be neglected;
  - 3.8 times more likely to be physically abused;
  - 3.1 times more likely to be sexually abused;
  - 3.9 times more likely to be emotionally abused.

(Sullivan and Knutson, 2000, cited in NSPCC, 2003).

Smaller-scale UK-based studies have indicated similar levels of maltreatment (Kennedy, 1989; Westcott, 1993, cited in NSPCC, 2003)

- Disabled children or children with learning disabilities are 20 per cent more likely than average to run away. This may lead to them being accommodated (Rees and Lee, 2005).

Particular concerns for disabled looked after children on their journey through care

Although some disabled children become looked after by virtue of needing a specialist placement (such as a 52-week special school placement), there are others who are looked after first, and their disability is a secondary issue. However, the disability may have an impact on their experiences in care, and they may share certain characteristics.

- Disabled children may present a range of communication difficulties related to autism, speech and language difficulties or learning disability. They may not be easily understood and may need to use communication aids or sign language such as Makaton.
- Children with disabilities remain looked after for longer, and are more likely to have an unsuitable placement. Evidence concerning placement stability is variable; Baker (2011) reviewed one study showing that disabled children with ongoing health conditions and learning difficulties had fewer placement moves; another which found a low disruption rate for children with physical disabilities; and yet another where children with learning difficulties had a higher likelihood of disruption.
- A return home is less likely for the disabled child, and when reunification does happen, it is usually later than for other children in comparable circumstances (Littell and Schuerman, 1995).

- Disabled looked after children are often older than the average and have higher levels of challenging behaviour (Sinclair *et al*, 2007).
- Looked after children with disabilities are at increased risk of needing safeguarding as they are often in care for longer periods, may have multiple carers in different roles and settings, and may have communication difficulties that can decrease their ability to recognise and report abuse (Marchant, 2011).
- Disabled looked after children may be in a less than ideal placement due to the difficulty of finding placements that can meet their complex needs. Finding permanent, stable placements for disabled children can be problematic and choice is often restricted; some are adopted, often by their foster carers, and although long-term foster care can be successful, risk of placement breakdown remains, particularly when the young person's behaviour is challenging.
- While the majority of disabled looked after children are placed in foster care, they are more likely to live in residential units than their peers (Sinclair *et al*, 2007), and they are three times more likely to attend a residential educational establishment than other looked after children (Gordon *et al*, 2000). The most significantly impaired are the most likely to be placed in a boarding school or residential college (Hirst and Baldwin, 1994). Most disabled children in residential settings have multiple impairments and "challenging behaviour" (Gordon *et al*, 2000).
- Their health histories may be complex and it can be difficult to access a comprehensive health history, particularly when multiple teams have been involved with the child. Holistic assessments are often lacking as emphasis may be more on the disability than on the child.
- Universal health screening and health promotion are often missed when children are seen by secondary and tertiary services, which could result in missed immunisations and lack of understanding of health issues.
- Looked after children with significant disabilities are more likely to be in out-of-area placements, especially where specialist schools or units are needed. Distant placement can make it hard for birth families to visit and remain fully engaged with the child, particularly when placements are lengthy (Baker, 2006).
- There is often anxiety about the transition from foster care into independence or adult services as the young person approaches the age of 18. This can be compounded by a lack of adequate transition planning, coupled with the difficulties in identifying appropriate follow-on services, as adult disability services have different criteria from those of children's services.
- Foster carers may need special training to be able to meet the needs of disabled children and may have developed effective communication and particular expertise in meeting the needs of the child in their care.
- It is essential that young people with disabilities have access to the same leaving care services as their non-disabled peers (see Chapter 12).

Special considerations for meeting health needs

- Advance planning may be required to facilitate communication with the child, and it is especially important that birth parents are invited to the health assessment to assist in understanding the wishes and feelings of the disabled child, to provide health history, and to give consent if needed.
- Obtaining consent may be more complex for children with disabilities, as it may be more difficult to determine whether the child or young person has the capacity to give consent. For young people without capacity to consent, the agency must ensure that parental consent is obtained for children accommodated under s.20, or for care orders, that consent is given by someone with parental responsibility (see Chapter 6). Even where consent is given for assessment, or the local authority has a duty to arrange an assessment, the child may refuse such an assessment if of sufficient understanding, and this may need to be considered.
- It is important to decide who has overall responsibility for a disabled looked after child. This includes determining who carries responsibility for ongoing and emergency/acute health needs, as well as the particular issues resulting from being a looked after child or young person. Clear plans and good communication are required.
- There is no need to duplicate health assessments, and a specialist report from the disability team that has extensive knowledge and has long followed the child may be more appropriate than requesting that a looked after health assessment be conducted by someone else. However, each case should be considered individually and an over-view from the looked after children's team, looking at the "bigger picture", advising on gaps in provision and health promotion, may be appropriate.
- Co-ordination of services for disabled children can be particularly challenging due to the number of services that may be involved and the need for clarity concerning who will offer them.
- Health professionals should be aware of the criteria for access to local services and mechanisms to accelerate concerns if the child fails to receive required provision.
- It is important to ensure that procedures and policies are in place to promote the well-being of looked after children with specific needs/disabilities.
- Special consideration should be given to provision of services to residential units for children with autism, physical disabilities, etc. These children will be under the care of paediatricians and therapists prior to placement and clarity about roles and responsibilities is essential.
- Health professionals should routinely be included in discussions concerning out-of-area placements (e.g. placement panels in Wales (Welsh Assembly Government, 2007)) to ensure continuity of health care and information sharing.

Common disabilities

There is a wide range of disability within the looked after children population. Very often there is an emerging picture of a child's disability, and their difficulties can become more apparent or more significant over time. It can be difficult to unpick the reasons for an individual child's behaviour as the child's life experiences will have a significant impact. Exposure to drugs and substances antenatally, domestic violence, poor parenting and changes of carer are not uncommon in looked after children and their effects can be cumulative and intertwined.

Some conditions co-exist, symptoms may overlap, and it may take time to arrive at a diagnosis or diagnoses. A diagnosis in itself may not necessarily be helpful – what is most important is to be able to recognise a child's difficulties and address their needs.

Developmental delay

We know that developmental delay or impairment, the "bread and butter" of community paediatrics, can be the result of neglect, abuse and poor parenting. It can also occur following injury or be related to other medical/genetic conditions, such as Down's syndrome (duplication of all or part of chromosome 21) or Fragile X syndrome (a genetic condition inherited in an X-linked dominant pattern, where males are usually more severely affected). Often, we need to investigate and monitor children to understand the extent and possible cause of their developmental delay. Recording catch-up in development is extremely helpful in determining the cause of any delay. Developmental assessments identify specific or global delay and can signpost clinicians to the appropriateness of further investigations or specific input from, for example, speech and language therapy. The multi-agency team is likely to have ongoing input with looked after children with developmental delay, particularly those with severe neurodevelopmental disability.

Delay in speech and language development can range from mild to severe language difficulties, and from children who have a specific language delay or disorder but have age-appropriate skills in other areas of development, to those whose language difficulties co-exist with other difficulties. Speech and language difficulties are relatively common in looked after children and it is important to remember that there can be an interrelationship with neglect. Of paramount importance is the need for children's voices to be heard and taken into account in planning their care. It is therefore very important to explore and record the best means of communication with the looked after child, and give consideration to the need for a communication passport – a document recording communication needs, preferences and abilities, used for communication between professionals.

The guide, *Parenting a Child with Dyslexia* (Stanway and Miles, 2012), may assist prospective carers to better understand the needs of such children and consider their ability to parent them.

Physical disabilities

Some children have significant physical disabilities. This includes those who have good cognitive skills and have a primary difficulty in their motor development, e.g. conditions such as cerebral palsy and muscular dystrophy. It also includes children with a physical illness that has an impact on daily living, learning and accessing the school curriculum, children with medical needs requiring additional support (e.g. tracheostomy, gastrostomy), and children with sensory impairments (e.g. hearing or visual impairments).

Looked after children will have the same range of physical health problems and disabilities as the general child population. The medical management of these will generally be the same, except that there will need to be careful consideration of the child's social circumstances and clarification of consent issues as well as the need for training of carers, for example, of children with severe epilepsy.

Prenatal substance exposure

Some health conditions related to maternal prenatal alcohol and substance use, including FASD, are explored in Chapter 2. The guide, *Parenting a Child Affected by Parental Substance Misuse* (Forrester, 2012), may assist prospective carers to better understand the needs of such children and assess their ability to parent them. *Children Exposed to Parental Substance Misuse* (Phillips, 2004) includes more information about this subject and will be very useful for health practitioners.

Mental health difficulties

It is well recognised that looked after children have high levels of mental health difficulties (Meltzer *et al*, 2003), and many of these can be considered disabilities (see the detailed discussion on mental health in Chapter 4). Co-morbidity or mental illness may also result from the disability (McCann *et al*, 1996).

BAAF's guides, *Parenting a Child with Emotional and Behavioural Difficulties* (Hughes, 2012) and *Parenting a Child with Mental Health Issues* (Jackson, 2012), may assist prospective carers to better understand the needs of such children and consider their ability to parent them.

Autism spectrum disorders (ASD)

Autism is a lifelong disorder that has a great impact on the child or young person and their family or carers. The term ASD covers:

- Autistic disorder
- Asperger's Syndrome
- Disintegrative disorder
- Other autism-like conditions (atypical autism or pervasive developmental disorder not otherwise specified (PDDNOS))

These disorders all include the following "triad of impairments":

- difficulties in relating with others socially and in a reciprocal manner;
- difficulties in communicating reciprocally (expressive and comprehension difficulties and non-verbal communication);
- rigid and restricted behaviour and imagination (routines, stereotypes) (Gillberg and Coleman, 2000).

Sensory integration difficulties are also extremely common and are being included in the diagnostic criteria for ASD in latest guidance.

The core autism behaviours are typically present in early childhood, but features are not always apparent until the circumstances of the child or young person change, for example, when the child goes to nursery or primary school or moves to secondary school.

The child or young person with ASD is an individual whose presentation and level of difficulties depends on the severity of the impairments in each of the four areas above and any associated difficulties, co-morbid conditions and level of intellectual ability.

Learning disability is more common in children with ASD and the proportion of children with ASD increases as the level of learning disability increases. However, all children with ASD have learning difficulties, however intellectually able they may be. The diagnosis encompasses able but socially gauche individuals who will find their niche in the world and manage independently, as well as those with severe learning difficulties and/or challenging behaviour who will require intensive support at home or in a residential setting throughout their lives (Brooks *et al*, 2004).

Co-morbidities include epilepsy, vision or hearing impairments, and associated medical disorders such as Fragile X, tuberous sclerosis, mood disorder, attention deficit hyperactivity disorder (ADHD) and Tourette syndrome. Autistic phenotype can also be seen in children who have suffered severe neglect (Colvert *et al*, 2008).

The needs of the child or young person with ASD will depend on their individual combination of difficulties. Their behaviour must be understood in terms of both their developmental stage and their ASD. The National Autistic Society, for example, runs excellent training for professionals, parents and carers.

Communication: An experienced speech and language therapist should assess all children. Non-verbal children and those with limited functional language may use PECS (Picture Exchange Communication System). This should be available across settings, with carers and teachers trained in its use. Children may have lots of language but very concrete (literal) understanding (and a need to avoid metaphor) and poor conversational skills. Children may be poor at asking for help, or unable to do this, and carers need to be aware of this.

Sensory integration: Children may be either over- or under-sensitive to sensory stimuli, resulting in hyper- or hypo-arousal. Some children can fluctuate between these states. Environmental issues that overstimulate can cause huge anxiety and contribute to challenging behaviour. An occupational therapy (OT) assessment can provide advice and suggest equipment that may help to lower anxiety. This needs to be available across settings.

Diet: Extremely limited diets are common. This may be part of the ASD need for sameness or a sensory issue, and is commonly a combination of both. In some cases, unless these are taken into account, a child may eat so little that their health is at risk. Speech and language therapists, occupational therapists, dieticians, a paediatrician and a psychologist may need to work together with carers. Constipation is common and must be tackled.

Sleep: Children with ASD have problems with their circadian rhythm, which can disrupt sleep. An elaborate routine may be a prelude to bedtime. Sensory issues may influence their sleep. Good sleep hygiene, melatonin and advice about bedding from an OT may be helpful.

Behaviour: A need for routine and for everyone around them to conform to this can provide a real challenge to any family life that is far from regimented. A balance must be struck that allows the child to feel relaxed and happy without them controlling everything so closely that when the unexpected happens they are deeply distressed. Good advice and an understanding of how behaviour presents across settings is needed. Communication and sensory issues have to be addressed. A child may not say that they are in pain but their behaviour may deteriorate. A CAMHS opinion may be needed for some children whose anxiety is helped by medication, or who have a co-existing mood disorder. As for other challenging children without ASD, a behaviour management strategy and a restraint policy that is accredited by BILD (British Institute of Learning Disabilities) is needed to safeguard the child. Staff and carers require training.

Safety: Children with ASD are vulnerable. They may have no idea of stranger danger or road sense. A more able child may not understand the true nature of friendship and be manipulated by others.

Transitions: A need for sameness and to know what will happen next is common in ASD. High anxiety will be precipitated by uncertainty and change. Preparation and information are vital, and may be given verbally when appropriate and/or by use of a visual schedule, and may be necessary for some or all of the time. Changes of carer, placement, plans for the day, etc, require this approach for many children on the autistic spectrum. Attending for health care is a prime example and may be challenging for a number of reasons. Waiting, environmental stimuli and the unknown may all cause anxiety.

The guide, *Parenting a Child with Autism Spectrum Disorder* (Carter, 2013), may assist prospective carers to better understand the needs of children with autism and assess their ability to parent them.

Practitioners should also be familiar with NICE guidance:

- Clinical Guideline 128: *Autism: Recognition, referral and diagnosis of children and young people on the autism spectrum* (2011)
- Clinical Guideline 170: *Autism: Management of autism in children and young people* (2013a)
- Quality Standard 51: *Autism* (2014)

Attention Deficit Hyperactivity Disorder (ADHD)

Practitioners should be familiar with NICE guidance Clinical Guideline 72: *Attention Deficit Hyperactivity Disorder (ADHD)* (NICE, 2008, updated 2013), from which the following information has been adapted.

ADHD is a heterogeneous behavioural syndrome characterised by the core symptoms of hyperactivity, impulsivity and inattention. While these symptoms tend to cluster together, some children are predominantly hyperactive and impulsive, while others are principally inattentive.

Symptoms of ADHD are distributed throughout the population and vary in severity; only those with significant impairment meet criteria for a diagnosis of ADHD. Symptoms of ADHD can overlap with symptoms of other related disorders, and ADHD cannot be considered a categorical diagnosis. Therefore, care in differential diagnosis is needed. Common co-existing conditions in children with ADHD are disorders of mood, conduct, learning, motor control and communication, and anxiety disorders.

Not every person with ADHD has all of the symptoms of hyperactivity, impulsivity and inattention. However, for a person to be diagnosed with ADHD, their symptoms should be associated with at least a moderate degree of psychological, social and/or educational or occupational impairment.

Moderate ADHD in children and young people is taken to be present when the symptoms of hyperactivity, impulsivity and/or inattention, or all three, occur together, and are associated with at least moderate impairment, which should be present in multiple settings (for example, home and school or a healthcare setting) and in multiple domains (domains refers to a type of social or personal functioning in which people ordinarily achieve competence, such as achievement in schoolwork or homework; dealing with physical risks and avoiding common hazards; and forming positive relationships with family and peers), where the level appropriate to the child's chronological and mental age has not been reached.

In general, ADHD is a persisting disorder, and most young people will go on to have significant difficulties in adulthood. In later adolescence and continuing into adulthood, the range of possible impairment includes educational and occupational underachievement, dangerous driving, difficulties in carrying out daily activities such as shopping and organising household tasks, in making and keeping friends, in intimate relationships (for example, excessive disagreement) and with child care, as well as substance misuse, unemployment and involvement in crime.

Severe ADHD corresponds approximately to the ICD-10 diagnosis of hyperkinetic disorder. This is defined as the presence of hyperactivity, impulsivity and inattention in multiple settings, with severe impairment that is affecting multiple domains in multiple settings. Again, determining severity is a matter of clinical judgement.

For looked after children who present with ADHD-like symptoms, it is important to consider that symptoms could be related to neglect, emotional abuse or foetal alcohol exposure (NICE, 2008, updated 2013).

Practitioners should be familiar with the NICE guidance QS 39: *ADHD* (NICE, 2013b). The guide, *Parenting a Child with Attention Deficit Hyperactivity Disorder* (Jacobs and Miles, 2012), may assist prospective carers to better understand the needs of children with ADHD and assess their ability to parent them.

Learning disability

Learning disability tends to co-exist with other disabilities such as Down's syndrome and Fragile X syndrome. There is no consistent definition of learning disability across services (i.e. mild, moderate and severe mean different things in paediatrics, mental health, etc), and it is important to understand it in the context of what it means for the child in terms of functional capacity and his or her care needs.

The following information about Fragile X syndrome is taken from the Genetics Home Reference website (available at: http://ghr.nlm.nih.gov/condition/fragile-x-syndrome).

Fragile X syndrome is a genetic condition that causes a range of developmental problems, including learning disabilities and cognitive impairment. Usually males are more severely affected than females.

Affected individuals usually have delayed development of speech and language by age two. Most males with Fragile X syndrome have mild to moderate intellectual disability, while about one-third of affected females are intellectually disabled. Children with Fragile X syndrome may also have anxiety and hyperactive behaviour, such as fidgeting or impulsive actions. They may have attention deficit disorder (ADD), which includes an impaired ability to maintain attention and difficulty focusing on specific tasks. About one-third of individuals have features of autism spectrum disorders that affect communication and social interaction. Seizures occur in about 15 per cent of males and about five per cent of females.

Most males and about half of females with Fragile X syndrome have characteristic physical features that become more apparent with age. These features include a long and narrow face, large ears, a prominent jaw and forehead, unusually flexible fingers, flat feet and, in males, enlarged testicles (macroorchidism) after puberty.

Fragile X syndrome occurs in approximately one in 4,000 males and one in 8,000 females. It is inherited in an X-linked dominant pattern. A condition is considered X-linked if the mutated gene that causes the disorder is located on the X chromosome, one of the two sex chromosomes (the Y chromosome is the other sex chromosome). The inheritance is dominant if one copy of the altered gene in each cell is sufficient to cause the condition – X-linked dominant means that in females (who have two X chromosomes), a mutation in one of the two copies of a gene in each cell is sufficient to cause the disorder; in males (who have only one X chromosome), a mutation in the only copy of a gene in each cell causes the disorder. In most cases, males experience more severe symptoms of the disorder than females.

Further resources for genetic disorders

For reviews of specific genetic disorders, see the Gene Reviews section of the NIH website, available at: www.ncbi.nlm.nih.gov/books/NBK1116/. In addition, OMIM (an online compendium of human genes and genetic phenotypes) is useful for rare single gene disorders: www.ncbi.nlm.nih.gov/omim/. Genetics Home Reference is also very readable for non-medical colleagues and families: http://ghr.nlm.nih.gov/.

What health professionals should do

- Designated professionals should ensure that the needs of disabled looked after children are the subject of audit and included in the annual report, and should educate and advise commissioners on the health needs of these children to ensure that they make adequate provision, including placements, which can effectively meet complex and specific needs.
- Health professionals and commissioners should ensure that job plans provide sufficient time to carry out comprehensive assessments of children with communication difficulties, and to liaise with multiple other professionals involved with disabled children.
- When the child has a communication disorder, health professionals may be key to enabling effective communication with other professionals and in assisting children to express concerns and exercise choice.
- Remember that support for disabled children is often focused on meeting the needs relating to the child's disability rather than looking at the child's wider needs, including

safeguarding, so health assessments provide an important opportunity for a compre-hensive assessment.

- Be aware that sometimes indicators of abuse are mistakenly attributed to the child's disability.
- Work with social workers to ensure that they have a good understanding of the needs of individual disabled children.
- Develop good policies for foster carers, for example, concerning treatment protocols, use of medications and equipment and resuscitation, and assist with training foster carers who require particular skills in caring for individual children.
- Be prepared to explain the needs of disabled children within the care system to GPs and hospital colleagues, who often have little exposure to adopted children or those in the care system.
- Stress the importance of advance planning to provide a seamless service when a child is being moved to a new placement, so that all required services are in place, equipment and supplies provided, and the new carers trained.
- Ensure that there are procedures in place for arranging health assessments of looked after children in specialist schools/units.
- When considering carers for specialist schemes, such as short break schemes for disabled children or schemes for adolescents, the medical adviser/looked after children health professional needs to form a view on the carer's likely capacity to meet the child's needs. For instance, if a child requires constant supervision, a great deal of personal care and lifting and carrying, or is involved in risky behaviour, there may be significant implications for carers' own health and well-being.

Key points

- Due to variations in defining and recording disability, it is difficult to obtain accurate data concerning the prevalence of looked after disabled children; however, they are over-represented in care. A large number of children have at least one disability, and in England in recent years, disability has been the main category of need for approximately three–six per cent of children entering care.
- Families with disabled children frequently experience additional financial, practical and emotional demands, discrimination, isolation and lack of support, all of which can contribute to children becoming looked after.
- Disabled children have greater safeguarding needs, both while in the care of their parents and within the looked after system.
- Many families and foster carers with responsibility for a disabled child will benefit from planned short break care.
- Children with disabilities tend to stay in care for longer, and a higher proportion live in

residential placements because of challenging behaviour and for specialist education.

- When providing health services, it is essential to consider the range of possible communication difficulties of disabled children and make every effort to understand the child's concerns, wishes and feelings.
- Statutory health assessments provide an important opportunity for a comprehensive assessment of the child's wider needs, including safeguarding, as well as needs relating to their disability.
- Looked after children health teams have an important role in facilitating communication with disabled children, training social workers and carers, and facilitating or undertaking comprehensive statutory health assessments.
- Disability and looked after children health teams should develop protocols to determine who has responsibility for various aspects of health assessment and service provision for disabled looked after children.
- Designated professionals should ensure that the needs of disabled looked after children are included in the annual report/joint strategic needs assessment to assist commissioners to provide appropriate services, including the range of specialist services required for high-quality health care.

Bibliography

Anderson D., Dumont S., Jacobs P. and Azzaria L. (2007) 'The personal costs of caring for a child with a disability: a review of the literature', *Public Health Reports*, 122:1, pp 3–16

Baker C. (2006) 'Disabled foster children and contacts with their birth families', *Adoption & Fostering*, 30:2, pp 18–28

Baker C. (2011) *Permanence and Stability for Disabled Looked After Children* (Insight no. 11), Glasgow: IRISS, available at: www.iriss.org.uk/resources/permanence-and-stability-disabled-looked-after-children

Bebbington A. and Miles J. (1989) 'The background of children who enter local authority care', *British Journal of Social Work*, 19, pp 349–68

Brooks R., Marshallsay M. and Fraser W.I. (2004) 'Autism spectrum disorder: how to help children and families', *Current Paediatrics*, 14, pp 208–213

Carter P. (2013) *Parenting a Child with Autism Spectrum Disorder*, London: BAAF

Colvert E., Rutter M., Kreppner J., Beckett C., Castle J., Groothues C., Hawkins A., Stevens S. and Sonuga-Barke E. (2008) 'Do theory of mind and executive functioning deficits underlie the adverse outcomes associated with profound early deprivation?: Findings from the English and Romanian adoptees study', *Journal of Abnormal Child Psychology*, 36:7, pp 1057–68

Department for Education (2012) *Children Looked After by Local Authorities in England – Year Ending 31 March 2011*, available at: www.gov.uk/government/publications/children-looked-after-by-local-authorities-in-england-including-adoption

Department for Education (2013) *Children Looked After by Local Authorities in England – Year Ending 31 March 2012*, available at: www.gov.uk/government/publications/children-looked-after-by-local-authorities-in-england-including-adoption

Dobson B. and Middleton S. (1998) *Paying to Care: The cost of childhood disability*, York: YPS for the Joseph Rowntree Foundation

Dobson B., Middleton S. and Beardworth A. (2001) *The Impact of Childhood Disability on Family Life*, York: Joseph Rowntree Foundation

Forrester D. (2012) *Parenting a Child Affected by Parental Substance Misuse*, London: BAAF

Gillberg C. and Coleman M. (2000) *The Biology of the Autistic Syndromes* (3rd edition), Cambridge: MacKeith Press/Cambridge University Press

Gordon D., Levitas R., Pantazis C., Patsios D., Payne S., Townsend P., Adelman L., Ashworth K., Middleton S., Bradshaw J. and Williams J. (2000) *Poverty and Social Exclusion in Britain*, York: Joseph Rowntree Foundation

Hirst M. and Baldwin S. (1994) *Unequal Opportunities: Growing up disabled*, London: HMSO

Hughes D. (2012) *Parenting a Child with Emotional and Behavioural Difficulties*, London: BAAF

Jackson C. (2012) *Parenting a Child with Mental Health Issues*, London: BAAF

Jacobs B. and Miles L. (2012) *Parenting a Child with Attention Deficit Hyperactivity Disorder*, London: BAAF

Littell J. and Schuerman J. (1995) *A Synthesis of Research on Family Preservation and Family Reunification Programs*, Chicago, IL: Westat, James Bell Associates, and the Chapin Hall Center for Children at the University of Chicago

Marchant R. (2011) 'Looked after disabled children', *Community Care Inform*, available at: www.ccinform.co.uk/

McCann J., James A., Wilson S. and Dunn G. (1996) 'Prevalence of psychiatric disorders in young people in the care system', *British Medical Journal*, 313:15, pp 29–30

Melzer H., Corbin T., Gatward R., Goodman R. and Ford T. (2003) *The Mental Health of Young People Looked After by Local Authorities in England*, London: Stationery Office

NICE (2008) *Attention Deficit Hyperactivity Disorder* (*ADHD*) CG 72, London: NICE

NICE (2011) *Autism: Recognition, referral and diagnosis of children and young people on the autism spectrum*, CG 128, London: NICE

NICE (2013a) *Autism: Management of autism in children and young people*, CG 170, London: NICE

NICE (2013b) *Attention Deficit Hyperactivity Disorder*, QS 39, London: NICE

NICE (2014) *Autism*, QS 51, London: NICE

NSPCC (2003) *Report of the National Working Group on Child Protection and Disability (2003) "It doesn't happen to disabled children": child protection and disabled children*, London: NSPCC

NSPCC (2009) *Key Child Protection Statistics in Northern Ireland*, London: NSPCC

Phillips R. (ed) (2004) *Children Exposed to Parental Substance Misuse*, London: BAAF

Rees G. and Lee J. (2005) *Still Running II: Findings from the second national survey of young runaways*, London: The Children's Society

Rodgers H. and Waugh R. (2014a) *Children in Care in Northern Ireland 2012–2013*, Belfast: DHSSPS, available at www.dhsspsni.gov.uk/child-care-ni-2012–2013.pdf

Rodgers H. and Waugh I. (2014b) *Northern Ireland Care Leavers Aged 16–18*, Belfast: DHSSPS, available at: www.dhsspsni.gov.uk/ni_care_leavers_aged_16_-_18_2011-12.pdf

Sinclair I., Baker C., Lee J. and Gibbs I. (2007) *The Pursuit of Permanence: A study of the English care system*, London: Jessica Kingsley Publishers

Stanway C. and Miles L. (2012) *Parenting a Child with Dyslexia*, London: BAAF

Welsh Assembly Government (2007) *Towards a Stable Life and a Brighter Future*, Cardiff: WAG

Welsh Government (2013) *Children Starting to be Looked After during Year to 31 March by Local Authority and Need for Care*, Cardiff: StatsWales

10 Black and minority ethnic children*

Savita de Sousa

This chapter is intended to raise awareness of the health needs of children from all black and minority ethnic communities in the UK. However, it is important to note that there is a lack of data on many communities. General principles will be discussed and examples provided wherever possible. This chapter focuses only on issues specific to black and mixed ethnicity children; Chapters 2, 3 and 4 in this book cover physical and mental issues common to all children. Some of the issues discussed in Chapters 11 and 13 (on unaccompanied asylum-seeking children and on those adopted from abroad) will also be of significance to some BAME children.

Children from black and mixed ethnicities (BAME) are over-represented in the care system, while those from Asian backgrounds are under-represented (Owen and Statham, 2009). Both groups have particular needs relating to their minority backgrounds. While health practitioners need to have an understanding of the diverse cultures of BAME children, as well as an awareness of the impact of their own cultures and those of their organisations on their work, it is important not to attribute all the causes of emotional suffering and health problems faced by BAME children to ethnic or cultural factors.

Who are these children?

In the UK today, there is considerable diversity of racial, ethnic, cultural, linguistic and religious backgrounds, and this is reflected amongst looked after children. Children from diverse backgrounds are generally included within the term black and minority ethnic (BAME). The term "ethnic minorities" was used by the Commission for Racial Equality to signify the importance of cultural and religious difference and the experience of racism. This term has evolved over time, becoming more common as the term "black" has become less all-inclusive of those experiencing racial discrimination. The term BAME is an attempt at comprehensive coverage.

It is also important to remember that this term can include families and children from other backgrounds, such as Welsh- or Irish-speaking, Gypsies and Travellers, Eastern European, or Jewish. Also included within the BAME group are trafficked children, who may be at particular risk of sexual prostitution, exploitative domestic servitude, enforced criminal activity or the removal of organs (Council of Europe, 2005/8). With diversity also

---

* See the Appendix at the end of the chapter for explanations of terminology.

come different cultural norms concerning relationships between the sexes, roles of extended family, and child-rearing practices, all of which must be taken into consideration in assessment and service delivery.

BAME communities represent a very diverse and dynamic population in terms of their reasons for migration, with changing health needs and priorities over time. The health needs of second generation BAME children will be different from those of their parents; similarly, the needs of communities that might have been living in the UK for generations will be different to those that have recently migrated to the country.

The profiles of children in family-finding publications such as Be My Parent clearly indicate that many of the BAME children needing placements have complex backgrounds and may be widely diverse in their ethnicity. There is also likely to be diversity in culture, language, religion and other significant factors, all of which will have varying degrees of importance in the daily lives of individual children. It is important that practitioners avoid labelling a child and therefore ignoring some elements in their background.

In reality, many white children may consider themselves to have a mixed ethnicity if one parent is British and the other is from a European country. The majority of mothers of mixed ethnicity looked after children are of white or mixed ethnicity themselves; are disadvantaged in some way; and have less support from their extended families than other parents (Selwyn *et al*, 2010). A study (Caballero *et al*, 2008) of the 2001 census 'Mixed Other' ethnicity category (which included White/Vietnamese, White/Caribbean, White/Chinese, White/Kosovan and African/Caribbean) showed that one-third to one-half of the respondents described themselves as growing up with a "mixed" culture, i.e. having a mixed racial or ethnic background; being transracially adopted; having a parent from a white ethnic background other than British; growing up speaking another language at home; living abroad as a child ("third culture" children); or having a step-parent from a different racial or ethnic background.

The diversity of the "minority ethnic" population in England and Wales is shown in the chart overleaf. Polish people whose place of birth is Poland are now included under the "Any other white" category, which has the largest increase in population. Across England and Wales, both London and the West Midlands have above average proportions of ethnic groups and a lower than average white ethnic population, whilst Wales has the smallest percentage of minority groups, followed by the South West and North East of England (Office for National Statistics, 2012).

Ethnicity and national identity in England and Wales

Much has been written about the connections between social deprivation, isolation and ill health (Belippa, 1991, p 23, cited in Dwivedi, 2002; Kober, 2003). Practitioners are encouraged to address the health needs of the British-born BAME child population alongside those of new immigrants, including those in semi-rural and rural boroughs where there are smaller numbers (Finney and Lymperopoulou, 2014).

The chart below shows the range of ethnicities of BAME children in public care in England and Wales in 2013. Figures on the ethnicity of looked after children in Northern Ireland are not available.

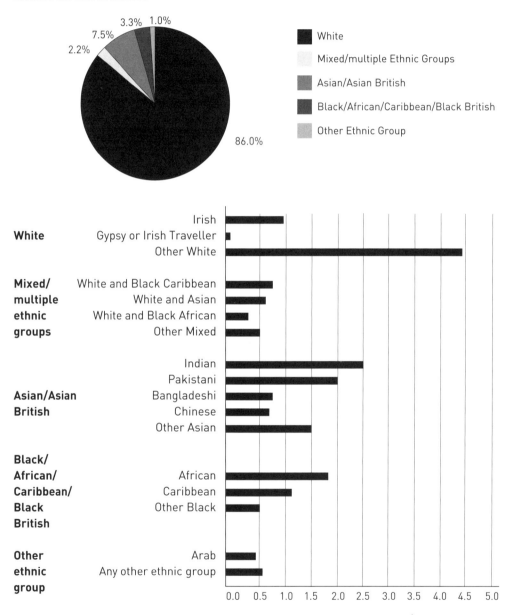

	England	Wales
Number of looked after children	**68,060**	**5,764**
White	53,030	
White British	50,620	
White Irish	310	
Traveller of Irish Heritage	60	
Gypsy/Roma	180	
Any other White background	1,860	
Mixed	6,090	175
White and Black Caribbean	2,270	
White and Black African	690	
White and Asian	1,160	
Any other mixed background	1,970	
Asian or Asian British	2,620	65
Indian	310	
Pakistani	770	
Bangladeshi	450	
Any other Asian background	1,090	
Black or Black British	4,470	45
Caribbean	1,530	
African	2,080	
Any other Black background	860	
Other ethnic groups	1,390	50
Chinese	70	
Any other ethnic group	1,320	
Other	500	170
Refused	30	
Information not yet available	470	

(*Summary of national statistics on ethnicity for children in care in England and Wales as at 31 March 2013* (*available at: www.gov.uk/government/publications*))

Legal issues, statutory duties and guidance

In the UK, the Equality Act 2010 brought about the same level of protection against discrimination and harassment on the grounds of race, ethnic or national origin. These principles are enshrined in the United Nations Convention on the Rights of the Child, which the UK has ratified. Article 8, for example, calls on states to 'respect the right of the child to preserve his or her identity'. In 1992, the Commission for Racial Equality (CRE) issued the *Race Relations Code of Practice in Primary Health Care Services* in collaboration with the various health agencies, with the aim of facilitating fair access to the provision of services. It recommends that practitioners acknowledge the experiences of racism and/or bullying where these may occur and become more 'emotionally available' to ethnic minorities (Davie *et al*, 2003).

England and Wales

The Children Act 1989, s.22(5)(c), places a duty on local authorities to have regard to a looked after child's 'racial origin, religious persuasion and cultural and linguistic background'. The principles of the Act also require practitioners to consider the wishes and feelings of the child. Furthermore, the *Working Together to Safeguard Children* guidance (DfE, 2013a) states that:

> *Every assessment should reflect the unique characteristics of the child within their family and community context. The Children Act 1989 promotes the view that all children and their parents should be considered as individuals and that family structures, culture, religion, ethnic origins and other characteristics should be respected.*

Section 1(5) of the Adoption and Children Act 2002 (England and Wales) requires that, when placing a child for adoption, the agency must give due consideration to the child's religious persuasion, racial origin and cultural and linguistic background. The Children and Families Act 2014 removed this requirement in respect of England only.

Northern Ireland

Article 75 and Schedule 9 to the Northern Ireland Act 1998 came into force on 1 January 2000 and placed a statutory obligation on public authorities, in carrying out their various functions relating to Northern Ireland, to have due regard to the need to promote equality of opportunity:

- between persons of different religious belief, political opinion, racial group, age, marital status or sexual orientation;
- between men and women generally;
- between persons with a disability and persons without; and
- between persons with dependents and persons without.

The Race Relations (Northern Ireland) Order 1997 follows closely the provisions of the 1976 Race Relations Act in the UK. It outlaws discrimination on grounds of colour, race, nationality or ethnic or national origin. The Irish Traveller community is specifically identified in the Order as a racial group against which racial discrimination is unlawful.

With regards to adoption, Article 16 of the Adoption (Northern Ireland) Order 1987 makes provision for parents to specify the religious persuasion in which a child is to be brought up. In cases where a court has given the adoption agency parental responsibility under Articles 17 or 18 of the Adoption (Northern Ireland) Order 1987, the adoption agency must give due consideration to the birth parent's religious persuasion when making placement decisions.

Factors contributing to family stress, becoming looked after and health inequalities

BAME children come into the public care system for the same reasons as other children, with the most common reasons being abuse and neglect. However, the families of BAME children experience additional stresses that may have an adverse impact on their health and contribute to the over-representation of these children in the care system. Some mixed heritage children come into the care system because of poverty and rejection by their white mothers' extended families (Barn, 1999b).

Migration and dislocation

Historically, the experience of migration to the UK has had a disruptive effect on many BAME families' coping strategies. The loss and separation of extended family networks have led to child-rearing difficulties, which have often contributed to children being received into care. The loss of support networks and cultural communities, compounded by little access to appropriate support (Belippa, 1991, cited in Dwivedi, 2002) has resulted in various family and parenting difficulties.

- In some African-Caribbean families, migration has caused the roles and relationships between men and women to become disrupted, often leading to single mothers having to rely on male relatives to provide role models for their sons.
- West African parents studying in the UK and experiencing unaffordable childcare services often arranged for their children to be cared for in private fostering homes, some of whose care is still a cause of concern for the Government today.
- Asian children in families that had migrated entered the care system because of the neglect caused by their mothers' isolation and depression, or because young women were assumed to be running away from home in search of personal freedom (Ahmed and Atkin, 1996).
- English is not the first language of many migrant families, and this can create isolation as well as adding complexity and stress to daily living.
- Feelings of isolation and adjusting to separation from their immediate or extended

family, culture and familiar environment may lead to psychological problems in parents, which may affect their children.

Racism

Racism is the belief that some races or ethnic groups are superior to others, which is then extended to justifications that create inequality.
(Bhopal, cited in Dwivedi, 2002)

In 1999, the Macpherson Report (Macpherson, 1999) identified the notion of institutional racism within public services. It led to the recognition that service provision for BAME children and their families should include outreach, interpreter and translation services, as well as culturally sensitive and cross-cultural practice.

Racism can have a far-reaching impact.

- BAME families are over-represented among the unemployed, those on lowest incomes, those who are socially excluded, and those living in deprived areas and in poor housing (Arora *et al*, 2000). When BAME families do find work, they tend to work long hours, on night shifts and earn low wages.
- Stereotypical beliefs about South Asian families 'looking after their own' (Ahmed and Atkin, 1996) may lead to neglect in terms of preventative services, while African and Caribbean cultures are often not recognised or may be seen as threatening and therefore in need of control (Ahmed *et al*, 1998).
- Racism can contribute to anxiety, fear and social exclusion.
- All of these factors are also associated with poorer health of parents and can affect the psychological development of their children (Braun, cited in Dwivedi, 2002).

Poverty

Social exclusion, particularly poor housing, poor environments and poverty in general, contributes significantly to family stress and has been identified as the prime determinant of ill-health. Reports suggest that a child is much more likely to live in poverty, regardless of whether their parents are in employment or not, if they are from BAME groups (Kober, 2003). National data suggest that more than half of African-Caribbean children live in areas of high unemployment, and that Bangladeshi and Pakistani children are consistently amongst the poorest of the poor. There is evidence that children brought up in disadvantaged inner city areas are at greater risk of accidents and emotional disorders than those brought up in other environments (Barnardo's and Leeds University, 2002).

Different cultural understandings of health and services

Practitioners should be aware that BAME families might not access services, particularly mental health services, because of differences in cultural values and ideologies, a lack of interpreting services, or unfamiliarity with the services available and roles of various practitioners. For children, this can lead to missed routine health screening and lack of recognition and treatment of acute and chronic illness. Untreated health conditions in adults may have an adverse effect on the quality of family life, ability to parent effectively, and the economic well-being of the family.

Physical health needs of BAME children

The physical health needs of BAME children are in most respects the same as for all children (see Chapters 2 and 3). It is important to keep in mind that BAME children who have recently arrived in the UK may not have had full childhood screening and immunisations in their country of origin, and that these will need to be reviewed (see Chapters 11 and 13 on unaccompanied asylum-seeking children and children adopted from abroad for further discussion). Guidance for 'vaccination of individuals with uncertain or incomplete immunisation status' should be followed (Health Protection Agency, 2012). They may also be at risk of infectious diseases such as hepatitis, HIV and malaria, which are highly prevalent in some countries of origin.

It is important to keep in mind that there are differences amongst the various ethnic groups. A number of studies have shown a higher infant mortality rate amongst poorer black communities, particularly within families from Bangladesh, Pakistan and the Caribbean (Smaje, 1999).

Growth

As for all children, it is important to monitor growth. However, practitioners should be aware that some BAME children may appear outside normal centiles on UK standardised growth charts, for example, ethnically tall (e.g. some African ethnicities) or short (e.g. Thai). Therefore, interpretation of the growth charts should be carefully undertaken in conjunction with the physical examination and body mass index (BMI).

Haemoglobinopathies

Haemaglobinopathies occur throughout the world. The commonest – sickle cell disease – occurs in black Africans, and those from the Caribbean, parts of the Middle East and some parts of Asia. Thalassaemia is common in parts of Mediterranean Europe and South East Asia. Children from these areas and those where the racial origin of birth parents is unclear should be tested. Detection of the homozygous state is important for the medical management and health prognosis of the child, while being aware that the child is a carrier of a haemoglobinopathy is important for the child's future. Haemoglobinopathy screening should include full blood count and ferritin as well as a request for haemoglobin electrophoresis.

G6PD deficiency

G6PD deficiency affects around 400 million people worldwide, with the highest prevalence in Africa (up to 20 per cent of the population), Southern Europe (4–30 per cent) and South East Asia. Boys carrying the G6PD gene suffer haemolytic anaemia when exposed to some oxidative drugs, fava beans or infections. Blood testing is recommended for boys.

Hair and skin care

Black skin needs to be kept moisturised at all times as it is prone to dryness, particularly due to lime in hard water. Eczema is often mistakenly diagnosed as ashen skin in black children.

Good, thorough hair care is especially important for black children. Their hair may look strong and resilient but in fact is delicate, breaks easily when wet, and has a tendency to dryness. Talking to black children about the ethnic traditions associated with different hairstyles can help them to develop a sense of pride in their own racial and ethnic identity.

Female genital mutilation

Female genital mutilation (FGM), also known as female circumcision, is a procedure which intentionally alters or injures the female genital organs to varying degrees, for cultural, religious and social reasons. It is illegal in the UK. In some communities, it is believed to be beneficial for a girl or woman, and seen as the proper way to raise a girl, to reduce libido and discourage sexual activity before marriage, and prepare for adulthood and marriage.

The procedure is traditionally carried out on pre-pubertal girls by a woman with no medical training, using scalpels, razor blades, knives, scissors or pieces of glass. Girls may have to be restrained as anaesthetics are not generally used. Immediate effects include pain, bleeding, shock, damage to surrounding structures, risk of infections, including blood-borne, and occasionally death. The longer-term effects are numerous and include pain during sex and lack of pleasurable sensation, scarring, chronic pelvic and urinary infections, complications in pregnancy, and neonatal deaths. The procedure causes psychological trauma ranging from depressed libido, anxiety and depression to traumatic flashbacks. Young women receiving counselling in the UK report feeling angry and betrayed by their parents.

FGM is prevalent in Africa, the Middle East and Asia, and is most likely to occur in areas of the UK with communities of first-generation immigrants, refugees and asylum seekers from these regions. Although the true extent of FGM is unknown, estimates suggest that over 20,000 girls under the age of 15 are at risk of FGM in the UK each year. Some families may take the girls to their countries of origin for the procedure, although this is also illegal in the UK and offenders who are caught face a fine and imprisonment.

Health and social care professionals should be familiar with *Multi-Agency Practice Guidelines on Female Genital Mutilation* (HM Government, 2011), which provides advice and guidance on protecting girls who may be at risk of FGM, and on the care and treatment of women who have already undergone FGM. Further information is available from NHS Choices at www.nhs.uk/conditions/female-genital-mutilation/pages/introduction.aspx, and in Chapter 11.

Learning difficulties

Specific attention should be paid to the incidence of learning difficulties amongst some BAME communities. The prevalence of learning difficulties amongst South Asian children and young adults has been linked to high levels of material and social deprivation, poor access to health care, misclassification and higher rates of environmental or genetic risk factors (as outlined above). Prevalence within other minority ethnic groups is not as well documented, although practice shows relatively high prevalence within the African-Caribbean community (O'Hara, 2003).

Disability

It is important to keep in mind that BAME children will have the same range of disabilities as any other children, and these are discussed in depth in Chapter 9. Research into the "multicultural question" within services for children and adolescents with disabilities has revealed problems such as over-diagnosis and denial of access to adequate services for children from minority ethnic communities, as well as disproportionate representation in services that target children and adolescents with disabilities. Practitioners should be mindful that BAME disabled children face challenges and discrimination linked to their disability as well as their ethnicity (Cuadra, 2012).

Psychological and emotional health needs of BAME children

The mental health needs of children discussed in Chapter 4 will be equally relevant to BAME looked after children. In addition, these children may have particular mental health needs related to their experiences of growing up in a predominantly white culture. There is very little research on the mental health experiences and needs of BAME children in the public care system. Factors that commonly contribute to the development of mental illness in BAME children include racism, unemployment, domestic violence and substance misuse, and the psychological impact of cross-cultural tensions. In some communities, the most common examples are forced marriages and female genital mutilation (FGM). These tensions can lead to isolation from participation in both the BAME community and wider society. Key findings from the Minority Voices research study of CAMHS services (Street *et al*, 2005) show geographical differences – from a range of developed services in partnership with community services in some localities, to little or no provision in others. A key issue for practitioners is how best to reach out to and engage with BAME young people who might be in need of mental health services.

As with some looked after children, dependence on drugs, alcohol or other substances is also a problem for some BAME young people. A comparison of prevalence and treatment data suggests that young women and young Asians may be under-represented in the treatment system, while black and mixed heritage young people appear to be over-represented in treatment (DfES, Home Office and DH, 2005).

Cultural differences may cause both different presentations and understandings of mental illness. Language barriers pose additional challenges when dealing with mental health problems, and use of interpreters adds another level of complexity and potential for misunderstanding.

The negative portrayal of BAME people and their cultures in the media can damage the self-esteem and racial identities of some BAME children who might not recover from the experience. Equally, when BAME children experience bullying and racial abuse in school, the community or the extended family of their adopters and/or foster carers, they can feel isolated and "hopeless" (Dwivedi, 2002). And, in turn, "white" children from majority groups can develop a superiority complex based on stereotypes of BAME people and their cultures (Pugh, cited in Dwivedi, 2002). If a child is able to relate to a spiritual or religious dimension, they might be better able to cope with the negative feelings engendered as a result of their experiences of racism.

Identity issues for BAME children

Identity development is an important health issue for all children who are unable to live with their birth families, but may be particularly difficult for BAME children who are separated from their ethnic, cultural and religious communities. Each of the child's parents may be strongly embedded in their heritage, loosely linked to it or may have rejected it altogether. The parents' identification with their own heritage may influence their views on the placement for their child. The child's experience of any of this will also be wide-ranging. For some, their experience of their culture will have been an important part of their early experience and will have come to form a part of their ethnic identity. For others who have been removed from their parents at birth or shortly afterwards, their heritage may exist rather as a set of complex facts about them and who they might become, but remain unrealised in actual lived experience. BAME looked after children who are placed in transracial and transcultural placements are more likely to ask themselves: 'Who am I and how do I fit in?' Knowledge of their origins might help them to cope with "difference" in their adoptive and foster care families, as well as the loss and negation of their birth families.

Banks (cited in Dwivedi, 2002, pp 151–167) developed the concept of a "positive black identity" to show that children can engage with their racial, ethnic or cultural group 'without shame and can accept their colour difference without feelings or beliefs of self-devaluation'. A positive black identity contributes to a black (and minority ethnic) child's healthy development by providing a psychological defence against racist experiences, and provides 'a sense of belonging and a foundation . . . for carrying out transactions with people, cultures and human situations beyond the world of blackness' (Cross, cited by Banks in Dwivedi, 2002, p 154).

Like all children in the public care system, BAME children are likely to have negative identity formations because of broken attachments and loss of contact with their birth families. If BAME children are to achieve their potential as adults, it is essential that their ethnic, cultural, religious and linguistic identities are promoted and nurtured by their foster and adoptive families. However, before children can explore their identities, they first have to understand that their ethnicity is "fixed". These stages of social constancy are often overlooked and they should be considered alongside those of ethnic identity (Dwivedi (2002, pp 304–5). When working with individual children, practitioners need to explore with them how they view their ethnic background and what meaning this has for them.

Stages of ethnic identity development

Crumbley (1999) explains the different stages of ethnic identity development, as follows:

Birth–age 3

Toddlers become aware of physical race and skin colour differences and learn names for specific groups. They do not comprehend the real meanings of these labels and may be puzzled by the use of colours to describe both people and objects.

Ages 4–6

Pre-schoolers can usually identify their own racial or ethnic group and may place a positive or negative value on their own or other groups. Feelings about groups are acquired by absorbing societal messages from around them, even in the absence of contact or parental instruction.

Ages 7–11

Firmer understanding of their own racial and ethnic identity and, given the opportunity, children will explore what it means to be a member of this group. This is a prime age for participating in group activities with a cultural or educational focus, as well as a time when role models are especially important.

Ages 12–18

Individualistic progression. A time of exploration, including exploring the significance of race, ethnicity, culture, adoption and examining how these apply to the individual. Past experiences determine positive, negative or transitional identity.

DNA testing to determine racial background

Some agencies have been interested in the use of DNA testing to determine racial background for looked after children where parental racial group is uncertain, for example, when a child's father is unknown. However, testing for this purpose has not been validated, and does not provide information about an individual's immediate antecedents. A statement on the use of DNA testing to determine racial background is in Appendix A and also available on the BAAF website at: www.baaf.org.uk/sites/default/files/uploads/res/lpp/ethnictesting.pdf. This outlines the reasons why the BAAF Health Group Advisory Committee, following consultation with colleagues in clinical genetics departments and the British Society for Human Genetics, does not recommend the use of DNA testing to determine ethnicity.

Cultural competence

Cultural competence could be defined as a set of congruent behaviours, attitudes and policies that come together in a system, agency or among professionals and enables them to work effectively in cross-cultural situations. It is the integration and transformation of knowledge about individuals and groups of people into specific standards, policies, practices and attitudes used in appropriate cultural settings to increase the quality of services, thereby producing better outcomes. Below, we reproduce an extract from *Making Good Assessments*, (Beesley, 2010), which explores cultural competence.

There are five essential elements that contribute to the emergence of satisfactory levels of cultural competency.

Valuing diversity – This refers to the ability to accept and respect differences. People come from very different backgrounds and their customs, thoughts, ways of communicating, values, traditions, and institutions vary accordingly. The choices that individuals make are powerfully affected by culture. Cultural experiences influence choices and outlooks on life. Even how one chooses to define family is determined by culture. All these need to be recognised as important building blocks of the individual's identity and should inform decisions made about them. Valuing the culture and contribution of members of black and minority ethnic communities and their experiences is particularly crucial for effective engagement of individuals from these communities, due to some of the negative attitudes and prejudices that pertain within the wider community.

Being aware of the impact of the social care professional or the institution on the individual or the group – This refers to the awareness of those assessing needs or offering services being aware of how their actions affect people from other cultures. The "outsider" in this situation is not outside the system but rather becomes a part of the cultural equation. And hence a culturally competent piece of work is really an encounter between the professional's and the service user's cultural and personal narratives. Therefore, rather than presupposing objectivism, an effective cultural competent engagement would entail perspectivism – the notion that one's view of reality depends on one's perspectives which are informed by their own ecological niche. The most important actions to be conscious of are usually taken for granted. It is important to try and put ourselves in the shoes of the service user and reflect on their experiences of power, access to services, racism, etc.

Being conscious of the "dynamics" inherent when cultures interact – There are many factors that can affect cross-cultural interactions. For example, biases based on historical cultural experiences can explain some current attitudes: for instance, some groups or individuals may have faced discrimination from members of dominant cultural groups and this may have created some mistrust, or indeed there may be dogmatic beliefs about institutions and professions (e.g. that social workers break up homes). Awareness of the presence of such understandable mistrust would lead a culturally competent service to avoid confirming such negative associations.

Institutionalising cultural knowledge – This refers to the knowledge developed regarding culture and cultural dynamics, being integrated into every facet of practice and policy. Staff must be trained, and effectively utilise the knowledge gained. Policies that are responsive to cultural diversity should be developed. Materials should reflect positive images of all people, and be valid for use with each group. Fully integrated cultural knowledge may affect global changes in service delivery. Staff must become familiar with the cultural differences and the impact of different customs on people's lives.

Developing adaptations to service delivery reflecting an understanding of diversity between and within cultures – Activities and services have to transform to account for the presence of services from different cultural groups. Unlike the change that occurs once understanding and knowledge have been gained, this could be an adaptation that has to occur in reaction to the situation on the ground. For instance, the recruiting of interpreters and cultural consultants is something that cannot wait until a particular culture is fully understood or adequate level of knowledge has been gained. Rather, the presence of people for whom interpreters and cultural consultants are required in order to ensure provision of services and equality of opportunities should drive the need to acquire such services.

For effective cultural competence to occur, these five elements must be manifested in every level of the service delivery system. They should be reflected in attitudes, structures, policies, and services.

McPhatter (1997) suggests that practitioners consider the following questions:

- How much personal/social time do I spend with people who are culturally similar to or different from me?
- When I am with culturally different people, do I reflect my own cultural preferences or do I spend time openly learning about the unique aspects of another person's culture?
- How comfortable am I in a different culture when I am in the minority? How do I feel and behave?
- How much time do I spend engaged in cross-cultural professional exchanges? Am I prepared to engage in serious discussion that might reveal my lack of knowledge?
- What have I done to increase my knowledge and understanding of culturally and ethnically distinct groups? Where are my gaps in knowledge, and what am I prepared to do about them?
- What is my commitment to becoming culturally competent, and what efforts am I prepared to make to achieve this?
- To what extent have I extended myself in approaching professional colleagues with the goal of bridging cultural differences?
- Am I willing to discontinue representing myself as knowledgeable and as having expertise in areas of cultural diversity that I have not actually achieved?
- Without being culturally competent, can I continue to work with people from different backgrounds? What can I do to ensure that they get a good service based on cultural competence?

Why is cultural competence important?

The ethnic and cultural composition of the UK is changing to include many groups from a variety of religious, cultural and linguistic backgrounds. This means that a growing proportion of service users would benefit from services that require an enhanced level of cultural competence in professionals, who need to appropriately engage them in order to assess their needs effectively and provide them with appropriate services.

Indeed, it is a legal requirement that professionals ensure the equality of access and outcomes for all service users and potential service users. The Race Relations Act 1976 (Statutory Duties) Order 2001 sets out the specific duty for public authorities listed in Schedule 1 of the Act to prepare and publish a race equality scheme by 31 May 2002. In order to meet this requirement, local authorities must:

- assess which of their services and policies are relevant to the general duty;
- assess and monitor services and policies, including services and policies proposed for introduction, to ensure that they are not affecting some groups negatively, and that all communities are satisfied with them;
- deal with evidence that its services and policies are not in line with the general duty;
- consult the general public, and particularly involve minority ethnic groups at all stages;

- deal with complaints about the way these duties are being met and other complaints about racial equality;
- publish the results of assessments, consultations and monitoring;
- ensure that everyone, whatever their ethnic background, has access to information about the local authority and its services;
- ensure that all staff understand their responsibilities under the duty;
- carry out a review of the scheme.

All over the world societies are struggling to manage difference. Communities are divided by politics, by religion, by culture, and all too often by ethnicity and race. The cost of failure is that this struggle is all too evident in countries riven by war and violent conflict. It is less obvious in nations where the division appears to be between a dominant majority and one or more minorities; but the essential challenge of finding a way for very different kinds of people to share the same space and resources and to prosper, is no different.
(Trevor Philips, former Chair of the Equality and Human Rights Commission, 2006–9)

Western perspectives	Other perspectives
The Western family unit prioritises the autonomy and rights of the individual child.	Some BAME families see children as belonging to the family and community rather than as an individual in their own right.
There is a tendency among some practitioners to view BAME families involving single mothers and absent fathers as pathological.	There is much diversity amongst BAME families and many examples of single women who have successfully fostered and adopted children with complex needs.
Families would be expected to seek help with parenting if needed. Practitioners may perceive not seeking help as secrecy or a refusal to obtain help for their children	BAME parents often believe solutions should be found within the family or community, and may feel stigmatised by seeking help outside their community.
Mental health is a well-established health concept.	Some cultures do not recognise the concept of mental health and are more likely to perceive their child's emotional problems as deviant behaviour warranting consultation with relatives or religious leaders rather than professionals.

Common dilemmas

Practitioners in health, social care and other disciplines bring to their work with all children and families a code of practice, which is influenced by their own childhood experiences, their psychologies, cultural ideologies, professional training, and the country's legislative framework. For example, the practitioner's ethnicity and cultural ideology may lead them to see only the weaknesses and not the strengths of a family's cultural practices, and in so doing, a practitioner might mistake cultural differences for pathology. See Dwivedi (cited in Davie *et al*, 2003, pp 153–165) for examples of different cultural perspectives on parenting and health issues.

Seeing BAME children as children first may mean that specific emotional, mental and physical needs related to their ethnic, religious, cultural and linguistic identities are neglected.

Although in England and Wales the Children Act 1989 states that a child's race, culture, religion, disability and language should be given due consideration in the assessment, planning and delivery of services, Selwyn *et al* (2010) noted in their research that the ethnicity of all the children in their sample of three local authorities in England had not been recorded on case files. This practice is likely to have a differential impact on the decisions relating to the care of BAME children. There is also little research on the health needs, particularly the mental health needs, of black and minority ethnic children in the public care system.

But the most problematic concern in England is the striking out of the requirement to give due consideration to ethnicity when making decisions about the adoption of the child (repeal of s.1(5) of the Adoption and Children Act 2002 in the Children and Families Act 2014). In general, transracial and transcultural placements have good outcomes for children; however, the experiences of transracially adopted adults reveal confusion about their identities. The dilemma for some practitioners is the lack of evidence around identity as a research concept, the debates concerning the importance of ethnic identity and the practical difficulties of making matched placements in a timeframe which meets the child's other needs.

What health professionals should do

- Develop knowledge about the additional needs of BAME children and become an advocate for them, while also remembering that this is a diverse group with diverse needs.
- Designated professionals should ensure that the needs of BAME children are the subject of audit and included in the annual report, and should educate and advise commissioners on the health needs of these children to ensure that they make adequate provision, including placements that can effectively meet their needs (which will include issues involving identity).
- Develop cultural competence and access appropriate training.
- Learn about different BAME communities, particularly those present locally.
- Ensure familiarity with the law concerning equality and diversity.

- Challenge discriminatory beliefs and practices.
- Encourage carers to access relevant advice on skin and hair care, as appropriate.

Key points

- BAME children become looked after for the same reasons as all children, but their families experience additional stresses related to migration, cultural displacement, loss of extended family networks, and racism, which contribute to the over-representation of these children in the care system.
- Practitioners need to be mindful in their assessments and interventions of the BAME child's diverse ethnic, cultural, religious and linguistic identities, and their impact on the child's health and well-being.
- It is important not to generalise and assume that all BAME families and children are the same. Practitioners need to explore with individual children how they view their ethnic background and what meaning this has for them.
- It is essential for practitioners to be aware of the impact of their own beliefs and values so that they can offer culturally sensitive and antidiscriminatory practice.
- Issues of identity can be particularly difficult for children living away from their families and culture, or if there is missing information about the ethnic background of a parent.
- Balancing children's needs for placements that reflect their ethnic, cultural, religious and linguistic backgrounds against their needs for stable and loving families is a complex process.

Bibliography

Ahmed S., Cheetham J. and Small J. (1996) *Social Work with Black Children and their Families*, London: BAAF/Batsford

Ahmed W. and Atkin K. (1996) *"Race" and Community Care*, Buckingham: Open University Press

Ahmed W., Darr A., Jones L. and Nisar G. (1998) *Deafness and Ethnicity: Services, policies and politics*, Bristol: Policy Press

Allen D. and Adams P. (2013) *Social Work with Gypsy, Roma and Traveller Children*, London: BAAF

Arora S., Coker N., Gilliam S. and Ismail H. (2000) *Improving the Health of Black and Minority Ethnic Groups: A guide for PCGs*, London: King's Fund

Barn R. (ed) (1999a) *Working with Black Children and Adolescents in Need*, London: BAAF

Barn R. (1999b) 'White mothers, mixed parentage children and child welfare', *British Journal of Social Work*, 29:2, pp 269–284

Barnardo's and Leeds University (2002) *A Health Needs Assessment of Black and Minority Ethnic Children's Needs*, Leeds: Leeds University

Beesley P. (2010) *Making Good Assesments*, London: BAAF

British Sociological Association (2014) *Equality and Diversity, Language and the BSA: Ethnicity and race*, Durham: BSA

Caballero C., Edwards R. and Puthussery S. (2008) *Parenting 'Mixed' Children: Negotiating difference and belonging in mixed race, ethnicity and faith families*, London: Joseph Rowntree Foundation

Commission for Racial Equality (1992) *The Race Relations Code of Practice in Primary Health Care Services*, London: CRE

Council of Europe (2005) *Convention on Action against Trafficking in Human Beings, Warsaw, presented to the UK Parliament by the Secretary of State for Foreign and Commonwealth Affairs by Command of Her Majesty*, Miscellaneous No. 7, Surrey: Office of Public Sector Information

Crumbley J. (1999) *Transracial Adoption and Foster Care: Practice issues for professionals*, Washington DC: Child Welfare League of America

Cuadra C. (2012) 'Diversity and equality in health and care', *Education for Primary Care*, 9:2, pp 125–140

Davie R., Upton G. and Varma V. (eds) (2003) *'The Voice of the Child': A handbook for professionals*, Oxford: Routledge

Department for Education (2013a) *Working Together to Safeguard Children*, London: DfE

Department for Education (2013b) *Statistics on Children Under Local Authority Care at National and Local Authority Level*, London: Department for Education

Department for Education and Skills, Home Office and Department of Health (2005) *Every Child Matters: Change for children*, London: Stationery Office

Department for Children, Schools and Families (2010) *Gypsy, Roma and Traveller Communities: Further information*, London: DCSF

Department of Health, Department for Education and Employment and Home Office (2000) *Framework for the Assessment of Children in Need and their Families*, London: Stationery Office

Dwivedi K. N. (ed) (2002) *Meeting the Needs of Ethnic Minority Children*, London: Jessica Kingsley Publishers

Equality and Human Rights Commission (2006) *Equality Act 2010: Glossary*, Glasgow: EHRC

Finney N. and Lymperopoulou K. with Kapoor N., Marshall A., Sabater A. and Simpson L. (2014) *Local Ethnic Inequalities, Ethnic Differences in Education, Employment, Health and Housing in Districts of England and Wales, 2001–2011*, London: University of Manchester

Gill O. and Jackson B. (1983) *Adoption and Race: Black, Asian, and mixed race children in white families*, London: Batsford Academic and Educational

Health Protection Agency (HPA) (2012) *Vaccination of Individuals with Uncertain or Incomplete Immunisation Status*, available at: www.hpa.org.uk/webc/HPAwebFile/HPAweb_C/1194947406156

HM Government (2011) *Multi-Agency Practice Guidelines: Female genital mutilation*, London: HM Government

HM Government (2013) *Working Together to Safeguard Children: A guide to inter-agency working to safeguard and promote the welfare of children*, London: DfE

Johnston J. (2009) *Barriers to Health: Migrant health and well-being in Belfast*, Belfast: Belfast Health Development Unit

Khanum J. and Raúf Q. (2011) *The (BAME) Lone Mother Equation: An examination of the barriers and enablers to empowerment for BAME lone mothers*, London: The Limehouse Project

Kober C. (2003) *Black and Ethnic Minority Children and Poverty: Exploring the issues, end child poverty*, London: National Children's Bureau

La Veist T. (ed) (2002) *Race, Ethnicity and Health*, San Francisco, CA: Jossey Bass

Macpherson W. (1999) *The Stephen Lawrence Inquiry*, London: House Of Commons Home Affairs Committee

Massey I. (1991) *More than Skin Deep*, London: Hodder and Stoughton

McPhatter A. R. (1997) 'Cultural competence in child welfare: what is it? How do we achieve it? What happens without it?', *Child Welfare*, 76:1, pp 255–278

NHS Choices (2013) *Female Genital Mutilation*, London: DH

Office for National Statistics (2012) *Ethnicity and National Identity in England and Wales 2011*, London: The National Archives

O'Hara J. (2003) 'Learning disabilities and ethnicity: achieving cultural competence', *Advances in Psychiatric Treatment*, 9, pp 166–174

Owen D. (2013) *Evidence on the Experience of Poverty among People from Minority Ethnic Groups in Northern Ireland*, York: Joseph Rowntree Foundation

Owen C. and Statham J. (2009) *Disproportionality in Child Welfare: Prevalence of black and ethnic minority children within "looked after" and "children in need" populations and on child protection registers in England*, London: DCSF

Phoenix A. and Husain F. (2007) *Parenting and Ethnicity*, London: Joseph Rowntree Foundation

Selwyn J., Harris P., Quinton D., Nawaz S., Wijedasa D. and Wood M. (2010) *Pathways to Permanence for Black, Asian and Mixed Ethnicity Children*, London: BAAF

Simon R. H. and Alstein H. (1992) *Adoption, Race, and Identity: From infancy through adolescence*, New York: Praeger

Smaje C. (1999) *Health, Race and Ethnicity, Making sense of the evidence*, London: Social Exclusion Unit

Street C., Stapelkamp C., Taylor E., Malek M. and Kurtz Z. (2005) *'Minority Voices': Research into the access and acceptability of services for the mental health of young people from black and minority ethnic groups*, London: Young Minds

Tizard A. and Phoenix B. (1994) 'Black identity and transracial adoption', in Gaber L. and Alderidge J. (eds) *Culture, Identity and Transracial Adoption: In the best interest of the child*, London: Free Association Books

Zimmerman C. and Borland R. (ed) (2009) *Caring for Trafficked Persons: Guidance for health providers*, Switzerland: International Organisation for Migration

Appendix: Use of terminology

In the UK, there is little consensus amongst academics and practitioners regarding the meaning and use of the different terms laid out below. It should also be noted that the language and terminology is constantly changing (British Sociological Association, 2014).

Black

A political definition that brings together communities affected by discrimination and under-representation. It represents people from African, Asian and Caribbean countries. Some South Asian groups do not identify with the term "black" and prefer to be referred to separately as Pakistanis, Bangladeshis, Indians, etc. Sociologists agree that it is important to distinguish between different ethnic groups in order to meet their different needs (British Sociological Association, 2014).

Black and minority ethnic (BME)

A wide term used to refer to the diverse communities in the UK whose ethnic or national origins are not wholly white British. Often the communities referred to are non-white although, depending on the context, they can also include white communities of non-British origin such as Polish and other Eastern European communities.

"Race"

A biological term which does not describe the different ethnic groups in the UK or the dynamic and constantly changing interactions between them (British Sociological Association, 2014). It is 'a protected characteristic under the Equality Act 2010 that includes people of colour, ethnic or national origins', including those of mixed heritage (Equality and Human Rights Commission, 2006). "Race" is also seen as an important 'determinant of health status and health care quality' (La Veist, 2002) and is used by sociologists to describe the social reality of black and minority ethnic children's everyday lives.

Culture

The system of knowledge, experiences, beliefs, values, attitudes, behaviours and traditions shared by a large group of people. Examples include cultural factors shared amongst families who have lived for generations in white, working class urban communities, or communities of people in the UK brought together by religion and country of origin, e.g. the Bangladeshi community.

Cultural racism

Cultural racism refers to the perception that the culture of minority ethnic groups is "deficient" in social customs, manners and appropriate attitudes (Massey, 1991).

Ethnicity

Ethnicity refers to a person's or group's "traits". Ethnic group refers to members of a group who share a common origin, way of living and sense of belonging. Individuals can both be stigmatised and/or empowered by belonging to an ethnic group (Equality and Human Rights Commission, 2006).

Mixed race
A misleading term since it implies that a "pure race" exists (British Sociological Association, 2014). Mixed *ethnicity* individuals are those identifying with any of the four "mixed" census categories. They are assumed to have multiple heritages as individuals (Equality and Human Rights Commission, 2006).

11 Unaccompanied asylum-seeking and other separated children

Emma Fillmore and Ann Lorek with Judith Dennis

Although only a small minority of looked after children will be asylum seekers and separated children, health professionals need an understanding of their circumstances and additional needs.

Definitions

Unaccompanied asylum-seeking child

According to the Home Office guidance, *Processing an Asylum Application from a Child* (2013), an unaccompanied asylum-seeking child (UASC) is 'a person under 18 years of age who is applying for asylum in their own right; and is separated from both parents and is not being cared for by an adult who in law or by custom has responsibility to do so'. They further advise that 'where the person's age is in doubt, he/she should be treated as a child unless and until a full age assessment shows him to be an adult'. "Unaccompanied child" is used with the same meaning throughout this chapter.

Trafficked children

Child trafficking is the recruitment, transportation, transfer, harbouring or receipt of a child, whether by force or not, by a third person or group, for the purpose of different types of exploitation. This includes sexual prostitution, exploitative domestic servitude, enforced criminal activity, or the removal of organs (Council of Europe, 2008).

Separated children

Separated children are all those outside their country of origin and separated from their parents or legal or customary primary caregiver (Dorling, 2013). This term is widely viewed as good practice because it describes the situation of many unaccompanied children as being separated from their families abroad. Trafficked children are often, but not always, included and defined as part of the UASC population (Pearce *et al*, 2009).

Age-disputed children

Age-disputed children are undocumented asylum applicants presenting as minors whose claimed date of birth is not accepted by the Home Office and/or the local authority/Health and Social Care Trust (in Northern Ireland) that has been approached to provide support (Dorling, 2013).

Who are these children and why are they in the UK?

Children can be separated from their parents and may seek asylum/protection for a number of reasons, and each child must be assessed with an open mind as to their potential welfare and health needs. Children may come from countries experiencing long-term or more recent conflict, which may be internal or between nations. Whilst the reason for leaving an area of conflict may appear obvious, for others it may be less clear, and local issues, for example, relating to inter-ethnic violence, plus opportunity, will affect the decision to leave their home and country.

Some children are in local authority care following family breakdown after arrival in the UK, for example, if an older sibling can no longer care for them, or due to breakdown of a private fostering arrangement, and others may have been trafficked or abandoned.

In 2013, the most common countries for child applicants to have originated from were Albania, Afghanistan and Eritrea, with an increasing number from Syria, consequent on world events (Refugee Council, 2014). Of 1,265 applications made by applicants seeking refugee status, 323 individuals had their age disputed. Methods of collecting and presenting the national data have been revised, and numbers change dependent on appeal. Most are given leave to stay temporarily.

In recent years, there has been increased recognition that children may enter the UK as victims of human trafficking for the purposes of labour, sexual exploitation and domestic servitude. Although in 2011 there were 234 children referred to the National Referral Mechanism (NRM), the true figure is likely to be much higher as victims of this hidden crime are often unable to come forward, or fear reprisals or problems with their immigration status. Eighty per cent of referred children were between 12 and 17 years old, and slightly more than half were female (Department of Justice, The Scottish Government, HM Government, 2012).

Legal framework

The recognised reasons for seeking asylum are fleeing war, torture, persecution, threat to life or political unrest. The Home Office has operational guidance around the political situation in different countries and when it may not be safe to return a young person (UK Visas and Immigration, 2014), and s.55 of the Borders, Citizenship and Immigration Act 2009 places a duty on them to perform their functions with regard to the need to safeguard and promote the welfare of children.

If the initial assessment by the authorities agrees that the young person seeking asylum is under 18 years old without an adult to care for them, then they are considered to be an unaccompanied asylum-seeking child, and the local authority concerned has a duty to accommodate the young person under s.20 of the Children Act 1989 or Article 21 of the Children (Northern Ireland) Order 1995. UASC will then usually have the right to all the statutory services available to other looked after children (accommodation, food, financial allowance, education, health assessments, looked after reviews, care plan, leaving care support), provided they meet the criteria. In England, the Department for Education's (DfE) statutory guidance, *Care of Unaccompanied and Trafficked Children* (2014), makes it clear that local authorities should fulfil their duties with regard to the child's circumstances and needs as unaccompanied or trafficked children. Unaccompanied children will usually be able to access legal aid to assist with their claim for asylum, although not for other immigration matters.

There is no specific guidance on the provision of accommodation for unaccompanied children in England and Wales, but they are subject to the statutory guidance, *Provision of Accommodation for 16 and 17-Year-Olds who may be Homeless and/or Require Accommodation* (Department for Communities and Local Government, and DfE, 2010).

Regional operational guidance published by the Health and Social Care Board, *Pathway for Safeguarding and Promoting the Welfare of Separated/Unaccompanied Children arriving in Northern Ireland* (2013), includes guidance on the provision of accommodation for children under the age of 16. Separated children are the responsibility of the Health and Social Care Trusts and are recognised as "children in need" under the Children (Northern Ireland) Order 1995. However, young people aged 16 or over and age-disputed young people may be placed in unregulated supported accommodation if the Trust deems this to be appropriate.

Unaccompanied children and care leavers whose asylum claims have not been finally determined will not be entitled to access social housing in their own right and will need to be provided with foster carers, a residential placement or supported lodgings. Bed and breakfast accommodation is not considered suitable for any looked after child – children under 16 should be placed in foster care or a residential unit. In each case, the needs of the specific child, rather than their status as an unaccompanied child, should dictate the choice of placement.

A child will be accommodated by a local authority under s.20 of the Children Act 1989 and Article 21 of the Children (Northern Ireland) Order 1995 when they are a child "in need" who requires accommodation, unless a person with parental responsibility for that child objects. In practice, a local authority will obtain the written agreement of a parent to a child's accommodation, covering issues such as consent to medical examination. This is clearly not possible for most unaccompanied children as their parents are usually not contactable. Section 20(11) of the Children Act 1989 and Article 22(5) of the Children (Northern Ireland) Order 1995 allow a child aged 16 or over to agree to his/her own accommodation. If the child is of sufficient age and understanding to consent to health assessment, a practitioner may accept that child's consent. If there are concerns that a child is not competent to consent to assessment, the local authority should consider obtaining parental responsibility for that child through a care order, which would enable the local authority to consent to the child's assessment. As for any looked after child, unaccompanied children should undergo statutory six-monthly health assessments if under five years old, and annual health assessment if aged five years and above.

Unaccompanied children are subject to an asylum determination process that is designed to be more appropriate for a child. They can make an application whilst they are a child, and could be granted asylum as a child. However, because children and young people may be given a form of leave recognising that they cannot be returned to their country of origin (see below), it may be years before a final decision is made on their claim. This can result in living with uncertainty for a long time and may add to the stress a young person goes through at critical stages in their life.

The possible outcomes of asylum application are as follows.

Refugee status

This provides internal protection under the UN Convention relating to the status of refugees. If this is awarded (termed asylum), it provides five years of leave to remain with the right to work and access benefits as appropriate. In 2013, of those unaccompanied children who received a decision whilst still a child, 20 per cent were found to be refugees.

Humanitarian protection

If a child is refused asylum, then consideration is given to human rights issues and humanitarian protection. If awarded, this provides five years of leave to remain with the right to work and mainstream benefits as appropriate.

Unaccompanied asylum-seeking children (UASC) leave

Those refused asylum and humanitarian protection may be granted UASC leave (formerly known as discretionary leave), if there are deemed to be no adequate reception arrangements in the country of origin. This will usually be granted for 30 months or until the unaccompanied child is 17-and-a-half years old (whichever is shorter). Others, including trafficked children, can also be granted this leave.

Refused asylum

When this occurs, the unaccompanied child must return to their country of origin. It is, however, very unusual as the Home Office will not remove an unaccompanied child unless safe and adequate reception arrangements are in place in their country of origin.

Adoption and special guardianship

Rarely, unaccompanied children who are very young may have a permanence plan that involves legal guardianship by an extended family member who is found in the UK, or adoption if no birth family can be traced either in the UK or the country of origin. If the child is adopted in the UK by British adopters, they will acquire British citizenship and the right to remain. Other permanence options will not confer citizenship and the child will still have to apply for leave to remain in the UK. Special guardianship is also an option, with the majority of orders made to former foster carers (DfE, 2012).

The importance of health assessments

Completion of health assessments and production of informative health assessment reports in a timely manner is important to the young person making applications to the Home Office. The inclusion of information on any early or current health and development difficulties or diagnoses, documentation of injuries with medical investigations, presence of mental health difficulties or diagnoses with prognosis, and any ongoing treatments needed is essential to help inform the correct legal decision around a young person's application.

For example, a young unaccompanied African boy aged 15 presented to the health team with weight loss, cough, lack of appetite and a skin rash. The results of medical investigations showing HIV infection and pulmonary tuberculosis, a plan for treatment, and prognosis without treatment, were included in the initial health assessment report to inform his appeal against the decision not to grant him refugee status. The appeal was successful on the grounds that he would die if returned to his country of origin, due to lack of treatment available for both conditions, and that prolonged treatment was required in the UK.

Young people may be unaware of their legal status and this should be clarified with the social worker. They have a right to receive legal aid to prepare their cases, to be accompanied to interview, to be represented at asylum appeals and to have their claims assessed by a specialist children's unit. Unaccompanied children should not be subject to immigration detention.

Trafficked children should be identified as being vulnerable and, if at risk of further abuse, child protection procedures should be followed. A referral should be made to the National Referral Mechanism, as they remain vulnerable, even if their asylum claim is not being met, and should be safeguarded (Coram Children's Legal Centre, 2012).

Age assessments

This is a complex issue frequently considered by social workers. Many unaccompanied children do not have passports or accurate documents with dates of birth (World Bank, 2012), and the information on record may not be consistent with what they say. Some countries, such as Ethiopia, use different calendars and dates of birth are not always easily interpreted. The child/young person may have had an interview assessment at the Home Office, but screening has been reported not to be child-focused and it is not unusual for the Home Office assessment not to concur with the social services assessment, as these young people's stories are often received in a 'culture of disbelief' (Crawley, 2007), which is also exhibited by professionals and the public. This replicates the early patterns of disbelief seen in child abuse cases in the 1960s and 70s, where the reports of traumatic experiences of children were not believed because they were so far removed from the cultural system of the listening adult. Similarly, many children who talk of experiences of rape, torture, war and persecution are not believed as these experiences are outside the social "norm" of the receiving country's culture (Children's Society, 2012).

Maturity is related to past experience and ethnicity. Children assessed as older than their actual age may therefore not be eligible for services that they need, and may be subjected to the immigration procedures of an adult, or be placed with an older peer group. Conversely, there is the concern that an adult or older child may be placed with younger children if their age is underestimated.

Royal College of Paediatrics and Child Health (RCPCH) guidance states that as x-rays should *not* be used for non-clinical reasons, they should not be obtained to assess age (Levenson and Sharma, 1999). Age assessment is not an exact science, and depends as much on the social as the clinical presentation. For a detailed discussion of age assessment, see Mather, 2006. There is no statutory guidance for conducting age assessment for unaccompanied children. Instead, there is a body of case law that sets out the process recommended for assessment. Two key judgements are *(R (B) v Merton London Borough Council* (2003) EWHC 1689 (Admin), and *R (FZ) v London Borough of Croydon* (2011) EWCA (Civ 59). More details of these and other relevant case law are contained in Dorling, 2013. The Merton guidance outlines the following.

- The local authority cannot adopt the decision by the Home Office without having gone through the process of age assessment.
- An appropriate adult should be in attendance at the assessment.
- The assessment should be conducted by two qualified social workers, one of whom is to be senior.
- The assessment should take into account: appearance, demeanour, credibility and background (education, health, family, social, culture, ethnicity).
- The young person must be given the opportunity to question or challenge questions or decisions made during the assessment.
- A paediatric assessment does not attract any greater weight than the observation and history taken by the experienced social worker.
- Medical investigations (dental x-rays, bone age, genital examinations) do not lend any further information to the assessment process (plus or minus two years is the most accuracy that can be obtained from bone age and dental x-rays) and are unnecessary.
- If in doubt, the local authority should give the benefit of the doubt to the young person and deem them a child.

It may be helpful to note if the young person presents as consistent with their stated age, whilst recognising that this is an inexact science as children mature at different rates, and are impacted by life events. Medical and developmental information from the health assessment by a paediatrician may assist the decision-maker (social worker) as background to their assessment process, and the final decision is with the local authority. Whilst the majority of these young people are eventually refused asylum, it should be noted that significant numbers are accepted. Home Office documentation may neither agree with what the child says, nor with social workers who carry out independent assessments, and some children assessed to be adult have subsequently found to have documentary evidence that they are minors (Bhaba and Finch, 2006; Crawley, 2007; Dennis, 2012).

Interpreters

Face-to-face, culturally and ethnically appropriate interpreters are essential if young people's voices are to be heard and essential health information shared. In some cases, it may be necessary to ensure that the interpreter is from the appropriate "side" of any divisions in the home country, so that the young person can speak freely. Appropriate training and awareness in conducting medical assessments with interpreters is necessary. It is important to be sensitive to concerns that the young person may have about confidentiality and risk to themselves and family members. They may also feel vulnerable if other people know their whereabouts, especially in situations of internal conflict or persecution in their country of origin. Even when young people become proficient in English, they often find discussing health problems (especially emotional health issues) very difficult if this is not conducted in their first language.

Health assessments

Unaccompanied children require a comprehensive assessment in the same way as any other child in care, but there are important additional factors related to their unique past experiences of loss and bereavement, often including war trauma, torture or trafficking. Unaccompanied children may have specific health issues relating to their country of origin, experiences on their journey, and situation and circumstances since entering the UK.

Knowledge of the medical, social and political situation of the young person's country of origin is paramount in assessment and planning for their health care. BAAF publishes a range of booklets for foster carers (Fursland, 2007), which focus on children arriving from different countries and provide specific information to give foster carers an understanding of the kind of country, society and family a child may have come from. Each booklet includes a general introduction to culture, habits and customs to help readers gain awareness about a child's background, and provides useful information.

Advice is available to GPs regarding the needs of these young people (Burnett and Fassil, 2002), but the statutory assessment may be the first one where time can be spent on a holistic assessment with an interpreter.

Arranging the assessment

An interpreter who is culturally and gender appropriate should be booked for face-to-face sessions. Usually, the local authority will arrange the interpreter as they may use the same person for the UASC in all their consultations (e.g. initial Home Office visit, education, GP, legal services).

At the outset, it is important to explain to the young person that they and their carer will both be seen individually, and then together. It is useful to talk things over together at the end, particularly if there is an interpreter present, provided consent and confidentiality issues are considered as for any young person. Many unaccompanied minors are old enough to consent for themselves (see Legal framework, above).

As for any child in care, it is important to allow enough time to gather comprehensive information at the initial meeting, as it is unfair to espect the young person to relive trauma and loss several times unless in a therapeutic setting, and this may also be one of the few occasions where there is an interpreter present.

Documentation

As for looked after children, a health assessment (generally using BAAF Form IHA–C or IHA–YP) will be required but an additional checklist may make the assessment process itself more appropriate to the young person's experiences and needs, and can include, for example, prompts for family tracing and other specific issues. Completion of the Strengths and Difficulties Questionnaire (SDQ) may not give the full picture for this client group, but is useful in providing additional or background information.

A structured approach will help in gathering more sensitive information, e.g. family circumstances, after more neutral information (demographics, health or education), and ideally should lead from a mental health screening about vulnerability to questions supporting and celebrating resilience. The collection of demographic information is a useful way to start to understand a little about the young person's country of origin and ethnicity. There may be particular issues arising from mixed marriage, or different cultures and religions. There may be specific health issues such as hepatitis B, haemo-globinopathies, vaccinations, and female genital mutilation (FGM).

As the life experiences of these young people may be quite different from those of their peers in the UK, a comprehensive assessment should be tailored to meet the individual needs of the young person, which should include the points detailed below.

Demographics

Verification of demographics from the young person themselves is important as they may have been given official documents that are not in agreement with their own understanding and information, and this can lead to conflict. This usually relates to lack of documentation (common in leaving a country at short notice and where many children worldwide do not have documentary validation of age), the age assessment process itself, and literacy difficulties, but difficulties with some national date systems can also make the interpretation of a birth date complex even for nationals (for example, children with birth dates under the Ethiopian calendar).

Past health and developmental issues

Verification of health history, including immunisations, may be impossible as documents are rarely collected if the young person left home at short notice, and immunisation history is not often known by the young person. The World Health Organisation (WHO) website (2014) provides country-specific information about national immunisation programmes and may be helpful in outlining the immunisation schedule that a child should have received. Whilst some countries have a good infrastructure, if there is no documentation and no definitive history it should not be assumed that the immunisations have been given, as they may have been disrupted by war or travel despite being compulsory in some countries (e.g. Iraq). The young person should be advised about restarting immunisations if there is either no record, or if there appear to be missing immunisations. Guidance for "vaccination of individuals with uncertain or incomplete immunisation status" should be followed (Health Protection Agency, 2012). BCG is often given at birth and a BCG scar should be documented. If there is no BCG scar, the young person may fall into the current Department of Health guidance (2012a) regarding immunisation of at-risk groups for tuberculosis. This should be discussed at the end of the assessment as part of the health plan, as it may involve consideration of screening for HIV before giving Mantoux and BCG. A history of contact with tuberculosis should lead to a referral for screening, irrespective of a BCG scar.

Enquiry about jaundice, fever and other symptoms may indicate past history, for example, of malaria, hepatitis, tuberculosis or haemoglobinopathy.

Injuries and ill-health due to torture, war trauma, and physical or sexual violence in the young person's country of origin and on the journey to the UK should be asked about and documented, and appropriate referrals will need to be made for follow-up of relevant physical and sexual health needs and to support mental health needs.

Education history and ability to read or write in the young person's own language may indicate whether there are previous learning or developmental difficulties or whether they have missed education, for example, due to internal conflict in the country of origin, and so may respond to regular appropriate education.

Current health

Clear history of the young person's concerns about their physical and mental health should be documented. It is helpful to structure the assessment such that more neutral information including demographics, health and social history precedes the history of the young person's exposure to trauma or violence and the outcome for their family. Mental and sexual health screening should also be carried out.

General health

Abdominal pains, backaches and headaches are common in this client group and may be related to stress or gastrointestinal infections. Poor nutrition and constipation are common with the disconnection from the cultural norms for eating and cooking, and introduction to Western foods (often takeaways). Food and behaviours are linked to both survival and a sense of sanctuary (Kohli *et al*, 2010). It is important to ask if the young person is eating a varied diet, has cooking equipment and can cook, and if they know what foods to buy or whether they have someone to support them in this. Parasites such as Giardia and Helicobacter should be considered. Vitamin D deficiency should also be considered, tested for, and treated with diet and supplements as necessary.

Skin complaints and dry skin are common in this group. Many skin complaints and infestations commence on the journey to the UK, due to crowded, poor travelling conditions with inadequate nutrition. Skin infestations, such as scabies and Tinea Capitis, are common and often not recognised by the young person, so may persist without the young person seeking medical care.

Growth

Growth measurements and documentation are important to identify and monitor nutritional and health issues. Note that when plotted onto UK standardised growth charts, many of the ethnically tall (e.g. African) or short (e.g. Thai) minors may appear outside normal centiles, and therefore interpretation of the growth charts should be carefully done in conjunction with the physical examination and body mass index (BMI).

Screening

These young people may never have been screened for vision, hearing and development, so baseline ophthalmology should be booked, and hearing checked if any concerns emerge. Standardised developmental assessments may be required in order to identify and investigate developmental needs. The young person may not have had routine neonatal screening of, for example, haemoglobinopathies, and their mother may not have been screened for hepatitis B, so further screening tests may be needed dependent on the age and presentation of the young person. Risk factors for blood-borne viruses should be considered as part of a comprehensive assessment, and screening for these arranged if indicated. *Guidelines for the Testing of Looked After Children who are at Risk of a Blood-Borne Infection* addresses this in detail (BAAF, 2008).

Health promotion

Health promotion appropriate for age is discussed in Chapter 8. It should be remembered that many topics and concepts of health promotion will be new to this client group (for example, do not assume that the young person is aware of contraceptives). Healthy eating may be made more complex if they do not have support with shopping for appropriate healthy foods or learning how to cook foods that are new to them.

Patterns of health-seeking behaviour (visits to the GP, etc) should be documented and it should be acknowledged that unaccompanied children will not be used to our health system. UASC often do not use pharmacy advice or over-the-counter remedies and present to a formal medical setting for minor ailments. They may be more inclined to use NHS walk-in or A & E settings rather than a GP surgery where they will have ongoing and holistic care.

Family and social history

It is important to ask what the young person may know of any illness in their family. It is helpful to ascertain whether they have any family living in their own country or any transit country.

From this starting point, the assessment can start to sensitively explore the issue of why they travelled to the UK, if they or their family experienced trauma or if they witnessed something that upset them. If their parents have died, it is important to ask when, and in what circumstances.

Case study

A 14-year-old young man from Afghanistan spoke of his experience of his mother and sister being killed in front of him with bayonets. He spoke of the image being like a veil in front of his eyes through which he had to view everything in his life from that moment onward. At night the picture was clearer as his eyes closed, so he spent all night awake to avoid the terrifying nightmare. He was exhausted, traumatised, falling asleep at school and unable to eat properly. He slowly accepted help from a counsellor at college who was from the local Afghani community, and with consultation from CAMHS he was able to reduce the vision and return to a better sleep/wake pattern. He later completed two years of CAMHS specialist input and progressed through college and on to employment.

Discussion should lead onto the question of family tracing, and whether this may be appropriate for the young person. They may need reassurance that it is carried out by organisations working to careful guidelines to keep them and their family safe. The British Red Cross international tracing and message service (British Red Cross, 2014) can be life-changing for a young person, and they may need support by their social worker to take this route, as their concern about risk to themselves and their families in the process may be high. Many young people express the wish to know what has happened to their families and find the Red Cross work in family tracing very helpful in helping them settle and reduce anxiety. Some can be reunited with siblings and other family members in the process.

Mental health

Documentation of sleeping and eating patterns, any self-harming behaviour, intrusive thoughts/memories, patterns of socialisation, access to education, mixing with local community, connections to faith community, and use of any medications may help build a picture of the young person's current physical and mental health needs.

Screening is needed as otherwise the assessor may miss those with post-traumatic stress disorder (PTSD) or suicidal tendency. A structured approach allows for sensitive questioning of their mood and any depression or suicidal ideation, or PTSD symptoms, as well as what is causing worry for them. Having assessed risk, it is important to lead on to questions of support and resilience. Do they have a trusted adult, or anyone they can talk to in confidence? Where do they get their strength?

It should be recognised that many unaccompanied children come from cultures where there is a different understanding of, and possibly less terminology to describe, mental health issues, and where discussion around mental health is uncommon. Therefore, most mental health issues will present initially as physical manifestations until the young person finds a trusted adult to whom they feel confident enough to open up. Many of these young people say that their experience is too painful to remember or recount and many need a lot of time to feel safe enough to begin to think about their trauma and rationalise it. Counselling is a Western concept and may not always be effective, although specialist input, including group work, is often helpful.

The mental health of refugees can deteriorate in the UK, and they are often under particular stress when their asylum claim goes through various stages, and multiple stresses can have a detrimental effect on children's mental health (Heptinstall *et al*, 2004).

The majority of young people say that the uncertainty of their immigration status is the key issue that causes them anxiety. This is demonstrated in poor mental health, with erratic eating habits, lack of sleep, psychosomatic symptoms, and evidence of depression, self-harm and social isolation (Sanchez-Cao *et al*, 2013).

It is important to advocate for support of mental health needs by normalising life for the young person as much as possible, including education, faith groups and supported care, as this will provide stability and is protective (Summerfield, 2002). However, some young people will need specialist mental health input to deal with issues of torture, loss, trauma, and bereavement (Sanchez-Cao *et al*, 2013).

Sexual health

Any sexual health needs of the young person should be established, including unprotected sex and contraceptive advice, and past history of being trafficked, sexual intercourse/rape, pregnancy and parenting or whether the young person has been cut by "circumcision" (see below). Some girls will already be pregnant, usually from sexual exploitation on their journey to, or after arrival in, the UK. Recent rape (within the week if a post-pubertal girl, or up to 72 hours for a boy) necessitates forensic medical examiner advice and, if appropriate, forensic child sexual abuse examination (under s.47 of the Children Act 1989), and many will need to be screened for sexually transmitted diseases. Many young people are ignorant of contraceptives and need further advice or signposting to services. Risk factors warranting screening for blood-borne viruses should always be considered and a low threshold for testing applied to all unaccompanied children, considering the high reported rates of sexual abuse/rape/exposure to HIV and hepatitis in countries of origin and during the journey to the UK.

Female genital mutilation (FGM)

Specific questions must be sensitively asked of girls from countries known to practise female genital mutilation (FGM), also called "circumcision" or "cutting". The young girl may not know if she has undergone FGM, but it is important that this is known at some point prior to sexual experience or childbirth, for health and social reasons. An examination by a suitably qualified clinician should be offered if the young woman wants to know her FGM status. The legal situation around FGM in this country should be made clear to the young person and any carers/community support workers from culturally similar backgrounds working with her. They need to understand that it is illegal either for girls to be circumcised in the UK, or for someone to take her to another country to have this procedure carried out. She should be reassured that there are specialist clinics that can provide confidential and specialist advice around childbearing and other concerns that she may have relating to FGM (NHS, 2012).

Safeguarding

It is essential to explore whether safeguarding issues, including any traumatic experiences, experience of abuse, trafficking or being a child soldier, have ever happened to the young person. Many have been trafficked (Somerset, 2004; Serious Organised Crime Agency (SOCA), 2011) or are vulnerable to sexual abuse. They may already have experienced sexual violence, which is more common in areas of conflict, and in the process of migration and settling in a new country (United Nations, 2012).

Try to understand something of what the young person's journey involved – this group of young people, both girls and boys, are particularly vulnerable to rape; explore if this has happened to them. Afghan boys have reported rape as a systematic problem, and around one-third of girls disclose rape, either in their own country or while travelling to the UK, or indeed on arrival as they remain vulnerable to trafficking and prostitution, as evidenced by a number of these young people who have disappeared from care. The possibility of trafficking needs to be considered as both boys and girls are trafficked for sexual or economic exploitation, as reported from a number of countries, including Nigeria, China, Afghanistan, Vietnam and countries in Eastern Europe (Child Exploitation and Online Protection Centre (CEOP), 2009). The opportunity for sexual abuse and trafficking is increased in any country where there is conflict. They may have themselves been perpetrators of violence and, for example, may disclose having been a child soldier, with associated difficulties in acceptance within their own communities. However, many young people do not disclose information until some while after the traumatic events have occurred, and it is important that their carers are aware that their past experiences may surface in discussions or sadness at home.

Experiences in the UK are important to note, such as age dispute and detention as an adult, bullying or other circumstances of concern.

As already noted, some unaccompanied young people have become pregnant, linked to sexual exploitation and vulnerability (United Nations, 2012) while in transit and once in the UK, with most having become pregnant before coming into the care of the local authority (John-Legere, 2012).

A number of the girls seen in clinics have been trafficked, or sexually exploited during humanitarian relief, or abandoned after an abusive situation. Thirteen of the first 36 girls seen in a clinic had been raped. An Afghan boy has disclosed that he was raped while leaving the country (Leather *et al*, 2003).

Safeguarding procedures should always be followed and referrals made to social care for section 47 enquiries if there is knowledge or suspicion that an unaccompanied child is likely to suffer, or actually suffering, significant harm.

Ask whether the young person is making friends, and if they are attending college, what subjects they would like to study and what aspirations they have. An important part of the settling process includes whether they can practise their religion.

If they have a partner or friends, it is important to ask sensitively about them in order to consider risk, and also to ask whether they have contact with drugs, alcohol, gangs or violence in their local area, as it is easy for young people to become particularly vulnerable when alone in a new environment. Questions around contact with the police or youth offending teams will also highlight vulnerability and risk. It is important to know whether they feel safe, and if there are any issues of bullying, risk or problems where they live.

Education

School life is part of the environment needed to support integration and normalising of the situation for these young people. Although they often find it hard to get a school placement, other activities, such as English language learning or a gym plus travel pass, are usually supported by the social worker. Learning may require more detailed assessment, but the commonest issue is the need to support access to an education placement as soon as possible, both from the point of view of learning and to help normalise their lives, and support mental health.

If any significant learning difficulties are suspected, then a clinical or educational psychological cognitive assessment should be considered, whilst recognising that past experience, lack of education and trauma can all cause significant cognitive deficits without inherent learning difficulties.

Educational, cultural and social supports are usually extremely helpful. Good role models are needed early in the placement, as is signposting to organisations, such as the Refugee Council, that have practitioner advice and can provide support, and local refugee support networks in the community for sports and social activities. These activities help the process of adjustment and settling (Brownlees and Finch, 2010). Young people in foster care often appear to fare better when in placements where they have access to support from other children or adults from their ethnic or faith communities (Brownlees and Finch, 2010).

Examination and investigations

A comprehensive physical examination is recommended and more than one consultation may be required to develop rapport and enable this to be carried out. Particular attention will need to be paid to concerns that have emerged from the young person's history, and appropriate arrangements may need to be made for further investigation or referral, and reflected in the health care plan. It is important to document, and if possible photograph, any injuries carefully as they may be relevant to abuse, or to the young person's asylum claim. Always assess the risk of infectious diseases, such as hepatitis B and other sexually transmitted diseases, and screen or refer accordingly.

Health care plan

A clearly written health care plan needs to include identified health issues with plans for involvement of specialist health services as required (e.g. CAMHS children in care service, chest/tuberculosis clinic, GP or immunisation clinic, HIV services, genito-urinary medicine (GUM)/contraception and sexual health (CASH) services, safeguarding services). Actions with timescales and persons responsible should be clearly identified in the plan.

The plan needs to be made with the consent of the young person, with discussion in their first language, as this may be one of the few contacts with health professionals where an interpreter is present.

Current placement

These young people may be placed in foster care, or in semi-independent accommodation. Their needs are unique and may be undisclosed, and foster carers and social workers need to be aware of the possibility of past trauma, as well as sensitive to cultural differences (Amarena and Kidane, 2004; Fursland, 2007). With consent and with the interpreter present, relevant issues can be shared at the health assessment, and this provides an opportunity for the young person to discuss with the carer or social worker if there are any difficulties in the placement that may impact on their mental health status, as well as give the carer or worker a chance to reiterate the health care plan.

Multi-agency approach

Given the complexity of their problems and needs, a multi-agency approach is useful in helping to signpost and provide appropriate care for these young people. This is not always possible at clinic level, but close working with social/children's services is essential to ensure that needs are met holistically. While these young people have needs common to all young people, it is important for someone in health care to develop expertise in dealing with the particular problems of this client group, and some consideration is given below to the option of specialist clinics. There is a strong need for dedicated and interested staff to develop and run specialist services for unaccompanied children, with a non-judgemental and empathetic approach to the young people attending. Good communication with other agencies is essential in order to link in with specialist support services (Chase *et al*, 2008).

Specialist clinics

Unaccompanied children are part of the responsibility of the designated doctor for looked after children, and require statutory assessments. Assessment skills can be obtained by any motivated doctor with an interest in these young people. It is essential that a culturally appropriate interpreter is present in order to assess needs holistically, as young people are often able to communicate socially but not to talk about their deepest needs. These needs are those of any young person, but UASC and separated children have often had past experiences that require understanding in order to explore them in a sensitive way. In one study, of the first 93 children seen in a multidisciplinary clinic, most had experienced traumatic circumstances, almost a third had parent(s) who had died, and half did not know if their parents were alive or safe (Leather *et al*, 2003). Many did not yet feel safe in the UK.

A specialist in the LAC service needs to understand some of the experiences of child soldiers or children who have undergone female genital mutilation or been trafficked. Specialist social work teams build up experience in addressing particular issues of loss and cultural adjustment. The specialist teams become more skilled in supporting adjustment and referring to specialist services if the child has, for example, depression or PTSD. Exploration of the option of specialist secure Red Cross family tracing is one way of starting to approach past issues and is often missed in generic looked after children assessments. Particular legal issues affect the care of, and contribute to stress within, this group of young people and these are explored in more depth in the next section. In summary, it is important that one member of the looked after team has specialist knowledge and interest relating to unaccompanied children, in order for their needs to be met appropriately, and for wider training to take place.

Common dilemmas

Legal issues

- Unaccompanied children are accommodated under s.20 of the Children Act 1989, but do not have a person with parental responsibility to give consent if the young person does not have capacity or is very young. Discussions with social care about obtaining a care order should occur prior to the health assessment if these concerns are raised early. Local authorities may be reluctant to obtain a care order due to cost and legal complexity. Resultant delay in the young person's health assessment, with no one having parental responsibility for a vulnerable young person, increases the risk of leaving significant health issues unaddressed and the young person not being able to access appropriate health care. Practitioners should keep in mind that parental consent is not required where a local authority has a duty to arrange a health assessment to safeguard the child's welfare, although the child with capacity to consent may refuse the assessment (see Chapter 6).
- The six-month period before UASC leave to remain runs out (at 18 years old) is a stressful period in a young person's life, with increasing concern regarding the threat of removal post-18 if their application is declined. During this period, it is not uncommon for unaccompanied young people to increasingly report health issues such as persistent headaches, eye strain, back pain, intrusive "flashback" memories, disturbed sleep patterns, nightmares, lack of concentration, poor academic progress and clinical signs and symptoms of depression. Patterns of self-harm, lack of sleep, stopping eating, weight loss, intrusive and morbid thoughts develop with increasing frequency and intensity during this pre-18 years period. The need for looked after

children CAMHS increases at this time. Paediatricians who have assessed and examined UASC are often asked for medical reports to support the young person's application to the Home Office for refugee status. Clarity around medical conditions, with evidence of injuries from war, torture or abuse, identified mental health issues, and need for specialist health services and medical treatments, should be included.

- Once a young person reaches 18, they are no longer a child in care and as such do not have the protection and provision afforded for a child in care. Those who qualify will have access to the same provisions as all care leavers, as discussed in the earlier section on leaving care. However, young people without this support often become destitute and isolated, with resultant deterioration in their physical and mental health.

- Failure to achieve refugee status by their claim to the Home Office being declined can also result in destitution. Young people then have the threat or experience of detention and deportation. Some "disappear", often living in poverty and obscurity, not being able to access mainstream health services. Young people are then highly vulnerable to exploitation, with entry into sex working, drug trafficking and unlawful and unprotected work becoming a common practice.

- Unaccompanied children have increased vulnerability to breaking UK law due to lack of knowledge and understanding of the UK law and systems. There are strict and rapid actions if the law is broken by an unaccompanied child – most commonly resulting in immediate detention and deportation. Professionals need to support unaccompanied children by explaining UK law and the consequences of breaking it.

Cultural issues

- Some young men who need health assessments may find talking to a female health professional difficult as this is outside their cultural norm. Also, discussing emotional and mental health issues is often beyond many young people's experience, and therefore obtaining an accurate picture of the young person's mental and emotional health may prove difficult. This needs careful and sensitive timing of questions, with information gathered from key workers, carers or social workers to build a picture of the young person's needs. Many young people do not want to access mental health services initially, due to lack of experience and trust of these services, and unwillingness to "open up" to a stranger.

- Obtaining consent, testing and treatment for blood-borne infections can be difficult, particularly in young people from countries (in Africa in particular) where HIV and AIDS continue to be very stigmatised. Convincing a young person that detecting and treating HIV is possible and beneficial for their health is a sensitive task that requires understanding of their country's belief system and the perceived loss or gain for the young person. Ongoing need for management and treatment for HIV, syphilis or hepatitis is important information that the young person can use in their claim for refugee status to the Home Office, as treatment for these illnesses in many countries of origin is not available or affordable and therefore the young person would be likely to die if deported.

What health professionals should do

- Designated professionals should ensure that the needs of unaccompanied asylum seeking children are included in the annual report, and should educate and advise commissioners on the health needs of these children to ensure that they make adequate provision, including placements which can effectively meet their complex needs.
- Gain an understanding of the range of experiences of this group and learn about the particular needs that result.
- Develop a database of local and national resources.
- Work closely with social services to ensure good communication, timely assessments and shared understanding of the needs of this population.
- Raise awareness of trafficked and unaccompanied asylum-seeking children with colleagues, and contribute to specialised training where relevant.
- Establish links with CAMHS and encourage development of specialised expertise in areas with significant numbers of unaccompanied children.
- Be an advocate for stability in schooling, leisure and routines, and signpost to relevant organisations.

Key points

- It is inappropriate for LAC health professionals to carry out age assessments, but it may be appropriate to comment if the young person's stated age is consistent with their presentation, or conversely if they appear mature for their stated age, keeping in mind cultural variations in appearance and development, and the effects of traumatic experiences and early responsibility.
- Unaccompanied asylum-seeking and trafficked children may have additional health considerations related to traumatic experiences and forced migration, and possible gaps in surveillance, immunisations and child health promotion.
- Always use culturally appropriate interpreters, subject to the views and wishes of the child or young person.
- Every child is unique – find out about their life journey.
- Screen for mental, physical and sexual health needs and make appropriate follow-up plans.
- Identify support and safeguarding needs (consider trafficking).
- There should be identified pathways for referral, in particular for any mental health and sexual health follow-up, and for BCG and other immunisations.

- The young person may need specialist mental health support, informed key working and advocacy.
- Don't assume that the young person can eat healthily, cook, or knows that it is possible to prevent pregnancy!
- Red Cross family tracing can transform lives.
- Promote resilience (see the section on resilience in Chapter 4).
- Establish good communication pathways with other professionals.

Recovery from the catastrophe of war is 'grounded in the resumption of the ordinary rhythms of everyday life – the familial, socio-cultural, religious, and economic activities that make the world intelligible'.
(Summerfield, 2002)

Bibliography

Amarena P. and Kidane S. (2004) *Fostering Unaccompanied Asylum Seeking Children*, London: BAAF

BAAF (2008) *Guidelines for the Testing of Looked After Children who are at Risk of a Blood-Borne Infection*, Practice Note 53, London: BAAF

Bhabha J. and Finch N. (2006) *Seeking Asylum Alone: Unaccompanied and separated children and refugee protection in the UK*, Cambridge, MA: Harvard University Committee on Human Rights Studies

British Red Cross (2014) *Finding Missing Family Members*, available at: www.redcross.org.uk/What-we-do/Finding-missing-family?gclid=CL-hroGEiLQCFe_MtAodBm0Axw

Brownlees L. and Finch N. (2010) *Levelling the Playing Field: A UK UNICEF report into provision of services to unaccompanied or separated migrant children in three local authority areas in England*, available at: www.unicef.org.uk/Documents/Publications/levelling-playing-field.pdf

Burnett A. and Fassil Y. (2002) *Meeting the Health Needs of Refugees and Asylum Seekers in the UK*, London: NHS/DH

Chase E., Knight A. and Statham J. (2008) *The Emotional Well-Being of Unaccompanied Young People Seeking Asylum in the UK*, research summary project report, London: IOE

Child Exploitation and Online Protection Centre (CEOP) (2009) *Strategic Threat Assessment: Child trafficking in the UK*, available at: www.ceop.police.uk/Documents/child_trafficking_report0409.pdf

Children's Society (2012) *Into the Unknown*, available at: www.childrenssociety.org.uk/sites/default/files/tcs/into-the-unknown--childrens-journeys-through-the-asylum-process--the-childrens-society.pdf

Coram Children's Legal Centre (2012) *Navigating the System: Advice provision for young refugees and migrants*, available at: www.seekingsupport.co.uk/images/navigating_the_system_final.pdf

Council of Europe (2008) *Council of Europe Convention on Action against Trafficking in Human Beings*, Warsaw: Council of Europe

Crawley H. (2007) *When is a Child not a Child? Asylum, age disputes and the process of age assessment*, available at: www.ilpa.org.uk/pages/publications.html

Dennis J. (2012) *Not a Minor Offence: Unaccompanied children locked up as part of the asylum system*, London: Refugee Council

Department for Communities and Local Government, and Department for Education (2010) *Provision of Accommodation for 16- and 17-Year-Olds who may be Homeless and/or Require Accommodation*, available at: www.gov.uk/government/publications/provision-of-accommodation -for-16-and-17-year-olds-who-may-be-homeless-and-or-require-accommodation

Department for Education (2012) *Children Looked After (SSDA903) Return*, available at: www. education.gov.uk/childrenandyoungpeople/strategy/research/a0063862/children-looked-after-ssda903-return

Department for Education (2014) *Care of Unaccompanied and Trafficked Children*, London: DfE, available at: www.gov.uk/goernment/uploads/system/uploads/attachment_data/file/330787/Care_ of_unaccompanied_and_trafficked_children.pdf

Department of Health (2012a) *Green Book*, available at: http://immunisation.dh.gov.uk/green-book-chapters/chapter-32/

Department of Health (2012b) *Immunisation Information*, available at: www.dh.gov.uk/en/ Publichealth/Information/index.htm

Department of Justice, The Scottish Government, HM Government (2012) *First Annual Report of the Inter-Departmental Ministerial Group on Human Trafficking*, London: Stationery Office, available at: www.official-documents.gov.uk/document/cm84/8421/8421.pdf

Dorling K. (2013) *Happy Birthday? Disputing the age of children in the immigration system*, London: Coram Children's Legal Centre, available at: www.childrenslegalcentre.com/userfiles/file/ HappyBirthday_Final.pdf

Franklin A. and Doyle L. (2013) *Still at Risk: A review of support for trafficked children*, London: Refugee Council and Children's Society, available at: www.refugeecouncil.org.uk/assets/0002/9408/ Still_at_Risk-Report-final.pdf

Fursland E (2007) *Caring for Unaccompanied Asylum-Seeking Children and Young People*, London: BAAF (country-specific booklets available on Afghanistan, China, Eritrea, Iran, Iraq and Somalia)

Health and Social Care Board (2013) *Pathway for Safeguarding and Promoting the Welfare of Separated/Unaccompanied Children arriving in Northern Ireland*, Belfast: Health and Social Care Board

Health Protection Agency (HPA) (2012) *Vaccination of Individuals with Uncertain or Incomplete Immunisation Status*, available at: www.hpa.org.uk/webc/HPAwebFile/HPAweb_C/1194947406156

Heptinstall E., Sethna V. and Taylor, E. (2004) 'PTSD and depression in refugee children: association with pre-migration trauma and post-migration stress', *European Child and Adolescent Psychiatry*, 13:6, pp 373–380

Home Office (2012) *Immigration Statistics, April to June 2012*, available at: www.homeoffice.gov.uk/publications/science-research-statistics/research-statistics/immigration-asylum-research/immigration-q2-2012/asylum2-q2-2012

Home Office (2013) *Processing an Asylum Application from a Child*, available at: www.gov.uk/government/uploads/system/uploads/attachment_data/file/257469/processingasylumapplication1.pdf

Immigration Law Practitioners' Association (ILPA) (2012) *Discretionary Leave*, Information Sheet, London: ILPA, available at: www.ilpa.org.uk/data/resources/15387/12.09-Discretionary-Leave.pdf

John-Legere S.S.M. (2012) *Factors Associated with Teenage Motherhood in Unaccompanied Asylum Seeking Children*, Public Health Masters Dissertation, London: King's College

Kidane S. (2001) *Food, Shelter and Half a Chance*, London: BAAF

Kohli R. K. S., Connolly H. and Warman A. (2010) 'Food and its meaning for asylum seeking children and young people in foster care', *Children's Geographies*, 8:3, pp 233–245

Leather S., Wickramasinghe R., Jennings N., Holland T., Sclare I. and Lorek (2003) *Findings from a Multi-Agency Clinic for Unaccompanied Refugee Children*, Presentation to BAACH Annual Scientific Meeting, 24 September

Levenson R. and Sharma A. (1999) *Health of Refugee Children: Guidelines for paediatricians*, London: RCPCH

Mather M. (2006) 'Determining the age of children: another paediatric point of view', *Adoption & Fostering*, 30:1, pp 81–83

NHS (2012) *NHS Sexual Health Services for Women with FGM*, available at: www.nhs.uk/NHSEngland/AboutNHSservices/sexual-health-services/Pages/fgm-health-services-for-women.aspx

Pearce J. J., Hynes H. and Bovarnick S. (2009) *Breaking the Wall of Silence: Practitioners' responses to trafficked children and young people*, London: University of Bedfordshire and NSPCC

Refugee Council (2012) *How can we Help you?*, available at: www.refugeecouncil.org.uk/practice

Refugee Council (2014) *Information: Asylum statistics*, available at: www.refugeecouncil.org.uk/assets/0003/1356/Asylum_Statistics_Feb_2014.pdf

Sanchez-Cao E., Kramer T. and Hodes M. (2013) 'Psychological distress and mental health service contacts of unaccompanied asylum seeking children', *Child Care Health Development*, 39:5, pp 651–59

Serious Organised Crime Agency (SOCA) (2011) *UKHTC: A baseline assessment on the nature and scale of human trafficking*, available at: www.soca.gov.uk

Somerset C. (2004) *Cause for Concern? London social services and child trafficking*, London: End Child Prostitution, Pornography and Trafficking (ECPAT)

Summerfield D. (2002) 'Effects of war: moral knowledge, revenge, reconciliation, and medicalised concepts of "recovery"', *British Medical Journal*, 325, pp 1105–7

UK Visas and Immigration (2014) *Country Information and Guidance*, available at: www.gov.uk/government/collections/country-information-and-guidance

UNICEF (1992) *UN Convention on the Rights of the Child (UNCRC)*, London: UNICEF, available at: www.unicef.org.uk/UNICEFs-Work/Our-mission/UN-Convention/

United Nations (2008) *Background Note Prepared by the Bureau for Crisis Prevention and Recovery, United Nations Development Program Sexual Violence against Women and Children in Armed Conflict*, Parliamentary Hearing at the UN, available at: www.ipu.org/splz-e/unga08/s2.pdf

United Nations (2012) *Report of the Special Representative of the Secretary General for Children and Armed Conflict*, available at: www.un.org/ga/search/view_doc.asp?symbol=A/67/256

World Bank (2012) *Completeness of Birth Registration (%)*, available at: http://data.worldbank.org/indicator/SP.REG.BRTH.ZS

World Health Organisation (WHO) (2014) *Country Specific Immunisation Information*, available at: www.who.int/topics/immunization/en/

12 Care leavers and those approaching leaving care

Hannah Smith, Nikki Shepherd, Louise Large, Stasia Brackenridge and Liz Gilmartin

It is generally acknowledged that the transition from adolescence to adulthood is a difficult experience for the majority of young people, but when combined with the complex care histories and journeys of care leavers, this transition can become overwhelming and fraught with anxiety. Without the support and advocacy of a caring family, the potential for care leavers to fall through gaps between children's and adult's services increases, and exacerbates care leaver vulnerability. Health professionals have an important role in promoting health and helping to empower young people as they prepare to leave care.

The legal framework and statutory duties

Health professionals need to have a clear understanding of the legal context and terminology of leaving care. The Care Leavers (England) Regulations 2010, the Children (Leaving Care) Act (Northern Ireland) 2002, the Children (Leaving Care) (Wales) Regulations 2001 and the Children Act 1989 s.23A-E and Schedule 2 provide the legal framework and statutory duties and responsibilities of agencies working with care leavers.

According to the regulations above, a young person's status as a care leaver can be divided into the following:

- **Eligible child** – a young person who is 16 or 17 and who has been looked after by the local authority/Health and Social Care Trust (in Northern Ireland) for at least a period of 13 weeks since the age of 14, and who is still looked after.
- **Relevant child** – a young person who is 16 or 17, who has left care after their 16th birthday and before leaving care was an eligible child.
- **Former relevant child** – a young person who is aged between 18 and 21 (or beyond if being helped with education or training) who, before turning 18, was either an eligible or a relevant child, or both.

A child who returns home for a period of six months ceases to be a relevant child unless the arrangement breaks down and they no longer live with their parent, in which case they again become a relevant child.

Health outcomes for care leavers

Young people leaving care are a particularly vulnerable group, and research has consistently found that their health and well-being is poorer than that of young people who have never been in care. (Broad, 2005)

Both young women and men in and leaving care are more likely than their peers to be teenage parents, with one study finding that almost half of young women leaving care became pregnant within 18 to 24 months (Biehal *et al*, 1995), and another reporting that a quarter were pregnant or young parents within a year of leaving care (Dixon, 2008). For some, this may be a positive choice (Dixon, 2008).

Many aspects of young people's health have been shown to worsen in the year after leaving care. Compared to measures taken within three months of leaving care, young people interviewed a year later were almost twice as likely to have problems with drugs or alcohol (increasing from 18 per cent to 32 per cent) and to report mental health problems (12 per cent to 24 per cent). There was also increased reporting of "other health problems" (28 per cent to 44 per cent), including asthma, weight loss, allergies, flu and illnesses related to drug or alcohol misuse and pregnancy (Dixon, 2008).

Services to meet the needs of older teenagers and care leavers

Looked after young people require, by law, an initial health assessment on entry to care followed by annual health reviews; the latter are usually carried out by specialist nurses. In Wales, the statutory guidance, *Towards a Stable Life and a Brighter Future* (Welsh Assembly Government, 2007), permits specialist nurses to undertake initial health assessments under the supervision of a doctor; throughout the UK, the expertise of a specialist nurse in enabling and encouraging young people to engage in discussions about their health concerns and assessments can be invaluable. This may include reassurance about confidentiality – a great concern for many young people, who may be very worried about where their information will be sent and discussed. Clear agreement about this should be reached with the young person, as per General Medical Council (GMC) guidelines in *Good Medical Practice* (2013) and *0–18 Years: Guidance for all doctors* (2007). It may also include reassurance about the nature of the health assessment itself, which many teenagers (and some social care staff) regard as an intrusion rather than an opportunity. Young people leaving care may require support to enable them to continue to obtain health advice and services at what is often a very stressful time for them.

Personal advisers work within a care leaver service as the lead professional, preparing and reviewing the pathway plan, co-ordinating the provision of services, and supporting the care leaver as he or she makes the transition to independence (Regulation 8, Care

Leavers (England) Regulations 2010; Regulaton 11, Children (Leaving Care) Regulations (Northern Ireland) 2005; and Regulation 12, Children (Leaving Care) (Wales) Regulations 2001). Pathway planning should consider all aspects of need – physical and emotional/mental health, housing, education, training, employment and lifestyle choices, including access to positive activities such as youth clubs, sports, arts and leisure, bringing together all agencies and services, including the voluntary sector, to provide a co-ordinated approach to planning and outcomes (Welsh Assembly Government, 2007; Department for Children, Schools and Families (DCSF) and Department of Health (DH), 2009). Personal advisers should work closely with the local looked after children health team and may benefit from multi-agency training in how to promote both physical and mental health.

The statutory guidance for England (DCSF and DH, 2009) endorses this co-ordinated approach:

> *Multi-agency approaches are particularly crucial for care leavers as at this stage health needs cannot be separated from wider needs. There is an important health promotion and health advisory role for the health services in supporting care leavers in registering with a GP and accessing a dentist when they move into independence. The young person's personal adviser will have a key role in getting care leavers registered with the health services.*

All health professionals seeing care leavers should be aware of the particular issues these young people have and of the need to promote their health and well-being at every opportunity. Looked after children health teams should have specialist knowledge, but school nurses, midwives, health visitors and others who have increased contact with young people in, or leaving, care should also have an enhanced appreciation of the particular issues and difficulties that these young people have in addressing their health needs and maintaining a healthy lifestyle.

When undertaking statutory assessments, particular consideration should be given to the following factors.

- The importance of encouraging and enabling young people to take appropriate responsibility for their own health. This will include ensuring that they feel confident to access routine health care, e.g. their GP, sexual health services and dentist, but may involve their need to manage specific health conditions, e.g. asthma, diabetes.
- The need to address specific physical health matters. This may include concerns that the young person has, e.g. dermatological problems that can affect appearance and are often of considerable concern to young people. The professional should enquire if the young person feels well and about any symptoms they have; if problems are uncovered, these should be discussed with the young person and actions agreed, with

clarity about the responsibility of the young person and the professional in resolving the issue. Enquiry should be made about any concerns with vision or hearing.

- Physical examination is not essential, particularly in the absence of symptoms. It should always be offered and encouraged but not at the expense of being able to engage a teenager who is anxious throughout the assessment about having to take their clothes off! They often visibly relax when this is explained at the start, although many will subsequently agree to it, possibly at a later appointment. Referral to the appropriate physician may be indicated if there are specific symptoms.

- Mental ill health (such as depression and self-harm), attachment and conduct disorders, and low self-esteem are extremely common in young people in care and care leavers; such difficulties should always be addressed in the health assessment and necessary referrals made.

- Remember to enquire about the young person's education or training, their housing/placement, progress towards independence, money matters, friends and contact with birth family members. Although not strictly health topics, they are inter-dependent in many ways; poor mental health makes it difficult to access education, for example, and being housed in an area where drug dealers are common can make it difficult to avoid using street drugs. Thus knowledge of these issues may indicate the need for further support/referral for the young person.

- Never miss the opportunity for health promotion (see Chapter 8). This will include discussion of diet, exercise and leisure pursuits as part of a healthy lifestyle. The professional should ensure that the young person is aware of their immunisation status and, if necessary, empowered to become fully immunised. The importance of good dental care, and routine screening, such as for cervical cancer, etc, should also be emphasised. Be prepared to address difficult issues, i.e. those that the young person may not wish to discuss, including smoking, alcohol consumption, street drug use, domestic violence, relationships and sexual activity, including contraception and sexually acquired infections. If the young person is reluctant to engage with your service, signpost them to appropriate local support services.

- Health professionals should familiarise themselves with what services are available locally, by internet or phone, where information and advice about health issues can be obtained. These may include smoking cessation, sensible alcohol use and safe sexual practices.

- Care leavers need a good understanding of their full health history, including genetic background, details of past infections and illnesses, allergies, immunisation status, etc (see detailed information on health assessment forms in Chapter 7) – gone should be the days when a woman tells the midwife that she has no information about genetic conditions in her birth family. It is also helpful to have "identifying", but not essential, health information such as the young person's time and place of birth, birth weight, mode of delivery, why sutures were required, etc; this may have no bearing on future health but enables the young person who has no contact with their birth family to know as much as possible about their past. Ideally, a written summary should be prepared and discussed with the young person at their health review; more than one opportunity to do this may be necessary. The advent of handheld records specifically for looked after children may also help this process, if they are used well and kept up to date.

Care leavers are entitled to support from children's services until the age of 21, or 25 if they remain in full-time education. In some areas, specialist looked after children's health professionals may continue to offer input and support to some care leavers. The complex and diverse nature of care leavers' individual needs cannot be over-emphasised; it is imperative for health professionals working with this group, and all adolescents in care, to be flexible, innovative, committed and tenacious to get the job done.

Specific health issues for care leavers and those approaching leaving care

Emotional health and well-being

Statutory guidance for England (DCSF and DH, 2009) recognises that when young people are consulted, their priorities are more often around their feelings about life, housing issues, having close personal relationships, their care experience and depression than about health issues. Care leavers need help to stop using unhealthy lifestyles as a way of reducing stress. Greater stability of placements whilst in care is of considerable importance in reducing the effects of stress and insecurity (Broad, 1999).

A small proportion of young people in care develop mental illnesses, such as schizo-phrenia and bipolar affective disorder, but the most common mental health difficulties for this group are attachment difficulties and disorders, anxiety and fears, depression, and conduct problems. Previous experiences of trauma and abuse can increase the risk of post-traumatic stress disorder (PTSD) and self-harming behaviours, including suicide attempts. In some situations, previous experiences of trauma can exacerbate the onset of psychosis in adolescence (Wade and Smart, 2002). Young people in care may be at greater risk of managing their despair and distress by high-risk behaviours such as use of drugs and alcohol, sexual promiscuity and prostitution, any of which may lead them into criminal acts. Also, use of cannabis can precipitate psychosis, particularly in genetically vulnerable individuals; one study showed a six-fold increase in risk (Rathbone *et al*, 2009). Comprehensive assessments can highlight known risk factors and point the way forward for early interventions.

Services need to be targeted yet flexible in their delivery. Some young people are sensitive to what they perceive as stigma associated with mental health services; this worry may be shared by some professionals and has sometimes acted as a barrier to accessing mental health support. However, multidisciplinary mental health teams that collaborate well with other involved agencies can facilitate effective interventions that may be directed to the young person, carer and/or birth family. Initial advice may be given to the parents, carers, social worker and teachers without the direct involvement of the young person; the teenager and carer may be seen together and direct work with the young person may come later. It is important for professionals, including commissioners, to have a broad understanding of "therapy" and that direct work with the young person is only one option of many, and not always the most effective. It is also vital for foster carers and residential unit staff to have a thorough understanding of teenage behaviour and attachment theory, and how to use this to manage young people who present problematic, distressed behaviours. School staff would also benefit from some knowledge in this area. Carers of particularly challenging young people should have rapid access to advice and support at all times; this may be from social care or mental health staff, or from other carers who have attained special expertise in managing such young people.

Where jointly commissioned specialist and dedicated mental health teams for looked after children exist, they are in a better position to develop comprehensive services. This then should facilitate more effective multidisciplinary working, communication and planning.

For information regarding mental health services beyond the age of 18 years, see Chapter 4. For out of area placements, see Chapter 17.

Risk-taking behaviour

Adolescence is naturally a time of physical and social change; participating in risky behaviours of various kinds is often part of growing up. It is known that young people leaving care experience greater and increasing disadvantages, more stressors and less support than their peers who leave home but still have the support of their family and the option to return home when difficulties present. Care leavers are often thrust into independent living at a far earlier age than their peers and therefore have a much shorter period of time to make the necessary transitions; also, they are often required to do so before they feel ready or equipped for independence. Many care leavers experience social exclusion; they are also more likely to be homeless, to misuse substances, to be unemployed/not in training, and also to be young parents. These circumstances are associated with poor living conditions, poverty, isolation and loneliness, all of which can have many impacts on health; risk-taking behaviours, such as alcohol and drug misuse, may offset the isolation and solitude or compensate for negative experiences, such as loss and rejection (Newburn and Pearson, 2002). In addition, low self-esteem and a sense of not being valued may cause many care leavers to engage in risk-taking behaviours, such as smoking, drinking, drug use and unprotected sexual activity (Mathews and Sykes,

2012). It is well documented that those not engaging in education are more likely to engage in risk-taking behaviours.

Substance use

Experimenting with drugs and alcohol is common amongst UK teenagers in general and statistics show that over a quarter (27 per cent) of young people aged between 16 and 19 years of age had used at least one illicit drug in the last year, and six per cent had used a Class A drug during this time (Home Office, 2003). Teenage drinking is also evident, involving almost a quarter (21 per cent) of 12–15-year-olds, with 15 being the average age for drinking alcohol on a regular basis (Home Office, 2003), although more recent statistics show a general decline in drug and alcohol use and smoking among 10- to 15-year-olds (Fuller, 2012). Within the population of care leavers, it was found that substances were used earlier (Newburn and Pearson, 2002) and more frequently than by their peers who had not been in the care system, and that care leavers have a higher risk of problematic misuse (Dixon *et al*, 2006). The same study showed that care leavers with substance misuse difficulties were more likely to become homeless and have other housing problems than those who did not. In many cases, young people leaving care survive on limited financial support and are unable to maintain social relationships or meet the daily demands of life (Mathews and Sykes, 2012). Along with this, the impact of poorer mental health and being more negative about their lives had links to substance misuse.

A study that looked at drug misuse among care leavers in transition to independent living showed higher self-reporting of drug use, compared with the general population. Almost three-quarters (73 per cent) said that they had used cannabis and a third (34 per cent) reported daily use. Many young people view smoking cannabis as harmless. Cocaine, heroin and ecstasy were also used on a monthly basis by between 10–15 per cent of the sample. Alcohol consumption was also an issue for young people leaving care, with nine per cent reporting daily use and a third (34 per cent) drinking at least once a week (Ward *et al*, 2003).

Offending behaviour

As indicated in Chapter 2, looked after young people and care leavers are more likely than the general population to be involved with the criminal justice system. It is important to remember that the experiences leading to young people becoming looked after are more likely to correlate with offending behaviour than being looked after *per se*.

Sinclair and Gibbs (1998) identified some association between the last care placement and offending. Young people who had moved on from foster care were less likely to have offended than those who had been accommodated in children's homes. However, this may reflect a tendency for residential care to accommodate more troubled young people. Offences included assault, fraud, criminal damage, drug use and dealing, alcohol-related violence and affray, burglary and theft (see also Schofield *et al*, 2014).

Since the implementation of the Legal Aid, Sentencing and Punishment of Offenders Act 2012 in December 2012, all young people who are remanded into custody in England and Wales automatically become looked after. A period of remand should last only for a short time and the automatic looked after status ends upon conviction, acquittal or grant of bail. Whether a young person remains looked after following the period of remand will depend on the individual circumstances of their case.

Young people leaving care are also at risk of becoming victims of crime. In one study, over a third (36 per cent) of participants had been a victim, commonly of burglary, assault and street robbery, and they may see themselves as being easy targets (Dixon *et al*, 2006).

Sexual health and contraception

Young people from a care background have the same worries and concerns regarding their sexual health as others of the same age (Stein and Wade, 2000; Dixon, 2008) but often lack the confidence to seek help on their own. Access to important sources of accurate information on sexual health, such as PSHE (personal, social and health education) lessons and school nurse "drop-in" sessions, is difficult for those whose attendance is poor or who change school repeatedly; "knowledge" gleaned from friends may be inaccurate or even hazardous. Many embark on parenthood with very basic knowledge regarding their bodies and how they work; young people in and leaving care are often unable to seek information and support from close family or adult friends. Professionals should not make the assumption that young people have the skills and knowledge to take responsibility or act appropriately when faced with an unplanned pregnancy or a burst condom. Advice on sexual health matters, including emergency contraception, is widely available.

Professionals should be aware of the services in their area and how to access them; these may include specific services for young people such as CASH (contraception and sexual health) clinics, which are free, accessible and operate on a drop-in basis. Some looked after children's health teams include a nurse-led sexual health service for young people leaving care, which has improved the uptake of health assessments and reduced the rates of teenage pregnancy and sexually transmitted infection (Griffiths, 2012). Other resources include pharmacies, GUM (genitourinary medicine) clinics, other sexual health advisory services such as GPs, Brook, British Pregnancy Advisory Service (BPAS) and, for emergency contraception only, walk-in centres and emergency departments. Thus expert advice is readily available, but it is vital to remember that vulnerable young people may need encouragement, practical help and support to access this, especially when it involves talking to a complete stranger.

Pregnancy

National figures indicate that about 30 per cent of young people leaving care become parents soon after or during the process of moving to independent living (Chase *et al*, 2004). They face the same issues as other teenage parents but their situation is often exacerbated by having little or no family support, inadequate preparation for parenthood, and few positive role models on which to base their own style of parenting. Some young people in and leaving care plan a pregnancy as they want a baby to love and care for (Corlyon and McGuire, 1997), irrespective of whether they are physically and emotionally ready. Some fail to disclose their pregnancy through fear of social services intervention; intervention is sometimes required but a wrap-around package of support for young parents is always recommended.

When a pregnancy is disclosed, it is essential to ensure that the young mother is registered with a GP and referred to a midwife. Many maternity units have a specialist midwife for teenage parents who is able to support the most vulnerable of young mothers; specialist services for pregnant drug users may also be available where necessary. Many young parents who have a care background will need an enhanced level of support from professionals but, given appropriate help, young people can and do parent successfully. It is important to recognise that young fathers often feel excluded by professionals and effort should be made to encourage their involvement with the pregnancy and child, once born. Successful schemes include the Family Nurse Partnership (FNP) in England and Wales, and recently introduced in Northern Ireland, which is a comprehensive package of support for first-time parents living in the most economically deprived areas. The dedicated family nurse works with first-time young mothers (and fathers if possible) from early pregnancy until the child is two years old. They use in-depth methods to work with young parents on attachment, relationships and psychological preparation for parenthood. Family nurses build supportive relationships with families and guide first-time teenage parents so that they adopt healthier lifestyles for themselves and their babies, provide good care for their babies and plan their futures. Not all young people will fit the criteria for this scheme; however, the FNP recognises and prioritises those from a background of care as the most vulnerable, requiring the highest level of support. Although the FNP programme is still being evaluated, outcomes for parents and children, including return to education and emotionally warm parenting, appear positive (Institute for the Study of Children, Families and Social Issues, 2011). It is important to remember that generic services, such as health visiting, also have a vital role in supporting young parents. Some local authorities and charities, such as Gingerbread, also provide enhanced support for young parents, including care leavers.

It is important to recognise that pregnancy is not an illness. In most cases, young women who are in education or training prior to pregnancy can continue quite safely; those who are not should be encouraged to re-enter education or training. Most establishments will encourage young people to achieve their academic goals, regardless of pregnancy, so they are better prepared for the labour market, have improved self-esteem and are better able to provide for their children.

Preparation for and transition to adulthood

Martin Narey, Chief Executive of Barnardo's at the time, commented:

> *The proportion of young people . . . who are on their own aged 16 and 17 – precisely the time when most children of that age still enjoy huge financial and emotional support from their parents – is astonishing. We should not scratch our heads and wonder why so many of them are in prison; where else are so many of them going to go? It is astonishing that some of them survive the process.* (House of Commons Children, Schools and Families Committee Looked After Children, 2009)

Demos (cited in Matthews and Sykes, 2012) compared leaving care with leaving prison, which precipitates a sudden change to independence whereas inmates were previously part of a system. There is clearly a need for a more holistic and gradual move to independence. Matthews and Sykes (2012) recommend that transition planning should be agreed with the young person and include distinct preparatory phases to develop key skills and facilitate increasing levels of independence, accompanied by reflection and support to identify and address potential challenges and develop resilience.

NICE guidelines (NICE/SCIE, 2010; 2013) recommend that young people moving to independent living should be encouraged and assisted to maintain contact with past foster and residential carers whom they value. This can provide a sense of continuity, ongoing support for all aspects of living, and be protective of the young person's mental and emotional well-being.

Health assessments, health promotion and continued support throughout time in care provide an opportunity to enhance knowledge and skills to equip young people to understand their own health history and to gradually increase their ability to take responsibility for their own choices, health behaviour and to learn how to access services. The value of good foster carers and residential care workers as consistent role models of a healthy lifestyle, including exercise, a good diet, appropriate use of preventative healthcare, etc, cannot be over-emphasised. The integration of such behaviour into daily life helps ensure that it becomes part of normal routine and is therefore more likely to be continued when the young person leaves care.

Care leaver health history

It is recommended that looked after children and care leavers should have access to their full health history. Recommendation 48 of NICE guidelines PH 28 (NICE/SCIE, 2010) states that the following actions should be taken as best practice.

Ensure that when young people are offered their final statutory health assessment, all available details of their medical history can be discussed.

Ensure young people are supported to understand their health and medical information.

Ensure young people are supported and encouraged to attend their final statutory health assessment.

Ensure that if a young person declines to attend their final statutory health assessment they are offered the choice of having a written copy of their basic medical history (such as immunisations and childhood illnesses) and that a health professional, in partnership with the young person's social worker, ensures that the young person knows how to obtain their social care and detailed health history.

Ensure that leaving care services that support young people when they move on to independent living have a process to contact health professionals when necessary to help the young person understand the information in their health history.

All these actions need to be undertaken in a sensitive and appropriate way. Some health teams and local authorities have developed a booklet for young people containing their personal health history and other relevant health information, and these have been well received by care leavers.

Access to universal services

Looked after children and care leavers should have access to the same services as the general population, even if they move across local authority or health boundaries. Care leavers must be offered continued access to support services. The specialist nurse should support the social worker or personal adviser to ensure that young people are registered locally with a GP and dentist, and know how to access other services, as detailed below.

- **How to register with a GP**: information needed to register, attending a new patient appointment, booking appointments and how to use the booking-in screen at the GP surgery.
- **How to register with a dentist**: the importance of making appointments and having regular dental checks.

- **Local opticians**: encouraging young people to have a regular check up, especially if they wear glasses or contact lenses.
- **Local pharmacy**: information about prescriptions and advice on common conditions and medications, etc.
- **Access to other health services**: contraceptive and sexual health (CASH) services, genitourinary medicine (GUM) clinics, drug and alcohol services, emotional health and well-being.
- **Local hospital**.
- **Walk in centres**, when their use is appropriate.
- **NHS information and advice**, available by phone, app or online.
- **NHS Low Income Scheme**: this helps with health costs on low income grounds. Form HC1 is used to apply and can be obtained from NHS hospitals, GP surgeries, opticians, dentists and Jobcentre Plus offices. To check eligibility, visit www.nhs.uk/NHSEngland/Healthcosts/Pages/nhs-low-income-scheme.asp.

Transition to adult health services

Health professionals and service providers in England should be familiar with Department for Education regulations (2010, updated 2014), which provide much useful information on transition to adulthood. A timely referral to adult services, where relevant, should be arranged, accompanied by a comprehensive summary of the young person's health history and a care plan.

This may be a particularly difficult area for disabled young people, including those with learning difficulties, and will require multidisciplinary planning and co-ordination. The DH and DCSF guidance (2008) may be helpful in addressing the transition for young people with complex health needs.

What health professionals should do

- Listen to the views of looked after young people and care leavers and ensure that their health needs are addressed in the children's health plan and annual reports, to assist commissioners.
- Provide flexible arrangements for health assessments that are convenient and non-stigmatising.
- Ensure that health promotion materials are available and relevant and develop a leaving care booklet with information on how to access services.
- Use statutory health assessments as an opportunity to educate young people about their personal health history and assist them in taking responsibility for their own health care.
- Provide each care leaver with a written health summary and assist with arrangements for transition to relevant adult services.

Key points

- Care leavers are at increased risk of social isolation, homelessness, poor educational outcomes, risk-taking and offending behaviour.
- Care leavers have a higher prevalence of physical and mental health problems, substance misuse, sexually transmitted infections and early parenthood.
- Every health-related contact provides an opportunity to promote health and assist young people in developing knowledge and skills to take responsibility for their own health.
- Foster and residential carers should be encouraged to promote health by modelling a healthy lifestyle and appropriate use of health services.
- Specialist nurses and personal advisers should provide effective pathway planning and additional support with transition to universal services and, where necessary, to specialist services.
- By the time they leave care, young people should have a good understanding of their personal health history, supported by a written summary.

Some useful agencies

- Local CAMHS
- National Youth Advocacy Service: www.nyas.net/
- SANE: Emotional well-being, www.sane.org.uk/
- Young Minds: www.youngminds.org.uk/
- Self-harm: www.mind.org.uk/help/diagnoses_and_conditions/self-harm
- Eating disorders: www.b-eat.co.uk/
- Bereavement: www.crusebereavementcare.org.uk/
- VOICE: leaving care England and Wales, www.voiceyp.org/
- VOYPIC (Voice of Young People in Care in Northern Ireland): www.voypic. org/
- Voices from Care Cymru: www.voicesfromcarecymru.org.uk/
- Samaritans: www.samaritans.org/

Bibliography

Biehal N., Clayden J., Stein M. and Wade J. (1995) *Moving On: Young people and leaving care schemes*, Barkingside: Barnardo's

Broad B. (1999) 'Improving the health of children and young people leaving care', *Adoption & Fostering*, 23:1, pp 40–47

Broad B. (2005) *Improving the Health and Well-Being of Young People Leaving Care*. Lyme Regis: Russell House Publishing

Chase E., Knight A., Warwick I., Aggleton P. and Brownjohn C. (2004) 'Rescue remedies: teenage conception among young people looked after by local authorities', *Community Care*, 1523, pp 40–1

Corlyon J. and McGuire C. (1997) *Young Parents in Public Care: Pregnancy and parenthood among young people looked after by local authorities*, London: NCB

Department for Children, Schools and Families and Department of Health (2004) *National Service Framework for Children, Young People and Maternity Services*, Standard 9, London: DCSF and DH

Department for Children, Schools and Families and Department of Health (2009) *Promoting the Health and Well-Being of Looked After Children*, London: Stationery Office

Department for Education (2010) *Planning Transition to Adulthood for Care Leavers: The Children Act 1989 Guidance and Regulations, Volume 3: Planning Transition to Adulthood for Care Leavers including The Care Leavers (England) Regulations 2010*, London: DfE, available online only at www. gov.uk/government/publications

Department of Health (2009) *Promoting the Health and Well Being of Looked After Children: Revised statutory guidance*, London: Stationery Office

Department of Health and Department for Children, Schools and Families (2008) *Transition: Moving on well – a good practice guide for health professionals and their partners on transition planning for young people with complex health needs or a disability*, London: DH and DCSF

Dimigen G., Del Priore C., Butler S., Evans S., Ferguson L. and Swan M. (1999) 'Psychiatric disorder among children at time of entering local authority care: questionnaire survey', *British Medical Journal*, 319, pp 675

Dixon J. (2008) 'Young people leaving care: health, well-being and outcomes', *Child and Family Social Work*, 13:2, pp 207–217

Dixon J., Wade J., Byford S., Weatherly H. and Lee J. (2006) *Young People Leaving Care: A study of costs and outcomes, report to the Department of Health*, York: University of York

Ford T., Vostanis P., Meltzer H. and Goodman R. (2007) 'Psychiatric disorder among British children looked after by local authorities: comparison with children living in private households', *British Journal of Psychiatry*, 198, pp 319–325

Fuller E. (2012) *Smoking, Drinking and Drug Use among Young People in England in 2011*, London: NHS, The Information Centre, available at: www.natcen.ac.uk/media/975589/sddfull.pdf

Garmezy N. (1996) 'Reflections and commentary on risk, resilience and development', in Haggerty R., Sherrod L.R., Garmezy N. and Rutter M. (eds) *Stress, Risk and Resilience in Children and Adolescents: Processes, mechanisms and interventions*, Cambridge: Cambridge University Press

General Medical Council (2007) *0–18 Years: Guidance for all doctors*, London: GMC

General Medical Council (2013) *Good Medical Practice*, London: GMC

Griffiths J. (2012) 'Promoting sexual health with young people leaving care: a nurse practice model', *Adoption & Fostering*, 36:1, pp 70–73

Home Office (2003) *Prevalence of Drug Use: Key findings from the British Crime Survey 2002/2003*, Findings 229: London: Home Office

House of Commons Children, Schools and Families Committee Looked After Children (2009) *Third Report of Session 2008–09 Volume 1*, London: Stationery Office

Institute for the Study of Children, Families and Social Issues (2011) *The Family-Nurse Partnership Programme in England, third report*, London: Birkbeck, University of London

Matthews S. and Sykes S. (2012) 'Exploring health priorities for young people leaving care', *Child Care in Practice*, 18:4, pp 393–407

Meltzer M., Gatward R., Corbin T. and Goodman R. (2003) *The Mental Health of Young People Looked After by Local Authorities in England*, London: Stationery Office

National Children's Bureau (2008) *Promoting the Health of Young People Leaving Care*, Healthy Care Briefing, available at: www.ncb.org.uk/healthycare

Newburn T. and Pearson G. (2002) *Drug Use Among Young People in Care, Youth Citizenship and Social Change,* Research Briefing Paper 7, Swindon: ESRC

NHS (2013) *Who Pays? Determining responsibility for payments to providers*, available at: www.england.nhs.uk/wp-content/uploads/2014/05/who-pays.pdf

NICE/SCIE (2010) *Promoting the Quality of Life of Looked After Children and Young People*, PH28, London: NICE/SCIE

NICE/SCIE (2013) *Looked After Children and Young People*, London: NICE/SCIE

Prison Reform Trust (1991) *The Identikit Prisoner*, London: Prison Reform Trust

Rathbone J., Variend H. and Mehta H. (2009) *Cannabis and schizophrenia*, Cochrane Schizophrenia Group, available at: http://onlinelibrary.wiley.com/book/10.1002/14651858/homepage/updated-sysrev.html.

Rutter M. (1990) 'Psychosocial resilience and protective mechanisms', in Rolf J., Masten A.S., Cichetti D., Nuechterlein K. H. and Weintraub S. (eds) *Risk and Protective Factors in the Development of Psychopathology*, Cambridge: Cambridge University Press, pp 181–214

Schofield G., Biggart L., Ward E., Scaife V., Dodsworth J., Haynes A. and Larsson B. (2014) *Looked After Children and Offending: Reducing risk and promoting resilience*, London: BAAF

Sinclair I. and Gibbs I. (1998) *Children's Homes: A study in diversity*, Chichester: Wiley

Stein M. and Wade J. (2000) *Helping Care Leavers: Problems and strategic responses*, London: DH

Tarren-Sweeney M. (2011) 'Concordance of mental health impairment and service utilisation among children in care', *Clinical Child Psychology and Psychiatry*, 15:4, pp 481–495

Wade A. and Smart C. (2002) *Facing Family Change: Children's circumstances, strategies and resources*, York: York Publishing Services

Ward J., Henderson Z. and Pearson G. (2003) *One Problem Among Many: Drug use among care leavers in transition to independent living*, London: HMSO

Welsh Assembly Government (2007) *Towards a Stable Life and a Brighter Future: Welsh Statutory Guidance*, Cardiff: WAG

Useful resources

NHS Direct, tel: 0845 4647, www.nhsdirect.nhs.uk

NHS Low Income Scheme, www.nhsbsa.nhs.uk/HealthCosts/1128.aspx

13 Children adopted from abroad

Kate Dickinson and Nicola Feuchtwang

Intercountry adoption (ICA) is relatively uncommon in the UK. However, there are clusters in certain geographical areas, so some medical advisers may encounter this more frequently than others.

Who are the children and where do they come from?

There is a widely held perception that ICA occurs as a humanitarian response to situations in which poorer countries are struggling to provide for their child population, perhaps due to conditions of extreme poverty, social upheaval, war or crisis. However, this is only part of the story and does not explain the worldwide trends and clusters of ICA from and to certain countries. International adoption is driven by the availability of adoptable children, and the procedures and regulations of both sending and receiving countries, which enable their placement with adopters. Trends in ICA fluctuate according to these variables.

According to Selman (2002), historically, the estimation of numbers of children moving between countries has been hampered by inaccuracies and incomplete recording. Nevertheless, it is clear that international adoption in the 20th century was dominated by adoption to the United States. European countries were the largest source of children until the late 1970s, when large numbers of children were adopted from South Korea and rising numbers from South and Central American countries, and India. In 2002, the sending countries were most likely to be China and Russia (Selman, 2002, pp 205–23). Large numbers of orphaned children were adopted from Japan and European countries following World War II (1939–45); numbers from Greece increased following civil war in that country (1946–49). A huge and prolonged surge of adoptions from South Korea occurred following the Korean conflict (1950–53), and additional adoptions from Vietnam followed the Vietnam War (1954–75) (Evan B Donaldson Adoption Institute, 2002). Most recent statistics suggest that in 2013, China was still the most common sending country to the US, with Ethiopia having overtaken Russia as the second most common sending country (US Department of State, 2014).

ICA in the UK is a relatively new phenomenon; numbers remain small but have risen substantially during the last 20 years. Accurate historical statistics of ICA in the UK do not exist, but the Department for Education (DfE) now keeps records of applications to adopt (Selman, 2002, p 208). These suggest that between January 2002 and December

2008, there was a total of 2,232 applications (DfE, 2012), compared to vastly greater numbers in the US.

In the late 20th century, owing to the Romanian revolution and the overthrow of Ceausescu, the world's spotlight fell on the plight of institutionalised children in Romania. Resulting procedures enabled a steady stream of children to flow from Romanian orphanages to the Western world, including the UK, until widespread disapproval of this practice led the Romanian Government to limit numbers (Selman, 2002, p 213). However, the focus on the damage caused to children by institutionalised care has continued, with UNICEF highlighting a continuing rate of infant institutionalisation in Central and Eastern Europe and Central Asia (UNICEF, 2010, p 24). This type of media campaign continues to fuel prospective adopters' interest in ICA.

The effect of population control in China led to the abandonment of baby girls and to overcrowded orphanages. The resulting media pressure led the Chinese Government to establish procedures and regulations which, after 1995, brought about the adoption of many Chinese girls to different countries, including the UK (Dowling and Brown, 2009, p 2).

According to the DfE, in the last five years Russia and India have overtaken China as the most popular countries for prospective intercountry adopters in the UK to adopt from. Table 1 shows the number of applications by prospective adopters for international adoptions from the top five countries between 2007 and 2011 (DfE). It can be seen that numbers of children adopted from China have dramatically declined during

Table 1
Number of applications by prospective adopters for international adoptions in the UK,* by the top five countries from which they apply to adopt, 2007–11

2007		*2008*		*2009*		*2010*		*2011*	
Total	**356**	**Total**	**225**	**Total**	**200**	**Total**	**146**	**Total**	**141**
China	127	Russia	59	Russia	54	India	37	Russia	31
Guatemala	46	China	32	India	29	Russia	33	India	25
India	37	India	28	Thailand	18	Ethiopia	14	Nigeria	13
Russia	32	Thailand	25	Ethiopia	17	Pakistan	9	Ethiopia	11
US	23	US	19	China	11	Kazakhstan	7	Pakistan	11

* It is important to note that these data should be regarded as a guide only. Not all of these applications will result in adoption and some may represent more than one child. The data are not validated and exclude applications by prospective adopters resident in Wales, Scotland, Northern Ireland and the Isle of Man who apply to adopt from countries that have implemented the 1993 Hague Convention on the Protection of Children and Co-operation in Respect of Intercountry Adoption and, since 1 April 2010, all applications from Scotland.

the period, whereas numbers from Ethiopia have become more significant. Overall, numbers of applications have substantially declined. Agencies closely monitor the international situation and signpost adopters with an interest in ICA. Day-by-day changes in countries' policies and sudden moratoria preventing the movement of children or changes in adopters' eligibility can close routes to ICA. Adopters establish networks, resulting in unusual clusters of adoptions from particular countries and trends in certain parts of the UK, and also develop country-specific resources to provide information and support.

Prospective intercountry adopters

Prospective adopters consider ICA for many individual reasons, which are often altruistic. Sometimes ICA is considered in order to avoid the complications of contact arrangements with birth family members that often result from domestic adoptions. Many adopters may hope to adopt a baby or very young child, but the combination of legalised abortion, easy access to birth control, and social and cultural change in the UK over the last few decades now enables young, single mothers to bring up their own children and has led to a dramatic reduction in the number of infants available for domestic adoption in the UK. However, the majority of children adopted from abroad are infants and toddlers. Also, the public perception is that these very young children are somehow less "risky" than older, domestically adopted children, despite there usually being very much more background information available about the children adopted within the UK.

Anecdotal evidence suggests that adopters may get caught up in the process of ICA and may miss the significance of possible health risks attached to children and accept missing information as the norm.

> We adopted our daughters from China 13 and 10 years ago, when they were both about a year old. We agreed to adopt based on a very simple medical report covering rudimentary health of the child. There was no medical information available about the parents, but we were given information about what inoculations had been done. These, however, were very different from what children would have had here in the UK and made for some very interesting discussions here at the local surgery as to what immunisations to use to play catch-up. We were very blessed that both girls were healthy.
> Comment from adoptive parents of two children adopted from China

The legal framework

Prospective intercountry adopters

Adults planning to adopt from abroad undergo the same process of adult health assessment as those applying for domestic adoption (see Chapter 15).

Children adopted from abroad

According to current regulations, a health assessment on the child is completed by a health professional in the country of origin. This assessment is recorded on the BAAF Form ICA, which is then forwarded to the DfE, Welsh Government or Department for Health and Social Services and Public Safety (DHSSPS) Northern Ireland, and then on to the adoption agency that approved the applicant/s. Assessments should include documentation of family history, perinatal and past medical history, current health and developmental status and discretionary screening tests (including HIV and hepatitis). We strongly recommend that prospective adopters discuss this information with the agency medical adviser at the time of matching, in order to promote their understanding of possible risk factors, including implications of missing health information, and the care that the child may need in the future.

England and Wales

Whilst there is no statutory requirement for children arriving in England and Wales to have a health assessment, this is strongly recommended as there is substantial evidence that children adopted from abroad have health and developmental needs that deserve early recognition.

Regulation 5 of the Adoptions with a Foreign Element Regulations 2005 requires that a local authority gives the Clinical Commissioning Group (England) or Local Health Board (Wales) written notification of the arrival of a child into the country, and sends the available health information to the prospective adopter's GP.

Northern Ireland

In Northern Ireland, the assessing social worker is required to set up a meeting with the prospective intercountry adopters and a paediatrician designated by the Trust under the Hague Convention (Northern Ireland) Regulations 2003, within 10 days of receipt of the medical information on the child. This requirement applies to all proposed adoptions (from overseas) in Northern Ireland. Adoption Regional Policy and Procedures (2010) require:

- all children to be seen by the social worker, the health visitor and the GP within seven days of arrival in Northern Ireland;

- the child and adopters/prospective adopters to be seen by a paediatrician within 21 days of arrival in Northern Ireland;
- all children brought from overseas to have a post-adoption or post-placement support plan in place within 28 days, which is reviewed on a three-monthly basis for as long as is considered necessary.

We had asked for a child with special needs, but her medical from China said that she was healthy but had a vaginal discharge. This turned out to be a recto-vaginal fistula requiring surgical correction with a colostomy, and then subsequent reversal of the colostomy. Both eardrums were perforated although one was saved by high-dose anaerobic antibiotics and the other was repaired with fairly good results.
Comment from adoptive parent of child adopted from China

Need for health screening of children in the UK

The health of children newly arrived from abroad is easily overlooked in the complex procedural hurdles that constitute the intercountry adoption process, and yet we know that many children arrive with unrecognised health problems. This may be for many different reasons.

- The adoption medical in the country of origin may consist only of a physical examination, while studies have shown that 80 per cent of underlying medical difficulties are not detected by physical examination alone (International Adoption Clinic, 2004 and Johnson, 2004, both cited in BAAF, 2004b, p 2).
- The examining professional may be a generalist and lack the skills for adequate assessment of paediatric health and development.
- Local medical culture may not identify risk factors for conditions that are less recognised in the child's country of origin, such as attachment disorders, autistic spectrum and attention disorders, and prenatal exposure to drugs and alcohol.
- There may be a language barrier preventing accurate interpretation of medical findings, and some countries use medical terminology that is not recognised in the UK.
- Some children may have been abandoned and lack any background history.
- Investigations and vaccination status may be unreliable.
- Previous abuse and neglect may not have been disclosed.
- In some parts of the world, there may be specific environmental risk factors that need to be considered.

When we adopted our son from Russia, we were sent scant medical facts and a photo and had only three days in which to give our decision back to them. We had some input from a medical facility in the US as we couldn't get the medical advice in the UK within the timescale. The medical information from Russia was also a bit daunting but we understood that the authorities there tend to exaggerate medical complications in order to justify adoption abroad and therefore save face.
Comment from adoptive parents of boy adopted from Russia

The medical questionnaire that we got completed in the country of origin was mainly about vaccines.
Comment from adoptive parents

Many children adopted from abroad have experienced institutional care with extreme emotional deprivation. There is a wealth of information available about the impact this may have on child development, including attachment behaviour. The English Romanian Adoptees (ERA) study, initiated in 1992, is a longitudinal study following children adopted by UK families from Romanian institutions (Rutter *et al*, 2009). The British Chinese Adoption Study provides the outcome for children adopted from Hong Kong into the UK during the 1960s (Feast *et al*, 2012). These studies provide invaluable information and contribute to our understanding of the consequences of such early adversity and prognosis for adopted people through adolescence and well into adulthood.

She had lactose intolerance so severe we thought she had Giardia at first. Otherwise she was physically healthy, but had significant emotional and psychological problems, on the lines of reactive attachment disorder with emotional dysregulation and difficulty in making and sustaining friendships. Her emotional needs have been far more far-reaching and harder to manage at times than her sister's considerable surgical needs! She is the only one of our children who was in an orphanage and she is the only one with emotional problems. We organised and funded play/art therapy as we knew that she had significant needs which just couldn't wait.
Comment from adoptive parents of child adopted from China

There is currently no statutory requirement for children arriving in the UK to have a medical examination, other than in Northern Ireland. However, in view of all of the above factors, screening shortly after arrival in the UK is strongly recommended.

Assessment process in the UK

Adoption agencies should ensure that prospective intercountry adopters are made aware of the need to assess and promote the child's health and development early in their adoption preparation. Medical adviser input into the training courses open to domestic and intercountry adopters is an ideal way to introduce prospective adopters to the importance of accessing a health assessment for their child following arrival in the UK. BAAF's Advice Note, *Children Adopted from Abroad: Key health and developmental issues* (BAAF, 2004a), will assist prospective intercountry adopters to understand the health risks and recommendations for screening. It also includes Form ICA–UK, which can be used to document the health assessment.

This information can assist the intercountry adopter to plan for the arrival of their child by obtaining any necessary vaccinations for themselves (e.g. hepatitis B) and arranging a health assessment for their child soon after arrival.

Although children adopted from abroad have many of the same health needs as domestically adopted children, they frequently also have additional needs from environmental risks. These might include infectious diseases common to their country of origin, or delayed development and attachment difficulties related to institutional care. While some countries with large numbers of ICA, such as the US, have responded to these factors by developing expertise in specialist clinics, this has not occurred in the UK where numbers of children adopted from overseas are small and families are geographically widespread. Ideally, and wherever possible, a health assessment should be carried out by a physician with expertise in developmental paediatrics. Medical advisers working in areas with geographical clusters of children adopted from abroad will have the opportunity to develop expertise, provided that this role is appropriately commissioned. Even though commissioning arrangements are lacking, in some areas medical advisers for adoption undertake these assessments, as they have a good understanding of these children's specialised needs. However, this is not sustainable and commissioners should be advised of the particular needs of children adopted from abroad, as they may not be aware of this vulnerable group. The assessment may be undertaken by the child's future GP, or the agency may have identified a paediatrician to offer advice at the time of matching, and undertake the assessment on arrival.

The adoption medical adviser did a really thorough examination and assessment of our son which put my mind at rest regarding his health and development. She referred him for speech therapy early on.
Comment from adoptive parents of boy adopted from Russia

Regardless of which doctor carries out the assessment, we strongly recommend use of Practice Note 46, *Health Screening of Children Adopted from Abroad* (BAAF, 2004b), which outlines the evidence base and recommendations for screening.

Some discretion will need to be exercised depending on the country and circumstances from which the child has been adopted. However, for children from developing and Eastern European countries, there should be good evidence on which to base a decision not to undertake screening. Unless the reliability of investigations and immunisations undertaken in the country of origin can be ascertained, repeat screening and immunisation are suggested. Children should be offered an assessment within four weeks of arrival in the UK (in Northern Ireland, within 21 days) or sooner if there is an established medical condition.

Practice Note 46 (BAAF, 2004b), addresses the following:

- physical examination;
- developmental assessment;
- growth and nutrition;
- hearing and vision;
- dental check;
- metabolic screening;
- G6PD deficiency;
- toxin exposure;
- parental substance misuse, including alcohol, heroin, amphetamines and cocaine;
- infectious disease risk and immunisation status;
- behavioural and emotional development.

Form ICA–UK provides a convenient means of documenting the findings and recommendations from the assessment.

What health professionals should do

- Encourage adoption agencies to make prospective intercountry adopters aware of the need to assess and promote the child's health early in their adoption preparation and assessment.
- Participate in adoption preparation so that prospective intercountry adopters are aware of the possible health risks and are able to proceed with informed consent.
- Work with your local agency and commissioners so that there is provision in your job plan to undertake advisory work, carry out health assessments on children upon arrival in the UK, and provide adoption support if needed.
- Access country-specific resources to enhance your understanding of ICA and health issues, particularly if you work in an area where there are clusters of families who have adopted from abroad.

There is a wealth of knowledge in the adoption communities regarding the problems which children may present with. For example, Children Adopted from China magazine has over the years covered topics such as hepatitis B and C, lead poisoning, Giardia, reactive attachment disorder, dental problems, etc. Medical advisers might

find it helpful to form a link with the support organisations for different sending countries, as the parents have usually gone to some lengths to inform themselves of the problems that are prevalent in that part of the world.
Comment from adoptive parents

Key points

- It is important to educate prospective intercountry adopters early in the preparation and assessment process about the wide range of potential health risks in children adopted from developing countries.
- Medical advisers play an important role in the interpretation of medical information at the matching stage to enable prospective adopters to understand the likely risk factors concerning a particular child's health and development.
- Except in Northern Ireland, there is no statutory requirement for children arriving in the UK to have a medical examination. However, there is convincing evidence that screening is warranted to detect medical and developmental problems that would otherwise be unrecognised.

Bibliography

BAAF (2004a) *Children Adopted from Abroad: Key health and developmental issues*, London: BAAF

BAAF (2004b) *Health Screening of Children Adopted from Abroad*, Practice Note 46, London: BAAF

Department for Education (2012) *Statistics – Intercountry Adoption*, available at: www.education.gov.uk/a0053996/statistics-intercountry-adoption

Department for Education and Skills (2005) *Adoptions with a Foreign Element Regulations*, London: DfES

Department of Health, Social Services and Public Safety (2003) *Intercountry Adoption (Hague Convention) Regulations (Northern Ireland)*, London: Stationery Office

Dowling M. and Brown G. (2009) *Globalisation and International Adoption from China*, Milton Keynes: Open University, Faculty of Health and Social Care

Evan B Donaldson Institute (2002) *International Adoption Facts*, available at: www.adoption institute.org/FactOverview/international.html

Feast J., Grant M., Rushton R., Simmonds J. and Sampeys C. (2012) *Adversity, Adoption and Afterwards: A mid-life follow-up study of women adopted from Hong Kong*, London: BAAF

Northern Ireland Health and Social Care Board (2010) *Adoption Regional Policy and Procedures*, Belfast: Northern Ireland Health and Social Care Board

Rutter M., Beckett C., Castle J., Kreppner J., Stevens S. and Sonuga-Barke E. (2009) *Policy and Practice Implications from the English-Romanian Adoption (ERA) Study: Forty-five key questions*, London: BAAF

Selman P. (2002) 'Intercountry adoption in the new millennium; the quiet migration revisited', *Population Research and Policy Review*, 21, pp 205–225

UNICEF (2010) *At Home or in a Home?*, available at: www.unicef.org/protection/Web-Unicef-rapport-home-20110623v2.pdf

US Department of State (2014) *FY 2013 Annual Report on Intercountry Adoption*, Washington DC: US Department of State, available at: www.adoption.state.gov/about_us/statistics.php

14 Privately fostered children

Hannah Smith, Florence Merredew and Savita de Sousa

Although children in private fostering arrangements are not "looked after children", it is important that health professionals have a good understanding of their situation, as they may come into contact with these children and must know what action to take. These are potentially "children in need", where safeguarding concerns may arise and they may become looked after.

The well-known case of Victoria Climbié illustrates several important issues. Victoria, aged eight, was murdered two years after moving from the Ivory Coast to live with her great-aunt in the UK. She was abused by the great-aunt and the aunt's partner until her death in 2000. The case sparked a massive shake-up of child protection services. A report into the circumstances of Victoria's death was led by Lord Herbert Laming (House of Commons Health Committee, 2003).

Victoria's suffering exposed flaws in all the main services involved in child protection. She was known to four London boroughs' social services departments (Haringey, Ealing, Brent and Enfield), three housing departments, two hospitals (Central Middlesex and North Middlesex), two Metropolitan Police child protection teams, and a specialist centre run by the NSPCC. Hers was a private fostering arrangement and, as for thousands of children who enter the UK every year under private fostering arrangements, it highlighted the significant risks that vulnerable children face when robust regulation processes are not in place.

It must be emphasised that the responsibility to investigate and regulate private fostering arrangements remains with the local authority and not with those who notify the local authority of possible concerns.

Definition of private fostering

A private fostering arrangement is one that provides for the care of a child under the age of 16 (under 18, if disabled) by someone other than a parent or a close relative, in that person's home, with the intention that it should last for 28 days or more (s.66, Children Act 1989). A child looked after by a local authority will not be privately fostered.

A relative, as defined by the Children Act 1989 and the Children (Northern Ireland) Order 1995, i.e. a grandparent, brother, sister, uncle or aunt (whether by full blood, half-blood or marriage) or step-parent who is caring for a child is not considered to be a private foster carer. Anyone from the extended family, e.g. a cousin or great-aunt, or a friend of the family, the parent of a friend of the child, or someone previously unknown to the child's family who is willing to foster the child, is considered to be a private foster carer.

The period during which the child is cared for and accommodated by the private foster carer would be continuous, but occasional short breaks do not break that continuity. Exemptions to this definition are set out in Schedule 8 to the Children Act 1989 (Department for Education and Skills (DfES), 2005a).

Reasons for private fostering

There are many reasons why a child might be privately fostered (HM Government, 2010). These children include:

- African and African–Caribbean children with families overseas;
- black, white and minority ethnic children with parents working or studying in the UK but not living with their children;
- children sent from abroad to stay with another family, usually to improve their educational opportunities;
- asylum-seeking and refugee children who are not looked after;
- trafficked children;
- local children and young people whose parents are not caring for them, for various reasons;
- local adolescents who, having broken ties with their parents, are staying in short-term arrangements with friends or other non-relatives;
- children living with host families while attending language schools;
- children at independent boarding schools who do not return home for holidays;
- children of Armed Forces families where the parents are living elsewhere;
- children brought to the UK from abroad with a view to adoption.

Research carried out by Shaw *et al* (2010) focused on drawing out the similarities between different types of arrangements. In particular, it seems that focusing on the different motivations and circumstances for placing children in private fostering allows the arrangements to fall (fairly) neatly into (fairly) discrete categories. They proposed and described a typology that encompasses all the private fostering arrangements outlined in this chapter, and which contains four broad categories:

- "child-centred" arrangements (arrangements made ostensibly to improve the life chances of the child in some way);
- "parent-centred" arrangements (arrangements made primarily to enable the parent to work or study);
- "carer-centred" arrangements (arrangements in which the carer has a major stake);

- "family crisis" arrangements (arrangements made in response to a parental problem, family crisis or breakdown).

These arrangements are often set up through informal networks without any knowledge of, or involvement from, local authorities, which is why these children can be very vulnerable, often isolated and at risk.

Notification to the local authority

Private foster carers and parents/those with parental responsibility are required to notify the local authority of their intention to foster, or to have a child privately fostered, or when a child is privately fostered in an emergency.

Teachers and health professionals should notify the local authority of a private fostering arrangement that comes to their attention, where they are not satisfied that the local authority has been or will be notified. For example:

> The first time I ever heard the term private fostering was in 1998 when a boy of seven was referred to me when I was working for a general practitioner practice. I did not know what it was and it had not come into my training. The only private foster children I now see are ones with problems . . . With regard to private fostering in general . . . if birth parents are to use private foster carers, then there are difficulties for them in assessing the carers. They can't do police checks. This can only be done effectively by officials. (Dr Taylor, cited in Holman, 2002)

Local authorities must satisfy themselves that the welfare of children who are, or will be, privately fostered within their area is being, or will be, satisfactorily safeguarded and promoted.

National notification statistics

An estimated 10,000 children are living in private fostering arrangements in England, yet at 31 March 2013, only 1,500 notifications of these arrangements were made to local authorities, according to the statistical first release for England from the DfE (2013). In Wales, 42 new private fostering arrangements started during the year ending 31 March 2013. Of these, 73 per cent of the children were born in the UK and 87 per cent were aged 10 or over (Welsh Government, 2013). In Northern Ireland, only two private fostering arrangements were reported by Health and Social Care Trusts in 2012/13, perhaps indicating a lack of awareness among professionals and the public of the need for these cases to be notified. In practice, most of the notifications to local authorities about private fostering arrangements come from professionals in health and education.

Most of these children will be safe, but others may be at risk of abuse and neglect at the hands of their private foster carers. As long as there is under-reporting of private fostering arrangements, children will remain at risk.

DfE (2013) figures on children cared for and accommodated in private fostering arrangements in England have been derived from statistical data supplied by the 152 local authorities in England. These figures are important because they monitor the impact of the legislative changes in 2005 under which local authorities have a duty to promote and encourage notification of private fostering arrangements. However, these figures are believed to be an underestimate of the total number of children in such arrangements.

Regulating private fostering

The framework for the inspection of local authority private fostering services shows how Ofsted's inspection principles and processes are applied, sets out the statutory basis for inspection and summarises the main features of the inspection (Ofsted, 2012). The inspection of Welsh local authority private fostering services is conducted by the Care and Social Services Inspectorate Wales (CSSIW). The Children (Private Arrangements for Fostering) (Wales) Regulations 2006 contain the same provisions, with minor amendments, as the English regulations. The references to the regulations below apply to both the English and Welsh versions. The Children (Northern Ireland) Order Guidance and Regulations, Volume 3: *Family Placements and Private Fostering*, outline arrangements for monitoring private fostering situations by Health and Social Care Trusts.

Duties of the local authority

It is the duty of every local authority to satisfy itself that the welfare of children privately fostered in its area is being satisfactorily safeguarded and promoted, as specified in the Children (Private Arrangements for Fostering) Regulations 2005 and the Children (Private Arrangements for Fostering) Regulations (Northern Ireland) 1996, and to ensure that such advice as appears to be required is given to private foster carers. In order to do so, local authority officers must visit privately fostered children at regular intervals and the minimum visiting requirements are set out in the regulations. The local authority officer should visit a child alone unless the officer considers it inappropriate.

Some local authorities have set up a specific multidisciplinary private fostering panel whose role is to advise the private fostering officer/social worker and to monitor the assessment reports so that the local authority is satisfied that the arrangements are appropriate for each child. Such panels may include a health professional or a representative from the UK Border Agency.

Safeguarding health

Regulation 4 of the Children (Private Arrangements for Fostering) Regulations 2005 specifies in Schedule 2 'that consideration has been given to, and necessary steps taken to make arrangements for, care of the child's health'. Regulations 7 and 8 specify in Schedule 3 'that the child's physical, intellectual, emotional, social and behavioural development is appropriate and satisfactory' and 'that the arrangements for care of the child's health are in place and, in particular, that the child is included on the list of a person who provides primary medical services pursuant to Part 1 of the National Health Service Act 1977'.

The Children (Private Arrangements for Fostering) Regulations (Northern Ireland) 1996, General Welfare of Children, s.2.2(f), state that arrangements should be made '. . . for the child's medical and dental care and treatment, and, in particular, that the child is included on the list of a general medical practitioner who provides general medical services under Part VI of the Health and Personal Social Services (Northern Ireland) Order 1972(1)'.

The Replacement Children Act 1989 Guidance Private Fostering (4.12) and the Welsh Guidance: NAFWC 11/06 (4.12) note that the quality and consistency of care are crucial to the child's physical, intellectual, social and behavioural development (health and well-being) and that appropriate and sufficient diet, exercise, play, intellectual stimulation, hobbies and interests, help as needed with language development, relationships, social skills and behaviour, along with relevant health promotion advice and information, may be needed to ensure development.

The Children (Northern Ireland) Order, Guidance and Regulations, Vol 3, 14.6: *Child Development* states:

> *The child's physical, intellectual, emotional, social and behavioural development would be expected to include appropriate and sufficient diet, exercise, play, intellectual stimulation, identification of abilities and disabilities, help (where necessary) with: language development, child's identity and self-esteem, relationships, social skills and behaviour, ensuring his needs are appropriately assessed and satisfactorily met and his views heard.*

> *The local authority must assess and decide whether a private foster carer has the capacity to look after the child and to meet their developmental needs. In order to understand the child's needs, the following will need to be considered:*

> - *quality and permanence of previous care and relationships, and effects of multiple carers;*
> - *developmental needs and progress;*
> - *how separation and loss are being handled;*
> - *wishes and feelings about private fostering arrangements;*

- *sense of self-worth, related to being loved, respected and accepted, and belonging in new family;*
- *self-image and sense of identity, including culture and ethnicity, knowing who parents are, and history of given name of child;*
- *disturbed behaviour may reflect emotional difficulties.*

Safeguarding issues

These children are often described as being "invisible", as their status is often not known to local authorities, schools or health professionals, and as such they are vulnerable to a range of safeguarding concerns. Contact with parents may be infrequent or nonexistent; private foster carers are often not identified or monitored; and they or their families may be abusers who have had their own children taken into care because of inadequate parenting. Carers may be well-intentioned but lack parenting skills and knowledge of the impact of separation and loss on the child. If the child is from a different cultural, ethnic, religious or linguistic background, the carer may have little or no understanding of how these factors impact on the child's health, well-being and identity. Awareness of private fostering should be incorporated into mandatory safeguarding training programmes.

According to *Working Together to Safeguard Children* (HM Government, 2010):

All professionals working with children have an important role in relation to safeguarding privately fostered children. If they become aware of a private fostering arrangement, and they are not confident that it has been notified to the local authority, they should contact the local authority themselves. Local safeguarding children boards can play a vital role in helping protect children who are privately fostered, exercising leadership and raising awareness in the community of the requirements and issues around private fostering. (paragraph 11.25)

Her Majesty's Chief Inspector for children's services at Ofsted, Christine Gilbert, said at a BAAF conference in 2009: 'Many local authorities are failing to check the suitability of private fostering arrangements, despite being ordered to do so after the death of Victoria Climbié in Haringey, north London.'

In reality, the notification system is not working as well as it should. Many local authorities do not receive any notifications from parents, private foster carers or third parties, such as agents bringing children into the UK, so they cannot assess the suitability of the arrangements.

In their monthly newsletter to Directors of Children's Services, Ofsted (2011) stated:

Inspections completed in 2010/11 in six volunteer authorities showed encouraging signs of progress in the effectiveness with which local authorities are delivering their responsibilities in relation to private fostering. HMCI has accepted a request from the Parliamentary Under-Secretary of State for Children, Tim Loughton MP, to undertake a further 12 inspections in 2012/13 to establish whether this improvement is more widespread. These inspections will take place in authorities selected by Ofsted, and we will give ten days' notice of the inspection.

In 2011, the DfE set the following objectives:

- changing the behaviour of key professionals who work with children in identifying private fostering situations in the course of their work;
- reducing the numbers of un-notified children living in private fostering arrangements.

Voices of young people concerning private fostering

Dubit is a specialist youth research agency commissioned by BAAF in 2010 to conduct an online survey with a nationally representative panel of 1,021 young people aged 9 to 16 from Dubit's Informer Panel – a panel of 37,000 young people aged 7–25 across the UK. Key findings from the survey (BAAF, 2010) revealed that:

- more than 1 in 10 children living in England and Wales could have been privately fostered;
- nearly half (46 per cent) of the privately fostered children surveyed said that they had anxieties while in those arrangements;
- forty-two per cent said that they didn't think anyone outside of the family was told that they were being privately fostered, creating large numbers of "invisible children";
- while most of the children who had been privately fostered said that they had a positive experience and were well cared for, 46 per cent said that they felt worried, lonely or sad;
- eight per cent of children being privately fostered said that they didn't know why they had been sent away;
- fourteen per cent of these young people said that they felt confused while being privately fostered;
- while 80 per cent of children felt that they were well looked after, 15 per cent said that the care was only "OK", and six per cent felt that they were not well looked after.

Private fostering spans most age groups, but this latest research suggests that it most commonly occurs with young people aged between 13 and 16. It is fairly evenly split between sexes and socio-economic groups. The survey found a particularly high predominance in London.

The reasons children become privately fostered can vary greatly. Responses to the survey revealed the following reasons for adolescents becoming privately fostered:

- Twenty-five per cent said that their parents were on holiday.
- Seventeen per cent said that their parents had long-term health problems.
- Seventeen per cent said that their parents were working away from home.
- Ten per cent said that their parents were living somewhere else.
- Nine per cent said that they had had a row with their parents.
- Five per cent said that their parents were in prison.
- Thirty-four per cent cited "other" as the reason why they became privately fostered.

Parental responsibility and consent

As for all children, a privately fostered child or young person with capacity to understand the issues and implications can give their own consent to health care (see Chapter 6). If they do not have this capacity, then a person with parental responsibility may arrange for some aspects of parental responsibility to be met by someone else on their behalf. Unfortunately, these arrangements are often not made when children are placed with a private foster carer. It is considered best practice for the parent/s to provide a written agreement authorising the private foster carer to give consent for routine health care such as assessments, screening and immunisation (and school trips, etc) as necessary, with copies being provided to the local authority and clinical commissioning group (CCG) or GP. There should be an agreed route for communication in urgent situations.

The child's health history

Informing the private foster carer of the child's health history is another area which is often neglected, with adverse effects for the privately fostered child. To ensure that carers and others are fully able to address the child's health needs, parents should provide carers, and inform the social worker, with a comprehensive health history, including:

- antenatal history and neonatal screening;
- childhood screening and development;
- immunisations;
- history of infectious diseases;
- hospital treatment – inpatient or outpatient;
- ongoing conditions, including congenital conditions;
- medications, allergies and required aids;
- special dietary needs;
- cultural needs;
- relevant family health history.

Full details concerning follow-up and appointments should be provided to the carer, who should also hold the Personal Child Health Record (PCHR) while the child is in their care.

What we know about the health of privately fostered children

There is a lack of formal research data on the health of these children, so it is not known whether their health is comparable to the general UK child population, or if they may experience health inequalities similar to looked after children. The Dubit survey previously described provides some indirect evidence and raises concerns about the mental health and vulnerability of young people in private fostering arrangements. However, there is no data on the health of young children.

Health care for privately fostered children

Privately fostered children are entitled to the same universal health services as other children and should be registered with a GP and have regular vision and dental checks and treatment. The local authority should establish that these arrangements are in place. Those children who are well should have the same routine surveillance and screening as offered to all children in the UK. However, if the child is unwell, it is important to consider additional factors such as sickle cell anaemia, malnutrition, TB, hepatitis, HIV, malaria, etc.

A child may have specific health care needs related to their ethnic or geographic origin. BAAF Practice Note 46, *Health Screening of Children Adopted from Abroad* (BAAF, 2004), and Practice Note 53, *Guidelines for the Testing of Looked After Children who are at Risk of a Blood-Borne Infection* (BAAF, 2008), provide information that is relevant for children born in other countries.

The Children (Northern Ireland) Order, Guidance and Regulations, Vol 3, 14.17: *Health Care*, states:

> Health care should be an essential part of a parent's responsibility in safeguarding and promoting the welfare of the child. Children of certain racial origins or from certain parts of the world may have particular health care needs and full consideration should be given to this aspect of the child's care. If a child is well and active no special screening may need to be undertaken, over and above routine screening and surveillance offered to all children. If, however, the child is unwell, racial or ethnic factors should be taken into account as they may be the key to the child's ill health. For example, children of particular racial origins or from the travelling community may be at risk from particular diseases such as tuberculosis, hepatitis B or congenital diseases.

Practitioner's experiences

Although there is a lack of research in this area, health practitioners have reported the following in working with privately fostered children:

- lack of health history, resulting in inappropriate therapeutic intervention;
- inadequate medical care for those children with sickle cell anaemia;
- poor skin and hair care for African–Caribbean and African children in transracial placements;
- lack of verbal stimulation to enhance language;
- missing out on school or under-achievement;
- emotional, physical and sexual abuse;
- children often subject to child protection investigation where social workers and managers were unaware that they were in private fostering arrangements.

Current practice in assessing the health of privately fostered children and young people

While older children and young people may be able to provide a significant amount of their own health information, there is variation between agencies as to whether social workers try to obtain health information directly from the child's parents, or rather from the private foster carer. There is also considerable variation concerning the extent of health information sought by agencies about privately fostered children, with some local authorities asking general questions about health, such as whether there are any health concerns, and when and for what reason the child last saw their GP, while other agencies seek completion of a comprehensive health questionnaire. Other agencies also contact the child's GP and dentist to ask about significant health issues and any treatment required. Some routinely contact the child's school to ask about any educational, health, social or behavioural concerns, and whether the school nurse has had any involvement with, or concerns about, the child.

If sufficient concern is raised about the suitability of the private fostering arrangement, then the local authority may consider it necessary to carry out a "child in need" assessment.

While currently very few health trusts flag the clinical records of children in private fostering arrangements, this can be helpful in raising awareness that these children are particularly vulnerable to safeguarding needs and that there may be issues concerning consent to health assessments, procedure and treatments.

Example of good practice

A London borough has a significant number of young people from Bangladesh who are living in private fostering arrangements. The authority has a team dedicated to children and young people in private fostering arrangements. In order to establish that their physical, intellectual, emotional, social and behavioural development is appropriate and satisfactory, and that suitable arrangements are in place for health provision, they undertake the following to assess the child's health.

- They contact the child's parent/s and private foster carer to check that there is an agreement in place for delegated authority for health and education, and to obtain health information.
- They obtain a health history including the current health of the child, e.g. development, diet, regular medication and allergies, prenatal and birth history, past hospital admissions, injuries, childhood illnesses and immunisations, and family history, particularly hereditary conditions.
- They ask about lifestyle issues relevant to the child's age.
- They contact the child's GP to confirm the child's health history and current health status, and ensure registration with a new GP if needed.
- They contact the child's dentist to confirm the date of the child's last appointment and current dental status, and ensure registration with a new dentist if needed.
- They contact the child's school to ask about current educational progress and whether there are any concerns about the child's health.

Assessment of the health of private foster carers

While there is no statutory requirement to assess the health of private foster carers, we believe that this is an important aspect of assessing the suitability of the placement for the child. There is currently a considerable range of approaches taken by local authorities, including the following.

- No assessment of the health of private foster carers.
- Obtaining consent from the carer to write to their GP to enquire whether there is any medical condition or issue that would affect the carer's ability to care for a child in a private fostering situation.
- Asking the carer to complete a health questionnaire, and proceeding to completion of BAAF Form AH if this leads to concerns about health.
- Routine completion of BAAF Form AH, although this was criticised in the inspection of private fostering services as these forms were designed for assessing the health of prospective adopters and foster carers.

Although the State is only justified in the interference with a parent's right to make any arrangements they choose for their child if there is a resulting risk to the child, we would argue that contacting the GP, with consent from the private foster carer, to enquire whether there is any health condition or lifestyle issue that would affect their ability to care for a child or young person in a private fostering situation, would be the minimum requirement upon which to assess whether any risk might be present. If this raises concern, then the agency should seek sufficient further information to determine whether the child is adequately safeguarded by this carer.

Checklist for a privately fostered child

The checklist and pathway below outline the steps that should be taken by health professionals to identify a privately fostered child.

- The child presents for the first time.
- Does the accompanying adult have Parental Responsibility (PR)? If not, who does?
- Does the child live with the person who has PR? If not, who does the child live with and how long have they lived there?
- Has the local authority been informed of this arrangement?
- In all cases, contact the local authority and provide details of the child and care arrangements.
- Update documentation.

Additionally, if a health practitioner is working with a parent who is likely to be hospitalised for a lengthy period of time (often involving mental health difficulties, but sometimes physical reasons), they should ask if suitable arrangements have been made for the care of the child.

What health professionals should do

- Emphasise that privately fostered children should be included in mandatory safeguarding provisions.
- Be familiar with local child protection protocols, including private fostering arrangements and notifications. Know the local lead for child protection, and lead officer responsible for receiving notifications for private fostering.
- Ensure a good understanding of what constitutes a private fostering arrangement and be able to identify children who potentially fit the criteria.
- Understand the role of health professionals in sharing information appropriately with the local authority, in order that the notification process is triggered and, where appropriate, local authorities can discharge their duties in regulating private fostering arrangements.
- Disseminate information and raise awareness of private fostering with colleagues at every opportunity.
- If any health practitioner suspects that a child may be privately fostered, they should take individual responsibility for making appropriate referrals to safeguard the child's welfare.

Pathway for identiying a private fostering arrangement (© Hannah Smith)

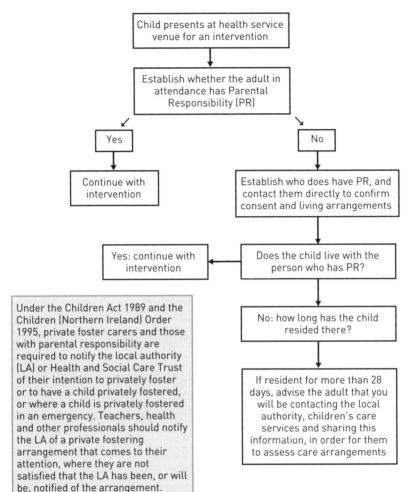

Key points

- A private fostering arrangement is one that provides for the care of a child under the age of 16 (under 18, if disabled) by someone other than a parent or a close relative, in that person's home, with the intention that it should last for 28 days or more.
- Children in private fostering arrangements are vulnerable to inadequate care, lack of health surveillance, abuse and neglect.
- All professionals who become aware of private fostering arrangements should notify the local authority.

- There is no requirement for a statutory health assessment for children in private fostering arrangements, but the local authority must ensure that consideration has been given to, and necessary steps taken to make arrangements for, care of the child's health.
- More research is needed on the health status and specific health needs of children in private fostering arrangements.
- There is practice variation across agencies and a lack of guidance concerning assessment of the health of private foster carers.

Bibliography

BAAF (2004) *Health Screening of Children Adopted from Abroad*, Practice Note 46, London: BAAF

BAAF (2008) *Guidelines for the Testing of Looked After Children at Risk of a Blood-Borne Infection*, Practice Note 53, London: BAAF

BAAF (2010) *Research with Young People Reveals Alarming Numbers of 'Invisible Children' and their Anxieties*, available at www.baaf.org.uk/media/releases/100222

Department for Education (2013) *Private Fostering Arrangements for England Year Ending 31 March 2013: Statistical first release*, London: DfE

Department for Education and Skills (2005a) *Schedule 8 to the Children Act 1989*, [exemptions P1], London: DfES

Department for Education and Skills (2005b) *National Minimum Standards for Private Fostering*, London: DfES

HM Government (2010) *Working Together to Safeguard Children: A guide to inter-agency working to safeguard and promote the welfare of children*, London: HM Government

Holman B (2002) *The Unknown Fostering: A study of private fostering*, Lyme Regis: Russell House Publishing

House of Commons Health Committee (2003) *The Victoria Climbié Inquiry Report*, Sixth Report of Session 2002–3, London: House of Commons Health Committee

Ofsted (2011) *Inspections of Arrangements for Discharging Duties and Responsibilities for Private Fostering* (Newsletter to Directors of Children's Services, England), London: Ofsted

Ofsted (2012) *Framework for the Inspection of Local Authority Private Fostering Services*, London: Ofsted

Shaw C., Brodie I., Ellis A., Graham B., Mainey A., de Sousa S. and Willmott N. (2010) *Research into Private Fostering*, London: DCSF

Welsh Government (2013) *Private Fostering in Wales, 2012–13*, Cardiff: Stats Wales

15 Adult health assessment

Judith Gould

The aim of substitute care is to provide children, many of whom will have complex needs, with nurturing carers and secure, stable placements lasting as long as a child requires them. Carers need to have robust physical and mental health to be able to cope readily with parenting these vulnerable and sometimes challenging children. A comprehensive health assessment should be carried out on all foster carers, kinship carers, special guardians and adopters to assist agencies in understanding the level of health risk that must be considered alongside a range of other factors in order to reach a decision about approval.

Medical advisers, panel members and decision-makers should apply the same health standards to foster carers and adopters, but agencies may decide to accept a higher level of health risk for placements with kinship carers and special guardians, in light of other benefits of the placement for specific children.

The primary purpose of the adult health assessment and medical adviser's advice is to inform the assessing social worker of any health issues that may need to be explored in the social work assessment of the prospective foster carers or adoptive parents, and to advise the agency and panel about health risks. Individual consideration must be given to the health of each applicant.

Guiding principles when considering difficult health issues in adults who wish to care for children (Mather and Lehner, 2010)
- The welfare of the child is paramount.
- Parenting capacities are more important than perfect health.
- Honesty and openness are essential in dealing with applicants.

Legal and statutory duties

Prospective adopters

The Adoption Agencies Regulations 2005 (England), Adoption Agencies (Wales) Regulations 2005 and Adoption Agencies Regulations (Northern Ireland) 1989 (see Appendix B) require that the adoption agency obtains a report prepared by a fully registered medical practitioner following a full examination (unless the medical adviser deems it unnecessary) as to the health of each person proposing to adopt a child. In Wales, the health assessment must be completed no more than six months prior to the panel. The Prospective Adopter's Report (PAR) should include a summary of the state of health of the prospective adopters, written by the medical adviser. In terms of evaluating the health of prospective adopters, the statutory involvement of the medical adviser ceases when the adoption order is granted. Further involvement is at the discretion of the adopters and will depend on each service agreement between NHS trusts and the agency. Clearly, however, in some situations it is good practice for the medical adviser to continue his or her involvement.

Adoption in England

New adoption applicants As a result of the Government's intention to recruit more adopters and speed up the approval process, a two-stage adoption process came into effect in England from July 2013. During Stage 1, described as the pre-assessment process, the prospective adopter learns about adoption through preparation groups, relevant reading, and exploration of the issues, with support from the agency, while the agency carries out the required statutory checks, including references and the health assessment. While Stage 1 should normally be completed within two months, there is recognition that this may take longer, for instance, when applicants need more time or in order to obtain comprehensive health information. Should the agency decide during or at the end of Stage 1 not to proceed with an application, the Independent Review Mechanism (IRM) is not available to the applicant, although applicants may make a complaint using the agency's local complaints procedure. At the end of Stage 1, the agency will decide whether the applicant can proceed to Stage 2, based on the outcome of the statutory checks. The applicant then decides when they are ready to start Stage 2; they can take up to a six-month break between the two stages.

If the applicant and agency decide to proceed, Stage 2 will then involve a detailed assessment culminating in a comprehensive Prospective Adopter's Report (PAR), to be considered by the adoption panel. It is expected that the agency decision-maker will make the decision about approval within four months of Stage 2 commencing.

Fast-track process A fast-track process has been introduced for adopters who have previously adopted in a court in England or Wales after having been approved under the Adoption Agencies Regulations 2005 (or corresponding Welsh provision), or intercountry adopters who have been assessed under the Adoptions with a Foreign Element Regulations 2005, and anyone who is a fully approved foster carer in England at the time they apply to adopt. It is important that the social worker works with the medical adviser to determine what is needed, as the statutory guidance gives responsibility to the medical adviser to decide whether a full or update report is required:

> *The agency must obtain a written report from a registered medical practitioner about the health of the prospective adopter following a full examination. The report must include the matters specified in Part 2, Schedule 4 of the AAR, **unless** the*

agency has received advice from its medical adviser that such an examination and report is unnecessary. (Department for Education (DfE), 2013)

Agencies will, in each individual case, need to determine whether prescribed checks and/or references should be sought, depending on the time since approval and, in the case of foster carers, the time since a child was placed with them. Agencies are required to complete the fast-track process within four months.

Medical advisers need to understand the new processes and should work with agencies to determine how these quicker timescales can be achieved.

Adoption in Northern Ireland and Wales

Some adoption agencies require all the statutory checks, including the health assessment, to be undertaken before the assessment begins, whilst others undertake checks and assessment concurrently. The comprehensive report prepared in Wales is the Prospective Adopter's Report (PAR Wales) and in Northern Ireland, the Form F Adoption NI is used. The whole process should take no longer than eight months.

At the time of writing, the two-stage process and fast-track approach are under consideration in Wales but not in Northern Ireland.

Prospective foster carers

The Fostering Services (England) Regulations 2011, the Children (Northern Ireland) Order 1995 Guidance and Regulations Volume 3, *Family Placements and Private Fostering*, and the Fostering Services (Wales) Regulations 2003 require details of the prospective foster carer's health, supported by a medical report, and BAAF's Health Group Advisory Committee strongly recommends the use of BAAF health assessment forms to provide a comprehensive assessment for fostering applicants.

Fostering in England

From July 2013, a two-stage process for assessing fostering applicants came into effect in England. Stage 1 includes various checks, including the health assessment, although this may be extended, for instance, when additional time is required to obtain comprehensive health information. The new fostering regulations require agencies to reach a decision about suitability to move to Stage 2 of the assessment within 10 days of receiving all of the Stage 1 information. As the timescales do not impose requirements on medical practitioners, the agency should consider receipt of the health assessment report from the agency medical adviser to be the start of the 10-day period, if that is the final piece of information that is awaited. There is no specified duration for Stages 1 or 2 for fostering applicants, but the whole assessment process should be completed within eight months.

Should the agency decide during or at the end of Stage 1 not to proceed with an application, the IRM is not available to the applicant, although they may make a complaint using the agency's local complaints procedure.

Fostering in Northern Ireland and Wales

At the time of writing, the two-stage process is under consideration in Wales but not in Northern Ireland.

Prospective special guardians

The Special Guardianship Regulations 2005 form part of the legislative framework for special guardianship orders in England. The special guardianship report to the court must include a health history of the prospective special guardian, including details of any serious physical or mental health illnesses, any hereditary disease or disorder or disability (Special Guardianship Regulations 2005), and also a summary prepared by the medical professional who provided the information. The Special Guardianship (Wales) Regulations 2005 require a similar health report. There are no provisions for special guardianship in Northern Ireland. The BAAF Health Group Advisory Committee recommends the use of BAAF health assessment forms for this assessment.

Medical adviser for adoption

(This information is taken from Lord and Cullen, 2012.)

Regulation 3(1)(b) of the Adoption Agencies and Independent Review of Determinations (Amendment) Regulations 2011 requires an agency in England to include on its panel central list the medical adviser to the adoption agency (or at least one if more than one medical adviser is appointed). Regulation 9(1) of the Adoption Agencies (Wales) Regulations 2005 requires the adoption agency to appoint at least one registered medical practitioner to be the agency's medical adviser. Regulation 6 of the Adoption Agencies Regulations (Northern Ireland) 1989 requires the adoption agency to nominate a medical practitioner to be the agency's medical adviser.

It is recommended that the agency makes arrangements for the appointment of its medical adviser with a local health trust's designated doctor for looked after children.

Medical adviser for fostering

There is no statutory requirement for a medical adviser to be appointed as a member of a fostering panel, but the panel must have access to medical advice if required. BAAF's Health Group Advisory Committee recommends that a medical adviser should review all health assessments on prospective carers, provide written advice and attend the panel. In some areas, specialist nurses for looked after children sit on fostering panels and may be well placed to advise on health concerns for looked after children, but they may not be able to comment on adult health issues.

Where medical issues are being considered, it is essential that supervising social workers and other non-medical professionals take advice from qualified and registered medical practitioners. It is not appropriate for non-medical staff to interpret medical information without such advice and guidance; neither is it appropriate to expect medical practitioners to make decisions about suitability to foster. There are clear processes for this, and health information needs to be seen as part of a wider picture.

Review of an agency decision

In England, the IRM is a process that an applicant may access when they are dissatisfied with the agency decision not to approve them as adoptive parents or foster carers (Adoption Statutory Guidance 2013, Chapter 3, and Fostering Services Guidance 2011, Chapter 5). As any medical concerns should be explored in Stage 1, they would not normally be considered by the panel.

In Wales, health assessments must be conducted within the formal assessment process so that, following presentation of a full report to the panel and the agency decision-maker, applicants for adoption or fostering can access the IRM Cymru.

In Northern Ireland, adoption policy and procedures currently require that health checks are part of the preliminary checks undertaken prior to the preparation course. Serious health concerns are still discussed at the panel at an early stage in relation to taking panel advice on whether a full assessment should be undertaken at that time. In fostering situations, while it is not stipulated that health checks are undertaken before the preparation course, it is relatively common practice to seek early advice from the panel in cases where there are serious health concerns. While there is no statutory IRM process, there is a process for reviewing panel recommendations and the decision-maker's decision.

General principles concerning health assessment

(This information is adapted from Mather and Lehner, 2010.)

The final decision regarding the approval of adopters and foster carers is not a medical one: it is ultimately made by the agency decision-maker, on the recommendation of the adoption or fostering panel or, for fostering in Northern Ireland, by the foster care panel. Although health information is important, it is not the sole criterion on which panel recommendations should be made. Medical reports are given to panels to assist in the approval and matching of prospective parents/carers with vulnerable children. They must not be used to exclude all but the very fit. *It is absolutely essential that the agency medical adviser does not see their role as one of accepting or rejecting a particular applicant purely on health grounds.* It is important that doctors and social workers should not use evidence about one health issue to reject applicants where in truth there is a range of issues of concern.

Parenting involves more than good health. It requires evidence of a prospective parent's or carer's values, attitudes, life experiences, commitment and flexibility in responding to the needs of individual children.

Comprehensive health assessments

When applying to adopt or foster, all applicants must usually have a comprehensive health assessment undertaken by their GP. In cases of serious illness, it is essential to obtain additional written permission to approach any specialists who have been responsible for the patient's care. In these cases, it is advisable to ask the consultant, in writing, very specific questions including the impact of the condition on daily functioning, the short- and long-term prognosis and the chance of a prolonged period of debilitating illness. It is also important to ensure that the consultant understands the need for robust physical and mental health to parent a child with complex needs, and the need for applicants to have a reasonable probability of being able to parent a child until adulthood.

Medical advisers and social workers should remember that adults whose application is turned down by an agency have a right to know on what grounds they were rejected. Hence, doctors and social workers should be scrupulously open and honest from the beginning.

In most cases, it is a couple, not an individual, who come forward to be considered as carers or adopters. Social workers and medical advisers need to carefully consider the illogical situation of rejecting a healthy, well-motivated applicant because of health problems in their partner. Where one applicant has significant health risks, the assessment must focus on the motivation and abilities of both partners and their support networks. The social worker will need to weigh up the potential impact of declining health in one partner on the capacity of the other to cope with their partner's illness. There will also be an unpredictable impact on the carer's birth children and any other children in placement, which needs to be carefully considered.

The panel also needs to evaluate the impact of premature parental death on children and young people who have already experienced significant losses. The conclusion might still be that the possible benefits to the child of lifetime family membership in a matched placement outweigh the overall risk.

The aim of substitute care is to provide vulnerable children with nurturing carers and secure, stable placements that last as long as the child needs them. It is illogical to have health standards that are based solely on the estimated length of the placement: short-term foster placements frequently become long-term by default. Medical advisers and agencies should apply the same health standards for foster carers and adopters, but agencies may decide to accept a higher level of health risk for placements with kinship carers and special guardians in light of the overall benefits to children.

Health standards for kinship carers, where different standards are often applied, are currently an issue of concern for medical advisers. In 2004/05, a large study examined in depth 113 kinship placements made between 1995 and 2001 (Hunt *et al*, 2008).

Concerns about the health of carers were identified in 22 cases at the time of care proceedings. These included diabetes, arthritis, stroke, previous heart attack, cancer, dementia, and psychiatric and degenerative disease in either the applicant or their partner. In this medium-term follow-up study, however, only one placement had broken down because of ill-health. A recent report on informal kinship care arrangements also showed that outcomes for these children were as good as or better than for stranger carers, but carers experienced significant adverse effects on their physical and mental health, and mental health in particular suffered when there was insufficient support to cope with the multiple stressors present (Selwyn *et al*, 2013, pp 47 and 55).

Difficult decisions about adult health must always be balanced against the large numbers of waiting children, particularly older children, sibling groups, black and minority ethnic children and children with other special needs. Whilst it is important to try to prevent the premature disruption of a placement because of carer illness or death, the quality of family life will always be more important to a child than the physical health of his or her carers.

Adult health assessment process and documentation

BAAF Form AH is recommended as the basis of this assessment and provides standardisation throughout the UK. This form is used for an initial health assessment on applicants for fostering, adoption, intercountry adoption, kinship care, special guardianship, and short break/respite care.

It is designed to obtain, based on health history, medical examination and medical data from records, an up-to-date, comprehensive and accurate report on the applicant's individual and family health history and current physical, emotional and mental health, including lifestyle factors that may have an impact on their ability to parent a vulnerable child. It assists the agency in assessing health and lifestyle risk factors that may affect the decision regarding the applicant's suitability to care for a child.

- **Part A** should be completed by the agency and the entire form given to the applicant.
- **Part B** should be completed by the applicant and the entire form given to their GP.
- **Part C** should be completed by the applicant's GP, unless special circumstances indicate that another doctor has better knowledge, and the entire completed form sent to the agency medical adviser.

Form AH complies with the requirements of the Adoption Agencies Regulations for England, Northern Ireland and Wales. BAAF advises that the same degree of health assessment should be completed when assessing foster carers and kinship carers. Letters to doctors requesting assessments and completion of reports from records should clearly explain the purpose for which the information is required, where to send the completed form, and where to send the completed account.

Obtaining further information

After review of the information provided in Form AH, it may be necessary to obtain additional written information from any consultant who has been responsible for the patient's care. Additional written permission to do this should be obtained from the applicant as the consent on Form AH is inadequate for further enquiries. Some medical advisers copy their letter to the applicant's consultant and the GP, indicating to the consultant that they have done so. An example of a request for further written information is provided below.

Dear Dr

Re: Name
     DoB
     Address

I write as medical adviser to………………adoption and permanency/fostering panel. Your previous patient has applied to be an adopter/foster carer/special guardian. I have permission to contact you and a copy of the consent is attached.

Carers are urgently required for children of different ages and with differing needs. Carers need to be mentally and physically robust and, for long-term placements, have a reasonable expectation of being able to care for the child into adult life. In making the decision, the panel will focus solely on the needs of the children.

I would be grateful for further details of the following:
1. Presentation of episodes; in particular, did they involve any risk to him/herself or others at the time?
2. Compliance and response to treatment.
3. Long-term prognosis.

I would appreciate a reply as soon as possible to prevent delay to the application. Please note that your reply may be copied to both your patient and the assessing social worker.

Yours sincerely

Medical Adviser

In England, Form AH must be completed during Stage 1 of the assessment for applicants to foster or adopt. In Northern Ireland, the Adoption Regional Policy and Procedures 2010 direct that medical reports should be obtained as part of preliminary checks in respect of adoption applicants prior to their participation in preparation and training. In Wales, early completion allows time to request additional information and for issues to be explored during the assessment, and can reduce delays. For adoptive applicants in Wales, Form AH needs to be completed no more than six months prior to the panel. In other areas, medical advisers may wish to request an update from the GP prior to the panel, if Form AH was completed more than six months previously.

Advice from the agency medical adviser

The medical adviser is required to write a summary on the prospective carer's or adopter's health, which forms part of the report for the panel. This summary should take account of medical history, current health and health-related lifestyle issues. The *BAAF Model Job Descriptions and Competencies for Medical Advisers in Adoption and Fostering* (BAAF, 2008a) states that the medical adviser should have undergone higher professional training in paediatrics. The adviser should also be well informed to advise on the implications for adoption and fostering of various adult health and lifestyle issues. Written advice is available in several publications which can be obtained from BAAF (BAAF, 2007, 2008b; Millar and Paulson-Ellis, 2009; Mather and Lehner, 2010), as well as in Health Notes in BAAF's *Adoption & Fostering* journal. Seeking the advice of fellow medical advisers both locally and nationally can be helpful when confronted with adult health dilemmas.

The role of medical adviser for voluntary adoption agencies, which largely recruit adult carers, may be undertaken by a GP with expertise or other registered medical practitioner who has relevant specialist training. However, they should have knowledge and expertise of children with very complex needs as these agencies are likely to be recruiting carers for such children.

Health review

Foster carers will regularly require a health review and those adopters who have not yet had a child placed will also require a review.

Adoption

The Adoption Agency Regulations 2005, Regulation 29 (in England), the Northern Ireland Adoption Regional Policy and Procedures 2010 and the Adoption Agencies (Wales) Regulations 2005, Regulation 30, require the agency to review the prospective adopter's approval periodically until a child is placed for adoption with them or a match is under active consideration. This review must be held a year after approval and then at yearly intervals, or earlier if the agency considers it necessary, for instance, if a couple separates or if there are substantive changes in health. At the review, the prospective adopter should be asked whether there has been any change in health since their previous health assessment. The agency medical adviser should be consulted as to whether it is necessary to obtain further information or carry out a comprehensive assessment. BAAF Form AH2, which was designed to provide an update from records of information on Form AH, may be used if further information is needed.

Foster care

There is no statutory requirement to review the health of foster carers, and agency practice has varied. Historically, the BAAF Health Group has recommended that foster carers should have routine health reviews at two-yearly intervals, alternating between a comprehensive health assessment necessitating a visit by the carer to their GP (using Form AH), and a request for information from the carers and their GP (using Form AH2). However, this approach overlooked the importance of ongoing monitoring and support by the agency of concerns regarding the health of carers, and tended to place the responsibility for health matters on health professionals rather than on social care professionals.

The BAAF Health Group Advisory Committee and social care colleagues have recently been considering more collaborative approaches to monitoring health that meet legal and good practice requirements. In managing health issues regarding foster carers, there are a number of principles that should inform practice.

- All prospective foster carers should be subject to the comprehensive health assessment process, including advice from a medical adviser, as previously discussed in this chapter.
- Foster carers should understand that it is their responsibility to inform their supervising social worker (or other member of the fostering service) about any changes to their health that might impact on their ability to foster, or might be perceived as likely to impact on their fostering.
- Similarly, supervising social workers should recognise that they have a responsibility to talk to foster carers about their health, and to raise any issues based on observations or other information provided to them. Best practice suggests that these discussions should take place in the context of a good professional relationship where the foster carer feels valued and supported.
- The foster carer review should also consider the matter of the foster carer's health, and the foster carer and supervising social worker should be asked to comment on this. Fostering services might wish to consider the use of an annual health questionnaire (by 2016, BAAF will have published a form developed by the Health Group – Form AH Review).
- Where medical issues are identified at a review, it is essential that non-medical professionals take advice from a medical adviser.
- When questions or concerns arise about health, there should always be an opportunity to seek further information from the foster carer's GP, relevant consultant or other qualified medical practitioner, to assess risks to health and parenting ability. Fostering services need to be reassured that foster carers are sufficiently healthy to undertake the fostering task, and to have information that allows them to effectively support the

carer. At times, the medical adviser may recommend that a comprehensive health assessment be completed (using Form AH); this should not be perceived as criticism of the foster carer, and there should be an expectation that foster carers comply with this request where it is reasonably made.

- In cases where there is doubt or disagreement about the significance of health concerns regarding foster carers, fostering services should err on the side of caution and require that the assessment be undertaken, or a named consultant be contacted. A robust safeguarding approach should be taken, that recognises that fostering services need good information about the health of their foster carers.
- If at any point a condition is identified that could impair the carer's ability to care safely, then in addition to ongoing monitoring by the social worker, medical advice should be sought concerning how and when to conduct the next review of the carer's health.
- Fostering services should recognise that periods of ill health are the norm for many parents and carers, and wherever possible should be looking at how best to support foster carers in such circumstances. Any supportive arrangements will need to take account of the needs of any children placed, and should consider the likely prognosis and timescales in each individual set of circumstances.
- Fostering services should promote healthy lifestyles, ensuring that foster carers are provided with relevant information about smoking, alcohol use, diet, exercise, obesity and stress management.
- A comprehensive health assessment with the carer's usual GP at regular intervals is a helpful part of a wider strategy, and the BAAF Health Group recommends that they occur at least every five years.

Form AH2 was designed to provide an update from records of information on Form AH. In view of the above recommendations, Form AH2 is no longer recommended for fostering and a health questionnaire, Form AH Review, will be published by 2016.

Fostering service policy

Fostering services should have a written policy, developed in consultation with the medical adviser, clearly stating how they deal with issues around health. The purpose of any such policy must be to ensure that foster carers are encouraged to live and promote a healthy lifestyle; to ensure that the fostering service is aware of any health concerns that may impact on the foster carer's ability to foster effectively; and to set out how the service might support foster carers who have short- or long-term ill health.

Difficulties in completion of adult health assessments

Prior to 2006, the Doctors and Dentists Review Body (DDRB) recommended national fees under collaborative arrangements for doctors providing work for social services.

Following concerns from the medical profession that the existing fee rates were no longer adequate, the DDRB ceased to recommend fees for this work. The British Medical Association advises individual doctors to establish and agree their own fees in advance of undertaking the work. If an applicant's GP refuses to undertake an adult health assessment, a less satisfactory option is for another GP to carry out the assessment, but access to the comprehensive records held by the applicant's usual GP is essential. Some regions have worked jointly with commissioners to agree a fee payable to GPs for completion of an adult health assessment/Form AH.

Confidentiality and data protection

Health reports form part of the applicant's case record, and the agency is required to treat such case records as confidential. The agency should have a policy concerning confidentiality of health issues, developed in consultation with their medical adviser. This policy should be shared with applicants early in the assessment process so that they understand that health information is not confidential to the medical adviser, and that a summary and health risk will be shared within the agency on a "need to know" basis. Applicants also need to be aware of the parameters for sharing health information outside of the agency, for example, with the agency placing the child. This may be particularly important for applicants with hepatitis and HIV where concern about stigma requires sensitive consideration of information sharing.

Although the applicant gives permission for the agency to have information regarding their health history, which can be shared within the agency on a "need to know" basis, this does not permit information about an applicant to be shared with their partner. The information regarding one applicant is confidential to that applicant, and this confidentiality must be respected, although if applicants are not being honest with their partners about their health, this will be an issue that the social worker will need to carefully explore.

Medical reports and all information about prospective foster carers are subject to s.7 of the Data Protection Act 1998, which grants applicants the right to see personal information held about them. This section does not apply in the case of applicants to adopt because adoption agency records are exempt from the provision about subject access, in terms of the Data Protection (Miscellaneous Subject Access Exemptions) (Amendment) Order 2000. (See BAAF, 2004, and Chapter 16, for further details.)

Common conditions and dilemmas

Obesity

NICE Guideline CG43, *Obesity: Guidance on the prevention, identification, assessment and management of overweight and obesity in adults and children* (2006), aims to stem the rising prevalence of obesity and diseases associated with it, increase the effectiveness of interventions to prevent overweight and obesity, and improve the care provided to adults and children with obesity. Mather and Lehner (2010) provide a comprehensive guide to the management of prospective substitute carers who are overweight and obese.

The prevalence of obesity in England has more than doubled in the last 25 years. The rapid increase in the prevalence of overweight (Body Mass Index (BMI) 25–30 kg/m2) and obesity (BMI greater than 30) has resulted in the proportion of adults in England with a healthy BMI of 18.5–24.0 decreasing between 1993 and 2010 from 41 per cent to 30.9 per cent among men, and 49.5 per cent to 40.4 per cent among women. In England, in 2010, 26.1 per cent of adults aged 16 years and over were obese (National Obesity Observatory, 2012).

Obesity has a severe impact on the health of individuals, increasing the risk of type-2 diabetes, some cancers, and heart and liver disease. Around 10 per cent of all cancer deaths among non-smokers are related to obesity (Butland et al, 2007). The risk of coronary artery disease increases 3.6 times for each unit increase in BMI, and the risk of developing type-2 diabetes is about 20 times greater for people who are very obese (BMI over 35), compared to individuals with a BMI of between 18 and 25 (Department of Health, 2011). These diseases can ultimately curtail life expectancy. A recent combined analysis of 57 international prospective studies found that BMI is a strong predictor of mortality among adults. Overall, moderate obesity (BMI 30–35) was found to reduce life expectancy by an average of three years, while morbid obesity (BMI 40–50) reduces life expectancy by eight to ten years (Dent and Swanston, 2010).

Not all obese individuals are at increased risk of cardiac disease. Those with abdominal obesity (a waist measurement greater than 100cm in men and 90cm in women) are at high risk of future serious health problems (Mather and Lehner, 2010). Smoking, lack of regular exercise (Clarke et al, 2009), heavy or binge drinking (Ruidavets et al, 2010), type-2 diabetes, and a family history of premature cardiovascular disease (Chow et al, 2007) all increase cardiovascular risk. There are a number of online calculation tools, such as the QRISK®2-2012 cardiovascular disease risk calculator (http://qrisk.org), which calculate the risk of an individual having a heart attack or stroke in the next ten years. To use this tool requires knowledge of an individual's age, sex, ethnicity, family history, smoking history, blood pressure and lipid profile. These tools enable medical advisers to make evidence-based risk assessments (Mather and Lehner, 2010).

Despite the large amount of research into obesity, the long-term physical and/or psychological impact on a child of being placed with obese substitute carers is unknown. Parenting is a challenging task. The weight at which obesity significantly limits a person's ability to parent a child is unknown. Can an obese adult provide a healthy environment for a child adopted, fostered or cared for by kinship carers? Mather and Lehner (2010) provide recommendations to social workers and panel members, children's services and placement agencies, and medical advisers.

Decision-making is often difficult when assessing prospective carers who are obese. Social workers, panels and agency decision-makers have to balance the potential health implications for the carer and child against the other benefits of the placement. Some recommendations for agencies and practitioners on decision-making involving obese applicants are detailed below.

Recommendations to children's services and placement agencies (Mather and Lehner, 2010)

- The importance of exercise and a healthy lifestyle and diet should be included in all initial training for prospective foster carers and adopters.
- The importance of a healthy lifestyle should be discussed at all reviews, especially where a carer has an elevated BMI or if a child is gaining excessive weight in placement.

Recommendations to social workers and panel members (adapted from Mather and Lehner, 2010)

- The recommendation about whether to approve an obese applicant is a joint one in which the medical adviser, social workers and panel members have an important role.
- As with any identified health issue, it is advisable to have a health assessment early in the assessment process. An update prior to the panel may be useful to establish the health status of the applicant.
- The assessing social worker should evaluate and evidence the applicant's understanding of obesity, a healthy diet for their family, and their attitude to physical activity, both for themselves and any children placed with them.
- The assessing social worker should make an assessment of the applicant's ability to engage in physical activity, for example, do they become breathless climbing a flight of stairs or could they chase a toddler who runs into the road?
- The social worker should consider the applicant's motivation to lose weight and whether they have the resources and support to succeed.

Recommendations to medical advisers (Mather and Lehner, 2010)

- For applicants who are overweight (BMI 25–30), assessment and annual reviews should provide an opportunity to promote healthy lifestyles in the interest of the applicant and their family.
- For applicants who are obese (BMI 30–40), waist measurement or hip to waist ratio, as recorded on the BAAF Form AH, should be used to identify applicants who are at high risk of obesity-related complications. Medical advisers should identify any additional risk factors from the Form AH. Applicants should be advised to visit their primary care team to discuss their weight, and arrange any further investigations indicated.
- For applicants who are morbidly obese (BMI over 40), medical advisers should request additional information from the GP and from the social work assessment, and make use of an online risk calculation tool. NICE has identified morbid obesity as a very serious health problem. Any decision on the application must be made on an individual basis following a multi-agency discussion. It is good practice for the medical adviser to refer an applicant with this degree of obesity back to their GP for further assessment, advice, and investigations if appropriate.

Smoking

There are approximately 10 million smokers in the UK. Non-smokers are put at risk by exposure to other people's smoke. This may be called passive or involuntary smoking, and there is much evidence of the harmful effects on children in "smoking" households, including respiratory disease, asthma attacks, cot deaths and middle ear infections. Also, children living with smokers are more likely to take up the habit as adolescents, with significant ill effects.

BAAF Practice Note 51, *Reducing the Risks of Environmental Tobacco Smoke for Looked After Children and their Carers* (BAAF, 2007), provides guidance to medical advisers, social workers and children's services on reducing these risks. Throughout the document, priority is given to the best interests of children and their carers, and the protection of their health. Below is reproduced a list of recommendations on reducing the risks of environmental tobacco for looked after children (taken from BAAF, 2007).

- Children under the age of five years should not be placed with carers who smoke.
- Children with a disability, respiratory problems, heart disease or glue ear should not be placed with smoking families.
- Carers who have successfully given up smoking should not be allowed to adopt or foster high-risk groups until they have given up smoking successfully for 12 months.
- Children from non-smoking families should not be placed with carers who smoke.

- The additional health risks to a child of being placed in a smoking household need to be carefully balanced against the benefits of the placement for the child.
- Carers who smoke should follow the National Safety Council guidelines, which advise on practical steps to minimise children's exposure to tobacco smoke.
- All agencies should encourage all carers to stop smoking, by providing information on the effects of smoking on adult health and the effects of passive smoking on children. Agencies should provide information on local and national NHS services for stopping smoking.

Electronic cigarettes

In recent years, electronic cigarettes (e-cigarettes) have become increasingly popular. In 2014, Action for Smoking and Health (ASH) estimated that use has tripled since 2012, with approximately 2.1 million individuals in the UK currently using e-cigarettes (ASH and The Fostering Network, 2014). These battery operated systems, which may or may not look like cigarettes, do not contain tobacco but deliver nicotine, flavourings (e.g. fruit, mint, and chocolate), and other chemicals via an inhaled vapour. Nicotine does not cause serious adverse health effects; it is the other components in combustible tobacco products which cause the most harm. This is reflected in the latest Public Health England (PHE) report which states that, 'the hazards associated with use of products (e-cigarettes) currently on the market is likely to be extremely low, and certainly much lower than smoking'. However, there is some evidence that e-cigarette vapour contains toxic substances which are carcinogenic and their safety in the long term has not yet been established (PHE, 2014).

E-cigarettes appear to have positive benefits for smokers when providing them with a route to abstinence, and the risk to children from passive smoke is lessened. BAAF recommends that users of e-cigarettes be considered in a different category to smokers. However, there are various concerns about their use and impact, which must be taken into consideration.

- E-cigarettes are not currently regulated as a tobacco product or a medicine in the UK, which means that there are no quality controls on the products or restrictions around advertising. However, from 2016 they will be regulated either by the Medicines and Healthcare Products Regulatory Agency (MHRA) as medicinal products, or by the EU Tobacco Products Directive as consumer products (European Commission, 2014).
- Although these devices have been promoted as a form of nicotine replacement to assist smokers with reducing cigarette use or quitting, it cannot be assumed in advance that users will successfully become non-smokers.
- Some research suggests that e-cigarettes are being increasingly used by middle and high school children, which raises concerns that they may act as a "gateway" for children and young people to start smoking (Hughes *et al*, 2013).

- They are marketed in various flavours which may be more attractive to children and young people.
- Liquid nicotine is highly toxic, particularly to small children, and poison centres report increasing incidents of nicotine ingestion by children (National Poisons Information Service (NPIS), 2014). Given their frequent use, it seems unlikely that users will lock away e-cigarettes as they would medication or other harmful products.
- The impact on children and young people of role modelling smoking behaviour by parents and carers is unclear but should not be underestimated.
- There is a risk that their use may "re-normalise" smoking, which could undermine the smoking bans recently established.

Mental health issues

One in four people will experience some kind of mental health problem in the course of a year. Mixed anxiety and depression is the most common mental disorder in Britain, while schizophrenia and bipolar disorder are much less common (MIND, 2013). Given the prevalence of mental health problems in the general population, mental health problems are common in adults who wish to foster or adopt.

With regard to mental illness and fostering and adoption, it is not so much the diagnosis that is important, but the level of functioning and ability to parent. Carers with significant mental health problems may be more focused on their own needs, and this can limit their ability to meet the child's needs. Children may be exposed to inconsistent parenting and changes in personality with episodic illness. It is also possible that some children may take on the role of caring for their parents, which may not be in their best interests.

The possible impact on the child of a carer with a history of mental health difficulties includes:

- an increased risk of an adverse developmental outcome;
- an increased risk of the child developing mental health problems; and
- an increased risk of abuse and neglect of the child.

As with any adult health concern, it is important to obtain a full history, which may involve requesting further information from the GP or specialist, with specific consent to do so, to gain an understanding of any precipitating factors, the course of the illness, response to treatment, and prognosis. The social worker assessment will need to explore the applicant's ability to recognise a relapse, and their willingness to seek treatment. It is not necessary that applicants should have discontinued antidepressant medication to be considered suitable. Any decision about treatment is the responsibility of the applicant and their medical practitioner.

As ever, the needs of the child or children are paramount and parenting capacity is more important than perfect health. The final decision regarding the approval of adopters and foster carers is made by the agency decision-maker, with the medical adviser being responsible for presenting any information about mental health problems so that the panel and decision-maker can make an informed decision. If there is a psychologist working with the adoption team, or with the looked after children team, their assessment and advice can be invaluable.

Age

Agencies have a responsibility to maximise the chances of applicants remaining fit and well into their child's young adulthood. Adoption Statutory Guidance 2013, Chapter 4.10, states that:

> . . . where older children need adoptive parents, older and more experienced adopters could take on the care of these children if they enjoy sufficient health and vigour to meet the child's varied demands.

The age of the prospective adopter must also be considered in the light of the age gap between them and the child placed with them. Adoption Statutory Guidance 2013, Chapter 4.11, goes on to state that:

> . . . the age of the prospective adopter must also be considered in the light of the gap in age between them and the child to be placed with them. Too large a gap may have an adverse effect upon the child and possibly upon their relationship with the adoptive parents.

For more information, see Lord and Cullen, 2012.

Alcohol

The UK Chief Medical Officers (CMO) recommend that men should not regularly drink more than 3–4 units of alcohol a day and women not more than 2–3 units a day. Both sexes should also abstain from drinking for 48 hours after a heavy session (Department of Health (DH), 2012). Liver problems, reduced fertility, high blood pressure, increased risk of various cancers and heart attack are some of the numerous harmful effects of regularly drinking more than the recommended levels. If there is any concern about a prospective foster carer's or adopter's level of alcohol consumption, the health assessment should seek evidence of physical, mental and emotional harm or adverse effects on relationships and parenting capacity.

A useful resource for medical advisers, social workers and prospective carers is the Drinkaware website (www.drinkaware.co.uk), which includes information on the impact of alcohol on health and well-being (Drinkaware, 2012).

An exploration of possible reasons for and the impact of problem drinking, and the applicant's understanding of how looked after and adopted children may have experienced alcohol and how this could affect parenting, should be included in the social worker's assessment.

Blood-borne virus infection

Hepatitis B (HBV), hepatitis C (HCV) and Human Immunodeficiency Virus (HIV) are infectious diseases that can cause fear in both professional and lay groups. Affected individuals and families face stigma, discrimination and social exclusion. In adults, HBV, HCV and HIV are transmitted through unprotected sexual intercourse with an infected person, through sharing contaminated needles, through blood transfusion in a country where blood donations are not screened, and through invasive medical/dental treatment using non-sterile instruments. HIV and HCV are not spread by social contact and daily activities such as coughing, kissing, or sharing bathrooms, cups or cutlery. Unless someone is highly infectious, HBV is not spread by social contact.

There is negligible risk to children cared for in the homes of carers with HBV, HCV and HIV, provided safe care procedures are followed. Transmission of HBV can be prevented by vaccinating all children cared for by HBV carers.

BAAF recommends that all carers should be given education about simple infection control measures that reduce the risk of the spread of blood-borne virus infection. All foster carers should be offered HBV immunisation.

With advances in treatment, more applicants with hepatitis and HIV are applying to foster and adopt, and although information sharing may be particularly complex, it should be approached in the same manner as for any other chronic condition. It is useful to consider what health information would generally be disclosed in a given situation, to whom, and for what purpose. General principles are outlined in Department for Children, Schools and Families (DCSF), 2008.

For further advice on management of children and carers who are at risk of a blood-borne infection, see BAAF, 2008b.

Fertility treatment

BAAF Form AH includes questions about failure to conceive. There are many reasons why individuals and couples cannot have children, and social workers will explore the impact of infertility as part of their assessment. The attendant feelings may vary dependant on the cause, individual circumstances, temperament and even the sex of the applicant, but primarily centre on loss, regret and failure. Most people come to terms with their infertility, at least to some degree, and embrace alternative ways of becoming a family.

The medical adviser may need to seek additional information from the GP or fertility specialist about the nature of fertility treatments, and when treatment has ceased. Additional written permission should be obtained, as the consent on Form AH is inadequate for further enquiries.

For more information, see Millar and Paulson-Ellis, 2009.

Treated cancers

A study of cancer survival by Macmillan Cancer Support (2011) found that people now live nearly six times longer after their cancer diagnosis than was the case 40 years ago. However, the surgery, radiotherapy or chemotherapy treatment that they need for their cancer can result in infertility.

If there is a history of cancer treatment in a prospective foster carer or adopter, it is useful for a full health assessment to be completed at an early stage in the assessment process. It is essential to contact the relevant consultant, in writing, asking specific questions about the impact of the disease on daily functioning and life expectancy. It is important that the consultant understands the need for robust physical and mental health to parent a child with complex needs, and the need for applicants to have a reasonable probability of being able to parent a child to adulthood, and preferably beyond. It is essential to obtain additional written permission to approach any specialist who has been involved in a patient's care. For most cancers, the consultant will be able to give a prediction of risk based on various factors.

While there is no consensus on how long an interval should elapse between treatment and acceptance of an application for assessment, agencies will need to explore the impact of the condition on the applicant and their partner and assess their psychological readiness to parent.

If there is concern that there is a discrepancy between the applicant's and consultant's understandings of the condition or the prognosis, it may be appropriate for the medical adviser to have a discussion with the GP or consultant concerning how the topic should be discussed.

Disability

Disabled people can and do foster and adopt. It is recommended that the agency medical adviser should request, with the written consent of the applicant, further information from the applicant's GP and any specialists involved. The medical adviser should be able to advise the assessing social worker on the potential implications of the applicant's condition.

A comprehensive assessment is required, examining the impact of any impairment, now and in the future, on the ability of the applicant to parent a child or children. The assessment should focus on the motivation and abilities of both partners and their support networks. Many disabled adults have become stronger from coping with their disability and will have experience of stigmatisation, which can make them strong advocates for their children. Assessment should explore how applicants would manage discriminatory comments made to a child or children.

Case examples

The following case examples illustrate the complexity of the medical issues that may need to be considered.

Case example 1: Disability, infertility and obesity

Mr and Mrs S applied to be considered to adopt a child. Mrs S is 35 years old; she is visually impaired and uses a guide dog. She is a non-smoker, and is a normal weight. Mr S is 40 years old. He had one episode of anxiety and depression 10 years previously, which resolved without treatment. He is obese, with a BMI of 34, and has never smoked. He has no family history of premature cardiovascular death, and his blood pressure and lipid profile are normal.

Mr and Mrs S have been unable to have birth children. Investigations have not identified any reason for their infertility. Mrs S is in full-time employment, and proposes to give up work when a child is placed.

Further information was requested, with her written consent, from Mrs S's ophthalmologist and GP. Her vision is limited to recognising light and dark, and is not expected to deteriorate.

The agency medical adviser recommended that Mr S should visit his GP or practice nurse to discuss his weight, and a copy of the advice was sent to the GP. The assessing social worker was advised to explore any possible triggers for Mr S's previous depression and anxiety and his ability to recognise any future episodes and seek appropriate support.

In her assessment, the assessing social worker explored the impact of Mrs S's visual impairment on her daily life and her ability to care for a child. Mrs S was able to describe how she would overcome these difficulties. She described how she was able to care for a friend's children at weekends, both with and without the support of Mr S. She was able to demonstrate the various aids available to visually impaired parents.

Mr and Mrs S were presented to the adoption panel, approval was recommended, and their application to adopt was approved by the agency decision-maker. Nine months later they were matched with a 15-month-old boy, whom they have subsequently adopted.

Case example 2: Obesity and kinship care

Mrs D applied to be a special guardian to her granddaughter, aged three months. She is 52 years old and is recently bereaved. She has two children still living at home. Form AH was completed by her GP. This identified that she had a diagnosis of fibromyalgia and was claiming disability benefit. She is obese with a BMI of 38, and she smokes 20 cigarettes daily. There is no family history of premature cardiovascular illness.

Further information was requested from Mrs D's GP, with her consent. Mrs D had not been seen by a consultant for her fibromyalgia for many years, and her GP was unaware of the impact of the illness on her daily activities. Blood pressure was within normal range and she had not had lipid levels checked.

The medical adviser recommended that the social worker explore the impact of Mrs D's fibromyalgia and obesity on her ability to parent a small child, and to explore her ability to provide a healthy lifestyle for a young child. In view of her increased risk of future cardiovascular disease, it was recommended that the assessing social worker discuss the importance of appointing a guardian in her will. The medical adviser recommended that Mrs D should visit her GP or practice nurse to discuss her weight and smoking, and a copy of the advice was sent to the GP.

Case example 3: Cancer survivors

Mr and Mrs P applied to adopt a child. Mrs P is 40 years old. Five years previously, she had been diagnosed with invasive carcinoma of the breast. She was otherwise fit and well and was a non-smoker and non-drinker. Mr P is 42 years old, fit and well. Prior to surgery and chemotherapy, Mrs P had some eggs harvested and frozen, but unfortunately in-vitro fertilisation was not successful. As well as exploring the impact of infertility on the couple and their relationship, the social worker explored with them possible future scenarios should the cancer recur, and assisted them in discussing how they might manage these.

With Mrs P's written consent, the medical adviser wrote to Mrs P's consultant surgeon, requesting information on the implications of Mrs P's disease. A copy of the letter was sent to Mrs P. The consultant replied with further information regarding her diagnosis and treatment, copying his reply to Mrs P. The consultant was able to use an adjuvent online prognostic calculator for breast cancer (Adjuvent! Online) which calculated her chance of surviving 10 years to be 82 per cent (see also Macmillan Cancer Support, 2011). This information was presented to the adoption panel, which supported the social worker's recommendation that the couple be approved to adopt one child. They are currently waiting to be matched with a child.

What health professionals should do

- Develop a good understanding of adult health issues relevant to substitute care, and maintain knowledge of the evidence base for common health issues.
- Participate in training social workers to assist with their understanding of pertinent health issues and their role in supporting carers.

- Contribute to decision-making by providing clear advice to the agency and panel regarding the health of applicants.
- Be available to discuss individual cases and address health promotion needs, as appropriate.
- Advise commissioners about the importance of the medical adviser role and the resources required to provide high quality services.

Key points

- The welfare of the child is paramount.
- Parenting capacities are more important than perfect health.
- Honesty and openness in dealing with applicants are essential.
- Carers need robust physical and mental health to parent vulnerable, and sometimes challenging, children with complex needs.
- Each applicant requires an individualised health assessment, based on comprehensive health and lifestyle information.
- The role of the medical adviser is to interpret health information and advise the agency and panel, not to approve or reject applicants on the basis of their health status.
- The medical adviser may need to obtain specific consent to seek further information from consultants and should ask specific questions relevant to the condition, possible course and prognosis.
- While health is important, the final decision regarding the approval of applicants is not a medical one.
- Medical advisers, panels and decision-makers should apply the same health standards for foster carers and adopters.
- It is important to balance health risk against positive attributes of a placement, and to consider additional support needs.
- Agencies should encourage applicants to utilise health promotion where relevant.
- Difficult decisions about adult health must always be balanced against the large numbers of waiting children.

Bibliograhy

Adjuvent! Online decision making tools for health care professionals. www.adjuventonline.com

ASH and The Fostering Network (2014) *Foster Care, Adoption and Electronic Cigarettes*, London: ASH/The Fostering Network

BAAF (2004) *Using the BAAF Health Assessment Forms*, Practice Note 47, London: BAAF

BAAF (2007) *Reducing the Risks of Environmental Tobacco Smoke for Looked After Children and their Carers*, Practice Note 51, London: BAAF

BAAF (2008a) *Model Job Descriptions and Competencies for Medical Advisers in Adoption and Fostering*, London: BAAF

BAAF (2008b) *Guidelines for the Testing of Looked After Children who are at Risk of a Blood-Borne Infection*, Practice Note 53, London: BAAF

Butland B., Jebb S., Kopelman P., McPherson K., Thomas S., Mardell J. and Parry V. (2007) *Tackling Obesities: Future choices project report*, London: Government Offices for Science, available at www.foresight.gov.uk

Chow C., Pell A., Walker A., O'Dowd C., Dominiczak A. and Pell J. (2007) 'Families of patients with premature coronary heart disease: an obvious but neglected target for primary prevention', *British Medical Journal*, 335:7618, p 481

Clarke R., Emberson J., Fletcher A., Breeze E., Marmot M. and Shipley M.J. (2009) 'Life expectancy in relation to cardiovascular risk factors: 38 year follow-up of 119,000 men in the Whitehall study', *British Medical Journal*, 16:b3513.doi:10.1136/bmj.b3513

Dent M. and Swanston D. (2010) *Obesity and Life Expectancy*, available at: www.noo.org.uk/NOO_pub/briefing_papers

Department for Children, Schools and Families (2008) *Information Sharing: Guidance for practitioners and managers*, available at: http://webarchive.nationalarchives.gov.uk/2013040115 1715/https://www.education.gov.uk/publications/eOrderingDownload/00807-2008BKT-EN-March09.pdf

Department for Education (2013) *Statutory Guidance on Adoption* (England), London: Stationery Office

Department of Health (2011) *Obesity General Information*, available at: www.dh.gov.uk/en/Publichealth/Obesity/DH_078098

Department of Health (2012) *Alcohol Advice*, available at: www.dh.gov.uk/en/Publichealth/Alcoholmisuse/DH_125368

Drinkaware (2012) *Alcohol Advice – for the facts about alcohol*, available at: www.drinkaware.co.uk

European Commission (2014) *Tobacco Products Directive 2014*, available at: http://ec.europa.eu/health/tobacco/docs/dir_201440_en.pdf

Hughes K, Hardcastle K, Bennett A, Ireland R, Sweeney S and Pike, K (2013) *E-Cigarette Access among Young People in Cheshire and Merseyside: Findings from the 2013 North West Trading Standards survey*, available at: www.cph.org.uk/wp-content/uploads/2014/03/E-cig-Trading-Standards-final-report.pdf

Hunt J., Waterhouse S. and Lutman E. (2008) *Keeping them in the Family: Outcomes for children placed in kinship care through care proceedings*, London: BAAF

Lord J. and Cullen D. (2012) *Effective Adoption Panels*, London: BAAF

Macmillan Cancer Support (2011) *Living after Diagnosis: Median cancer survival times*, available at: www.macmillan.org.uk/Documents/AboutUs/Research/Researchandevaluationreports/LivingAfterCancerMedianCancerSurvivalTimes.pdf

Mather M. and Lehner K. (2010) *Evaluating Obesity in Substitute Carers*, London: BAAF

Millar I. and Paulson-Ellis C. (2009) *Exploring Infertility in Adoption*, London: BAAF

MIND (2013) *How Common are Mental Health Problems?*, available at: www.mind.org.uk/ information-support/types-of-mental-health-problems/statistics-and-facts-about-mental-health/ how-common-are-mental-health-problems/

National Obesity Observatory (2012) *Trends in Obesity Prevalence*, available at: www.noo.org.uk/ NOO_about_obesity/trends

National Poisons Information Service (2014) *Report 2013–14*, available at: www.npis.org/ NPISAnnualReport2013-14.pdf

NICE (2006) *Obesity: Guidance on the prevention, identification, assessment and management of overweight and obesity in adults and children*, CG 43, London: NICE

Public Health England (2014) *Electronic Cigarettes,* London: PHE

QRISK®2-2012 Cardiovascular disease risk calculator (2012), http://qrisk.org

Ruidavets J.B., Ducimetiere P., Evans A., Montaye M., Haas B., Bingham A., Yarnell J., Amouyel P., Arveiler D., Kee F., Bongard V. and Ferrieres J. (2010) 'Patterns of alcohol consumption and ischemic heart disease in culturally divergent countries: the Prospective Epidemiological Study of Myocardial Infarction (PRIME)', *British Medical Journal*, 341:c6077doi:10.1136/bmj.c6077

Selwyn J., Farmer E., Meakings S. and Vaisey P. (2013) *The poor relations? Children and informal kinship carers speak out, A summary research report*, Bristol: Buttle UK/University of Bristol

16 Confidentiality, information sharing and management of health records

Alexandra Conroy Harris and Julia Feast

This chapter considers the importance of the handling of health records for looked after and adopted children, as well as confidentiality and information sharing. It also addresses the storage and retention of health records and access to their records by post-care and adopted adults.

The principles outlined by Dr Mary Mather in *Doctors for Children in Public Care* (2000) remain relevant today, and have been reproduced in this chapter with permission from the author, with updating of the legislative references and other details where required. Information in this chapter has been taken from Mather, 2000, except where stated otherwise.

The significance of continuous medical records for children

Medical students are traditionally taught that the taking of an accurate and comprehensive medical history will, in the vast majority of cases, also give them the diagnosis. This is particularly true in paediatrics. Childhood is a rapid and irreplaceable episode of growth and development that has profound implications for the future health of the adult the child will become.

A child's medical history starts before conception when the genetic material of both parents is combined to form a new and unique individual. This individual will, therefore, carry some genetic tendency to develop the same medical conditions that affect both of his or her parents. The child's medical history continues through pregnancy, delivery and the early neonatal period. During this time, in addition to the recognised medical complications of pregnancy, poor maternal diet and antenatal care and exposure to the effects of cigarette smoke, drugs or alcohol will all have an influence on the developing child. Early childhood experiences, the arrival of siblings, common childhood illnesses, admission to hospital, accidents, and exposure to the effects of poverty, deprivation, neglect and abuse all contribute important pieces of information to the child's medical history.

For a child who is brought up within his or her birth family, there is little need to depend on accurate medical record keeping. Most parents have an intimate knowledge of their own child's health and development. An accurate medical and developmental history carefully taken from a parent is an indispensable cornerstone of paediatric practice. For children separated from their birth families, however, all too often the story is one of loss or delay in the transfer of medical records, disrupted medical histories, and inadequate record keeping. The continuity of medical records is vital for children. For looked after children, who often have less than optimal health, failures in medical record keeping can have very serious consequences.

The following are examples of situations where incomplete records or poor sharing of information have adversely affected health.

- A child requiring prophylactic antibiotics for a renal tract problem was placed in foster care without this information being shared and without the required antibiotics. This child developed a urinary tract infection, which was preventable, and treatment was delayed as the carer had not been advised regarding possible symptoms.
- A 12-year-old boy was transferred without any medical records to an out-of-area placement. The night after he was transferred he was admitted to hospital, seriously ill with acute asthma. He spent three days in intensive care. The foster carer was not aware that he was asthmatic and his medication had been inadvertently stopped in his previous placement.
- A 29-year-old adopted woman was concerned about having children of her own because she had no knowledge of her own health history.

Confidentiality

All professionals are bound by confidentiality but, in addition, they develop professional codes of ethics and etiquette that are designed to safeguard this duty. These codes are also intended to promote each professional's ability to serve his or her clients' or patients' welfare and to preserve the reputation of the profession.

Confidentiality is not the same as secrecy. Confidentiality is an issue only in situations requiring the sharing of information. Legally, the duty of confidence is a duty owed by one person to another not to disclose information about the other without their consent. The duty arises not from the nature of the information, but from the circumstances in which it was given. The circumstances giving rise to a duty of confidence are principally:

- expressed agreement between the parties;
- the relationship between the parties where duty may be implied, for example, between the doctor and patient or social worker and client;
- statutory or subordinate legislation, for example, Adoption Agencies Regulations 2005.

The person to whom the duty is owed may waive it. For example, prospective adopters can agree that GPs may disclose information from their medical records to the adoption agency for the purposes of their assessment.

Health professionals should remember that confidentiality was also found to be a significant issue for many young people in care attending a health assessment (see Chapter 12). The fact that everything said or done during the assessment was likely to be reported to their social worker acted as a major deterrent to their seeking health care. Doctors should always act in the best interests of their patients and offer young people confidential health care whenever appropriate. Doctors must be honest with their patients and from the beginning inform them to whom their written reports will be sent. They must seek the young person's consent for the release of information and keep medical information confidential if specifically asked to do so by the "Gillick competent" patient. They should only break confidentiality when the young person is at risk of harm or abuse. It is good practice to offer copies of written reports to the young person concerned.

The sharing of information held by agencies

The sharing of information about looked after children within a multidisciplinary team is often a very difficult area of practice. The number and status of the people who require information varies with the service being provided. In work related to adoption, fostering and looked after children, there is a need for sharing within a multidisciplinary team. The primacy of the social work task has to be recognised by arrangements for all reports, including medical reports about the child and relevant adults, to be kept in the child's case record. This has long been a regulatory requirement in adoption (since the Adoption Agencies Regulations 1983, and now is set down in Regulation 12, Adoption Agencies Regulations 2005, Regulation 12, Adoption Agencies (Wales) Regulations 2005, and the Adoption Agencies Regulations (Northern Ireland) 1989).

Where information is given in confidence to an individual working for an agency, it is given to that agency as a body, and all employees and members of that agency are bound by the same duty of confidence. The agency's procedures should ensure that disclosure of the information within the agency is restricted to those who need to know it (see *R v Birmingham City Council ex parte O* [1983] 2 WLR 189). This could include, for example, members of the adoption panel considering the case of a particular individual, as well as those within the agency making decisions about an individual's approval as a foster carer or adopter. On the other hand, local authority councillors who are not members of the adoption panel will not usually need to have detailed information about individual cases.

Where information does need to be shared within the agency, the agency's procedures should ensure that the person to whom the information is given is fully aware of the fact that the information is given in confidence. It may be appropriate for the agency to expect a written undertaking to be given.

Agency procedures also need to provide for cases to be referred, if necessary, to an appropriate senior individual or body within the agency to make decisions on whether disclosure within the agency should be permitted. Consideration should also be given to the possibility of allowing only partial disclosure where this is sufficient for the purpose, for example, without revealing the names and/or addresses of certain people.

Agency policies

(Information provided by Alexandra Conroy Harris, BAAF Legal Adviser)

Adoption and fostering agencies should have comprehensive policies regarding confidentiality of health information, sharing of information within the agency and with other agencies as relevant, as well as retention and access to health information included in records held by adoption and fostering agencies. To protect confidentiality, identifying information should only be transferred electronically using secure systems designed for this purpose. The agency medical adviser and specialist nurse for looked after children can advise on such policies.

Breach of confidence

Where a person receives information that is given in breach of confidence, whether the breach is deliberate or inadvertent, the person receiving the information is still bound by the duty of confidence owed to the client concerned, even though one or more others have breached it.

The person to whom the duty of confidence is owed is the person who can enforce it (or waive it). This does not of course mean that an agency cannot or should not take appropriate disciplinary action against an employee who has broken confidence, even if the affected individual does not wish to take action.

Competing duties

The duty of confidence is not absolute and may be overridden in certain circumstances, for example, where this is necessary to avert a serious danger to another individual. Where children and families are concerned, there will often be complex conflicting rights. Information about a parent's health or lifestyle may well have a direct bearing on his or her child's health and well-being. It is likely that it would be considered justifiable to pass on this information, in breach of confidence if necessary, to ensure the child's well-being. Doctors will be familiar with the dilemma of receiving information given by an older child or young person, which they may feel is important for the child's parents or carers to know.

It is impossible to give comprehensive advice to cover all the possible conflicts that may arise. It will nearly always be desirable, where the possibility of disclosure in breach of confidence arises, for the person faced with this dilemma to endeavour first to persuade the client/patient to agree to the disclosure, and then to explain why this agreement is sought. Where such agreement is still not forthcoming, the professional/agency will have to weigh up the competing considerations and reach a decision. It is essential to record the reasons for reaching the decision.

Government guidance, *Information Sharing: Guidance for practitioners and managers* (Department for Children, Schools and Families (DCSF), 2008) sets out some helpful principles, although it does not address the specifics of this area of practice. In Northern Ireland, the guidance, *Records Management: Good management, good records* (Department of Health, Social Services and Public Safety (DHSSPS), 2011) also addresses this issue.

Court proceedings

It is very rare for a court to request medical or social work witnesses to divulge information given to them in confidence. Medical witnesses in cases of child abuse can, of course, divulge such information in the interests of the child since the General Medical Council in 1987 added this item to their criteria for permissible divulgence (General Medical Council, 1988). In some circumstances, however, it is within the power of the court, again in the interests of the child, to order a witness to break confidence, for example, if it is known that a doctor has, or may have, information about a person involved in the case that might affect the outcome. It can also order that sensitive information before the court should not be divulged to one of the parties to the case. For example, if the doctor cited above subsequently gave the information to the court, the court could prevent its being passed to another party of the proceedings. A witness requested to disclose is permitted to argue against the disclosure, but if the argument is not accepted by the court, a witness who continues to withhold information will be held to be in contempt of court.

All adoption agencies have named legal advisers who could discuss the implications with medical colleagues who are called as witnesses in court proceedings.

Adoption

An enhanced duty of confidentiality attaches to the information disclosed in connection with adoption. This is not merely because of the explicit requirements of the Adoption Agencies Regulations 2005, the Adoption Agencies Regulations (Northern Ireland) 1989 and the Adoption Agencies (Wales) Regulations 2005, but arises from the nature of adoption itself.

Adoption is unique in that it is the only process that irrevocably ends a child's legal relationship with his or her birth family and gives full parental responsibility to the adopters. It is therefore of the utmost importance that agencies and courts reaching decisions about adoption are given all relevant information. Individuals may be more prepared to disclose confidential information in connection with adoption than they would be in connection with more temporary arrangements. It is in the interests of future children that those asked to provide information will continue to do so, and therefore important that they should feel confident that the information will not be disclosed in breach of confidence, unless required by law.

Change of surname

It is important to know that, after placement and until an adoption order is made, it is unlawful to change the child's identity against the wishes of the birth parent(s) unless the court has given leave (s.28(2) and (3)(a), Adoption and Children Act 2002). Adults concerned with a child are prevented by law from 'causing the child to be known by a new surname' unless the birth parents give written consent or the court has agreed. The making of an adoption order gives the child a new legal identity as a member of an adopted family and in the vast majority of cases the child will receive a new surname. This may mean in practice that the child will have been with a family for a considerable period of time and may have an extensive medical file when this change of name occurs. This provision makes the task of co-ordinating medical records complex for the health professional.

Health professionals responsible for the health of adopted children will need to have access to the child's full health history, but they need to be aware of the possibility that not all the children will themselves know of their adopted status, and fewer may know their original name. Despite a greater openness in adoption today, it remains, in principle, a matter for an adoptive family to decide how widely they wish to share the information about the child's adopted status.

On reaching adulthood, adopted children will be entitled to obtain information as to their birth parentage, but until then it is the adoptive parents' privilege to decide whether and how far to give children this information. Children who are adopted when they are older will, of course, probably already have the information. When training and assessing adoptive parents, adoption agencies should emphasise the need for honesty and openness, at developmentally appropriate levels, when bringing up their adopted child.

The law makes no specific provision regarding the deletion or otherwise of a child's original name from medical or social work records. Historically, however, the NHS central registry has attempted not only to ensure that there was no link between the old and new names, but also that the fact of adoption was concealed. This increased the difficulty of the health professional's task to ensure that relevant records are available for the child's well-being. Once an adoption order is made, all decisions regarding the child's adopted status are the responsibility of the adoptive parents.

Handling medical records in the best interests of the child

(The following is an extract from an article by Dr Heather Payne, entitled 'Medical records on adopted children' (1992).)

The subject of medical records and adoption raises a number of practical issues and ethical tensions. The fundamental purpose of the records is to transmit information from one professional to another in order to promote the care and well-being of the patient. Separate, fragmented or duplicated records are not only unhelpful but positively dangerous in some circumstances.

It is essential that all the child's notes are maintained together. Any entries which refer to the child by a previous name should be placed in a sealed envelope (or electronic equivalent) but kept within the file with the child's new name. This means that in the event of an appropriate professional needing to know more about a child's medical history, the record can be accessed. It is important that references to a child's previous medical history are not removed. [A copy of] the adoption medical assessment should also be kept on the medical records.

The updating of medical records, including computerised records, raises additional questions about what should be placed on computer and whether the facts of the child's adoption should be recorded. Therefore a system needs to be devised for converting all the old name data to the new name data.

The medical adviser for adoption will have a responsibility in ensuring that there is a system for the change of records which can ensure that all the old information is maintained, and a system for tracing a child's previous name.

Sadly, more than 20 years later, these issues remain unresolved, and with changes in adoption practice and older children being adopted, the issue of records has become more complicated, and the introduction of electronic records has added a further layer of complexity. By the time a child is adopted and thus changes his or her name, he or she may have a number of records. These records will contain reports from other agencies, such as social services case conference minutes or educational statements. Important information will also be contained in the mother's obstetric notes and the family health visitor file.

A child placed for adoption at the age of five could have any or all of the following:

- A personal child health record.
- Child health surveillance information and immunisation data.
- School health records.
- Community-run clinic records such as vision, audiology or enuresis clinics.
- Child guidance or mental health records.
- Records from speech and language therapy, physiotherapy, occupational therapy or portage.
- Hospital records.
- GP's records.

All these records will contain information not only about the child, but also about the child's parents and siblings.

Current practice with records and NHS number

(Information provided by Florence Merredew, BAAF Health Group Development Officer) Existing practice was begun in the era when most adoptions were closed, with the illegitimate infants placed given a "fresh start" with a new NHS number. The adoption order triggered a notice to the NHS from the Central Registry Office so that a new NHS number was assigned. This was also meant to safeguard the placement in situations where the birth family opposed adoption and might have taken steps to trace the child, although in reality protection could only be partial as the new NHS number was assigned months after the placement began. However, for the many children with considerable medical records by the time of placement for adoption, assigning a new NHS number has resulted in significant problems related to lack of continuity of records.

Pressure for change

Below, information is provided about changes to the system of management of health records in England and Northern Ireland. There are no comparable actions taking place in Wales.

England

There has never been national guidance on the management of health records in adoption and so a variety of different practices have developed for the transfer of paper records. With the introduction of electronic records in England (NHS Connecting for Health (CFH)) several years ago, stakeholders were involved in discussions about implementation of a national system of management of electronic health records in adoption, and identified two important principles. The first was to provide continuity of health records when children are adopted, and the second was to protect confidentiality and specifically the demographics of the placement. Keeping the original NHS number on adoption, a view supported by BAAF's Health Group Advisory Committee, was felt to be the best way to maintain continuity of the health record, but another mechanism would be needed to protect the placement. Meeting these criteria within the electronic system has proved challenging, because the demographics form an integral part of each clinical encounter and so cannot be removed from the clinical record. Given this, the working group considered various options and submitted recommendations to Government.

In November 2009, the DCSF and DH published revised statutory guidance on promoting the health and well-being of looked after children (revision expected in 2015). Section 9.15.4 states:

> It is proposed that the practice of issuing a new NHS number when a child is adopted should be brought to an end. This is because important medical records are being lost due to the introduction of new NHS numbers. A date for the new policy is currently being agreed with stakeholders and from that date the following policy should be applied:

- *Adopted children retain their original NHS number.*
- *Arrangements should be put in place for local authorities to request the shielding of demographic data in the medical records of children placed for adoption where, after a risk assessment, it is deemed necessary (i.e. in the cases where birth family members will use all endeavours to trace an adopted child). This should be done through the NHS Information Centre applying the "S" flag in the NHS Connecting for Health system.*

To date, the proposed changes have not been implemented and the Government is still considering how best to proceed. In the meantime, the current policy of issuing a new NHS number on adoption will continue.

The use of different technology in various regions means that local solutions to the management of health records for adopted children will require collaboration between health, social care and information management professionals. Whatever system is adopted, the following principles and considerations are important.

- **Information should follow the child**: In general, it is better for the information to follow the child. With the passage of time, the location of the original paper files may be forgotten, particularly if the medical adviser leaves the employment of the agency or the adoptive family moves to a different part of the country.
- **Avoid secrecy**: If there is no need to keep information secret, then it should be available to make medical management better and to reduce the chance of error.
- **Sharing of relevant information**: Information should also be made available to the patient and the new family unless there is a good reason for it not to be, in which case the reason should be recorded.
- **Continuity of clinical records**: Availability of the entire original clinical record is vital when new information relevant to the child comes to light in the future. The child may develop a new condition for which past information is important, for example, cerebral palsy following birth trauma; or if difficult behaviour develops, the practitioner may want to review earlier records regarding possible prenatal exposure to substances. Alternatively, a birth parent could provide the adoption agency with information after the adoption which is relevant to the child, for example, a diagnosis of schizophrenia, malignant hyperpyrexia or Huntington's disease. For these reasons, clinical records in the child's original name and NHS number must not be deleted, and a summary is insufficient.
- **Protection of the new placement**: There should be a way to ensure that demographic details of the new placement are protected from any birth family members who might wish to interfere. While this may involve restricting access to the entire file through use of an S-flag, protocols may need to be developed to ensure that essential changes to the record occur at the appropriate time, for example, birth parents should no longer

be listed as next of kin once a child is placed for adoption. Consideration will also be needed as to whether there are multiple records or systems where changes need to be made.

- **Confidentiality**: Although most adoptions today are open, it is important to ensure that handling of clinical records does not inadvertently breach confidentiality, for instance, to a child who does not know they are adopted, or to reveal demographic information or sensitive details/information to an adopted child or young person before they are ready or prepared for it. A warning or flag may be helpful to alert users that the child is adopted and that there are additional concerns about confidentiality, etc.
- **Third party information**: It is important to keep in mind that child records may contain family demographic, health and social information. Inadvertent sharing of this information with the child or their adoptive family, without consent from the party of concern, is a breach of confidentiality. There may be situations where the practitioner makes a decision to share relevant third party health information without consent, but this requires careful thought, and is not the subject here (see Chapter 6).
- **Training**: All those involved with adopted children require comprehensive training in understanding the issues as well as new policies and procedures.
- **Individual consideration**: Any system needs to take account of these differing situations and should allow for difficult cases. These are children who most need an effective system and they should not be treated as "exceptions".

Northern Ireland

Consultation on the management of health records of adopted children is underway in Northern Ireland, regarding a proposal that the current practice of cleansing health records will cease, ensuring continuity of information.

Retention and storage of health records in adoption and fostering

(Information provided by Alexandra Conroy Harris, BAAF Legal Adviser)
Health records are "sensitive personal data" within the meaning of the Data Protection Act 1998. As such, they are subject to the processing and storage requirements of that Act, along with some additional requirements imposed by regulations relating to adoption and fostering.

Any person or organisation processing data must abide by the eight data protection principles. Processing is defined very widely and includes obtaining, holding, altering, disclosing and deleting the data.

The Data Protection Principles

1. Personal data shall be processed fairly and lawfully and, in particular, shall not be processed unless –

   (a) at least one of the conditions in Schedule 2 is met, and

   (b) in the case of sensitive personal data, at least one of the conditions in Schedule 3 is also met.

2. Personal data shall be obtained only for one or more specified and lawful purposes, and shall not be further processed in any manner incompatible with that purpose or those purposes.

3. Personal data shall be adequate, relevant and not excessive in relation to the purpose or purposes for which they are processed.

4. Personal data shall be accurate and, where necessary, kept up to date.

5. Personal data processed for any purpose or purposes shall not be kept for longer than is necessary for that purpose or those purposes.

6. Personal data shall be processed in accordance with the rights of data subjects under this Act.

7. Appropriate technical and organisational measures shall be taken against unauthorised or unlawful processing of personal data and against accidental loss or destruction of, or damage to, personal data.

8. Personal data shall not be transferred to a country or territory outside the European Economic Area unless that country or territory ensures an adequate level of protection for the rights and freedoms of data subjects in relation to the processing of personal data.

   (Schedule 1, Data Protection Act, 1998)

Adoption

The child

Adoption agencies have the duty to set up a child's case record and include in it the information and reports obtained as required by the Adoption Agencies Regulations 2005 in England, the Adoption Agencies (Wales) Regulations 2005 in Wales and the Adoption Agencies Regulations (Northern Ireland) 1989. This will be the report of any assessment carried out by the agency's medical adviser, as well as the neonatal report and any other information provided by other practitioners, and the summary and recommendations prepared by the medical adviser and included in the Child's Permanence Report (CPR) in England, Child's Adoption Report (CAR) in Wales, or the Child's Adoption Report (CAR-NI) in Northern Ireland. It will also include any health information that the agency has been able to obtain about the child's birth parents and siblings, as required by

Regulation 16(2) of both the English and Welsh Regulations and Schedule 1, Part 4 of the English Regulations, Schedule 1, Part 5 of the Welsh Regulations, and Schedule 7(2)(c) and (d) of the Northern Ireland Regulations.

Once a child is adopted, the Disclosure of Adoption Information (Post-Commencement Adoptions) Regulations 2005 in England and the Access to Information (Post-Commencement Adoptions) (Wales) Regulations 2005 require that the adopted person's file is kept for at least 100 years from the date of the adoption order. In Northern Ireland, Regulation 14 of the Adoption Agencies Regulations (Northern Ireland) 1989 requires adoption records to be retained for a minimum of 75 years following the granting of an adoption order.

If the child is not adopted, the information on the adoption file should be transferred to the child's care record. The Care Planning, Placement and Case Review (England) Regulations 2010, the Placement of Children (Wales) Regulations 2007 and the Arrangements for Placement of Children (General) Regulations (Northern Ireland) 1996 require that the care records be kept for at least 75 years from the child's birth or 15 years from the child's death, if they die under the age of 18. If the child has not been in care (for example, if a mother has changed her mind about relinquishing a baby and keeps the child with her after birth), the files should be destroyed when no further action is necessary.

The adopters

Similarly, the agency has a duty to set up a case record in respect of prospective adopters and include in it the information and reports required by the regulations. This will include the written report and any further information requested, as well as the summary to be included in the Prospective Adopter's Report.

The adoption agency must keep the records secure and ensure that there is no unauthorised access to or disclosure of the information contained in them. They must ensure that they are kept in a safe place and protected from destruction or damage.

There is no specific time period laid down for how long a prospective adopter's records should be kept. The regulations require that the information should be kept for as long as the agency thinks appropriate. The fifth Data Protection Principle will apply, and agencies should not keep any information for longer than is necessary. Where a child has been adopted, it might be considered appropriate to keep the adopter's file until six years past the child's 18th birthday (allowing for the limitation period on starting legal action), in case the child wishes to make a claim or complaint against the agency if the adoption is unsatisfactory. Prospective adopters may consent to the retention of their records to allow them to make a further application to the agency later. If applicants are not approved as adopters, their files should not be kept for significant periods. Retention for a short time would allow the exchange of concerns if the applicants approached another agency, but they should not be held indefinitely. Statutory guidance issued in England when the

Adoption and Children Act 2002 first came into force suggested that two years would be a reasonable time to retain the files of applicants not approved as adopters, and although this suggestion has not been repeated in the revised guidance, it might be considered a useful reference point for agencies in both England and Wales considering their retention and destruction policies. In Northern Ireland, the Adoption Regional Policy and Procedures (2010) require records relating to applicants not approved to adopt to be retained for at least 30 years.

Retention by health agencies of health records for adoption

As adoption agencies have such a clear duty to retain all the health information in respect of a child and prospective adopter, there will be little or no need for the medical adviser to keep substantial/duplicate records themselves. The fifth Data Protection Principle mitigates against unnecessary retention of data and the medical adviser will need to consider what it will be necessary to retain. Copies of the assessment report and any information that was provided to inform the assessment report, including any notes of consultations, may be held for as long as the case is being decided. This may include any period allowed for prospective adopters to apply to the Independent Review Mechanism in case further information is requested. It may also be appropriate to retain all notes in respect of a child until he or she is placed with their prospective adopters, as it will be good practice, where a child has specific health needs or developmental uncertainties, for the medical adviser to meet with the prospective adopters as part of the matching process.

When a prospective adopter has been approved, they will be subject to a review of their approval annually until a child is placed with them. The medical adviser will need to check with the prospective adopter's GP and any practitioner involved in ongoing monitoring or treatment of the adopter, whether anything about their health has changed. For this reason, it could be justifiable to retain the record of the assessment for as long as reviews continue.

Fostering
The child

A considerable variety of health records and reports, including neonatal, GP, community/child health database, school, health visitor, speech and language, consultant, CAMHS, etc, may be compiled by the LAC health team in carrying out comprehensive health assessments on BAAF Forms IHA and RHA. Information from these various health sources should be retained by health agencies according to their information governance policies.

To protect confidentiality, guidance on Forms IHA and RHA recommends as good practice that details of health in Part B should be retained within health agencies, and that only the summary and recommendations contained in Part C should be sent to the fostering agency. The records of a child in care must be kept by the local authority that has care of that child. The Care Planning, Placement and Review (England) Regulations 2010, the Placement of Children (Wales) Regulations 2007 and the Arrangements for Placement of Children (General) Regulations (Northern Ireland) 1996 require the entire care file to be kept until at least the child's 75th birthday, or, if the child dies before the age of 18, the 15th anniversary of the child's death.

The foster carers

The Fostering Services (England) Regulations 2011, the Fostering Services (Wales) Regulations 2003 and the draft Foster Placement and Fostering Agencies Regulations (Northern Ireland) 2014 require that the agency assessing a prospective foster carer obtain details of his or her health, supported by a medical report (usually provided by completion of BAAF Form AH). The prospective foster carer's report is then compiled from the information contained in the medical report. If there is any health concern recorded on the medical report, the medical adviser will be invited to comment on it and give an opinion on the impact of the information on the applicant's suitability to foster. For recommendations on best practice in adult health, see Chapter 15.

The regulations require the fostering service provider to open a case file and to include on it the report (BAAF Form F) of the assessment of the applicant's suitability to become a foster carer and the information obtained in relation to the assessment (which will include the medical report).

Regulation 32 of both the English and Welsh regulations requires the foster carer's file to be kept securely for at least 10 years from the date on which their approval is terminated. If the approval is refused, or the applicant withdraws during the assessment process, the records must be kept for at least three years from the refusal or withdrawal. The draft Foster Placement and Fostering Agencies Regulations (Northern Ireland) 2014, which are being consulted on at the time of writing, propose the retention of foster carers' records for 40 years from the date on which registration was terminated and for applicants not approved to foster, from the date on which this decision was made.

In the same way as for adoption, above, there is no statutory or regulatory requirement for the medical adviser to retain records for any length of time. Once the application has been dealt with, including any possible time for application to the Independent Review Mechanism (IRM), there is little reason for the medical adviser to keep copies of the foster carer's file. If further issues arise on which more medical advice is needed, the fostering service provider should have all the relevant information available on their own file to share with the medical adviser when necessary.

Retention by health agencies of health records for fostering

As noted above, it should not usually be necessary for a medical adviser or looked after children's health team to keep records for any length of time. However, different agencies may have different requirements of their medical advisers, so advisers should check their terms of engagement for any local requirements.

If a medical adviser or specialist nurse is also employed as part of the NHS, they may be able to store any records they keep at their surgery, clinic or hospital and will need to comply with that organisation's codes of practice for storage of records. If a medical adviser is retired from practice generally or is otherwise working on their own, they should be cautious about holding and storing records. They may need to register as a data controller in their own right, and must have satisfactory secure storage for paper records and electronic security for computers and other methods of data storage. Particular care will need to be taken when information is sent by email or transported in laptops or data sticks. Further advice and information about the requirements for storage of health records are available from the Information Commissioner's Office at www.ico.gov.uk/for_organisations/sector_guides/health.aspx.

Disclosure of health records

Adoption
The child's records
"Pre-commencement" – England and Wales
For adoptions that took place before the Adoption and Children Act 2002 came into force on 30 December 2005, the adoption agency has discretion under the Adoption Agencies Regulations 1983 to disclose the information held on the adopted person's file to that person, including in childhood, for example, if necessary to provide support. This may include any health information recorded on the file, and the agency may seek the medical adviser's help in deciding what should or should not be disclosed, or in interpreting medical information or outdated medical terms before disclosure. The adoption agency may disclose information to any other person if it decides that doing so is required for the purposes of its functions as an adoption agency.

"Post-commencement" – England and Wales
An adopted person is entitled, on reaching the age of 18, to receive a copy of the information that was disclosed to his or her prospective adopter/s at the time of his or her placement with them (s.60, Adoption and Children Act 2002). This will include the Child's Permanence Report (CPR) in England, or Child Assessment Report for Adoption (CARA) in Wales, containing the medical adviser's summary of the child's health assessment. The adopted adult may request access to further information held on the adoption file, including the full medical report, which the agency will have discretion to disclose under Regulation 42(2) of the Adoption Agencies Regulations 2005 in England and Regulation 43(2) of the Adoption Agencies (Wales) Regulations 2005. The agency may seek advice from the medical adviser before disclosing this information.

The adopter/s of a child may seek further access to their child's medical assessment, and may do so pursuant to s.62 of the Adoption and Children Act 2002. The agency has no duty to disclose any further information, but may do so if the child's welfare requires it. The agency may seek medical advice in considering such a request.

Northern Ireland

Regulation 15(2) of the Adoption Agencies Regulations (Northern Ireland) 1989 allows an adoption agency to disclose information from its files as it thinks fit for the purposes of carrying out its functions as an adoption agency. This will include medical information that could be disclosed to the child, an adopted adult, professionals involved in providing treatment or therapy to the family, or to the adoptive parents needing more information about their child's background.

Adopters' records

Prospective adopters' records must be kept confidential. The adopters themselves do not have the right of access to the information contained in their files by reason of the Data Protection (Miscellaneous Subject Access Exemptions) Order 2000, which excludes all adoption files from the general right to access information granted by s.7 of the Data Protection Act 1998. The adoption agency has the discretion to disclose information from the files under Regulation 15 of the Adoption Agencies Regulations 1983, Regulation 42(2) of the Adoption Agencies Regulations 2005, Regulation 43(2) of the Adoption Agencies (Wales) Regulations 2005 and Regulation 15 of the Adoption Agencies Regulations (Northern Ireland) 1989 for the purpose of carrying out their function as an adoption agency. This discretion would allow the disclosure of information either to the adopter themselves or to the adopted person, should the disclosure of that information be thought relevant and helpful to the agency's task of supporting adopters and adopted people.

Fostering and care records

Access to files held about foster carers and looked after children is subject to s.7 of the Data Protection Act 1998, which applies in England, Wales and Northern Ireland. This gives the subject of the files the right to access information held about them. Third party information held on the files should not be disclosed without the consent of that third party, unless it is reasonable in all the circumstances to disclose such information. For example, it would be reasonable to tell a young person that his mother was unable to care for him due to her mental health difficulties, despite a lack of consent from his mother to disclose this information. It might not be reasonable to tell a young person that his mother's mental health difficulties stem from a specific traumatic incident, if the mother has refused her consent to discuss this information with anyone. Where the information requested relates to a person's health, the agency may only disclose or refuse to disclose it following advice from the appropriate health professional about whether disclosure of the information would be likely to cause serious harm to the physical or mental health or condition of the data subject or any other person (Data Protection (Subject Access Modification) (Health) Order 2000). The appropriate health professional is the one who has most recently had care of the subject, but in access to records cases, the records may be many years old and the appropriate medical professional may have long since retired. In such a case, the agency may consult a medical professional with appropriate experience and qualifications, which may well be the agency's medical adviser.

Accessing information from adoption and care records

(Information provided by Julia Feast, BAAF Policy, Research and Development Consultant)

For adults brought up in their family of origin and not adopted or brought up in care, it is easy to take for granted the information that is usually available about family background and medical history. As a health professional, you may not have to advise and actively help an adopted adult or care leaver concerning how they can access information that is held on official records. However, it is still helpful to have some basic knowledge about the legislative framework and the process adopted adults and care leavers have to go through to access the information that is held about them. It is also important to be able to signpost people to other resources that may help them in their search for information.

What motivates people to access adoption and care records?

Many adopted people have told us how obtaining information about their birth family background and understanding why they were placed for adoption can help them build a fuller sense of identity. It can enable them to have a greater understanding of who they are and where they come from. Some adopted people want to obtain identifying information so that they can begin a search for birth family members. Others are keen to access information about their family of origin's medical history to help them respond to questions that they are often asked by health professionals, throughout their lifetime, about the medical conditions that exist in their family.

For adopted people who have grown up in a secure and loving family, it is likely that there will be photos and shared memories that they can recount across their lifespan. However, for people who have been brought up in care and who have had several placements throughout their childhood and adolescence, there can be many more challenges. For them, sharing memories and photographs, recounting family stories and significant events, which is normally an integral part of family life, may not be possible. As a result, they may need to gather information from records held by the local authority or voluntary agency, to help rebuild fractured identities and resolve deeply personal questions about their origins and histories. Others may want to confirm significant events in their lives, for example, when and why they came into care, where they lived and the decisions that were made about them. Some people want information to help them seek the relatives they have lost touch with. For others, it is to try and make contact with other significant people from their lives in care, for example, particular friends, foster carers or residential staff, as these people can be as important as birth family members. For some, it is curiosity and just wanting to know what records have been kept, where they lived, and why they were moved.

Adopted adults and care leavers may share a natural curiosity to find out about their origins and family medical history, but the level of their information needs may be different depending on the family experiences they had growing up.

As the legislative framework and processes for accessing information from official records are different for adopted adults and care leavers, they will be addressed separately below.

Adopted people: the legislative framework and process

In England and Wales, adoption first became legal in 1926, while in Northern Ireland this occurred in 1929. Accessing the original birth certificate and determining which agency arranged the adoption are crucial initial steps in obtaining further information from adoption agency records, and progressing to a search for birth family members if the individual wishes. The legislative framework and process depend on the date of adoption.

People adopted in England and Wales before 12 November 1975 and in Northern Ireland before 8 December 1987

Since 1975, adopted people aged 18 and over in England and Wales have had the right to apply to the Registrar General for access to their birth record (Children Act 1975). In Northern Ireland, this right was introduced in 1987 (Adoption (Northern Ireland) Order 1987). If the adopted person already knows their birth name, they can apply directly to the Registrar General (RG) for a copy of their original birth certificate. However, an adopted adult who does not know their birth name will have to access their birth record to obtain their original name and the names of their birth mother, and birth father if this is recorded. This is done by attending a "counselling interview" with an adoption social worker at the local authority where they live, or at the agency that arranged the adoption (if known), or at the Registrar General's office in Southport. They will then be given the necessary forms to apply for a copy of their birth certificate. Providing it was not a private adoption, the RG may also be able to let the adopted person know which agency arranged their adoption so that further information can be sought.

People adopted in England and Wales after 12 November 1975 and before 30 December 2005, and people adopted in Northern Ireland after 8 December 1987

The birth records "counselling interview" is optional for individuals adopted during this time period, and he/she can apply directly to the RG for a copy of their original birth certificate (s.51, Adoption Act 1976; Article 54, Adoption (Northern Ireland) Order 1987).

People adopted in England and Wales after 30 December 2005

Following the implementation of the Adoption and Children Act 2002, anyone adopted in England and Wales after 30 December 2005 should apply to the agency that arranged the adoption, rather than the RG, for the information they need to obtain a copy of their original birth certificate.

Accessing information from adoption records

Adoption records can be located at a range of agencies. The three main locations are the local authority, a voluntary adoption agency and the court where the adoption order was granted.

Under the Adoption Agencies Regulations 1983 (Regulation 15.2) in England and Wales and the Adoption Agencies Regulations (Northern Ireland) 1989 (Article 15(2)), local authorities, trusts and voluntary adoption agencies have the discretion to share information (including identifying information) from the records they hold. This means that adopted people do not have an automatic right to receive information from the agency's records; however, during the past few decades, adoption agencies have gained a greater understanding about the needs of adopted people. Through practice experience and hearing from adopted people directly, they have learned how information can help the adopted person answer important questions about their background, and also help them begin a search for birth family members. This has meant that agencies are usually willing to share information that is held on their records.

Adopted people who want to access information about their family background would normally be expected to have an appointment with an adoption social worker who will review the information in their records with them. The information held in an adoption record usually gives a lot more detail than is held on the birth certificate, for example, information about other birth family members such as names and ages, and also the reason why the adoption order was made. However, records can vary in length depending on the era and reason for the adoption order. In contemporary adoption, it would be expected that there would be comprehensive information held on the records, but for some adoptions from years ago there may be just a single summary sheet or very few pages. Unfortunately, some adoption records may have been destroyed by fire or flood.

The adoption social worker can also offer advice and information about searching for birth relatives if this is something that the adopted person wants to do and, providing they have the resources, may also be able to provide intermediary services.

For information about accessing records of a deceased adult, see Chapter 6.

The availability of support, advice and help

Health professionals should be able to signpost adopted people to sources of further information and support, for example, to the adoption support worker at the local authority where the adopted person resides. BAAF's Adoption, Search Reunion (ASR) website holds comprehensive information for adopted people about the legislative framework and obtaining information from adoption records, as well as access to many other resources such as a reading list and free tracing guide. There are two databases: one to help adopted people find where adoption records may be held, and another to help them find an agency where they can obtain a service and support. More information about the ASR website can be found at: www.adoptionsearchreunion.org.uk/Channels/. The ASR website also provides information about intermediary services for adopted people, adoptive parents and birth relatives.

The medical adviser's role

There is usually medical history information on the adoption records, the amount and quality of which will vary depending on the era when it was gathered. Some information will be straightforward, such as the adopted person's birth weight, immunisations and illnesses, but sometimes the medical information is much more complex. In such cases, the adoption social worker may seek the medical adviser's assistance to understand the medical information and the implications for the adopted person and his or her family (for example, the medical information may reveal a history of Huntington's disease or a genetic type of breast cancer). Consideration will need to be given to whether it would be best to involve the agency medical adviser or the adopted person's GP in disclosing sensitive health information.

The Adoption Registration Service, run by the NHS Information Centre, can provide the confidential transfer of information about hereditary medical conditions between the GPs of the adopted person and birth relatives, providing the adopted person and birth relative can be identified from the information available and are currently registered with a GP in England, Wales or the Isle of Man. For more information, visit: www.ic.nhs.uk/services/adoption-registration-service.

The area of information sharing, often many years after adoption, is complex and usually needs to be considered on an individual basis. While the "GP to GP" service can be very helpful, consideration needs to be given to whether it is the most appropriate approach to use in each individual case.

Care leavers: the legislative framework and process

Unlike adoption, where regulations provide for the agency to exercise discretion in sharing information (including identifying information) with the adopted adult from the records they hold, there is no specific provision for local authorities to share information from their care records with care leavers. Requests from care leavers for access to information from records of their childhood retained by the local authority in England, Northern Ireland and Wales currently come under the Data Protection Act 1998 (DPA). Prior to the DPA 1998, the governing legislation that enabled people brought up in care to access information came under DPA 1984, the Access to Personal Files Act 1987 and the associated Access to Personal Files (Social Services) Regulations 1989, and the Access to Personal Files and Medical Reports (Northern Ireland) Order 1991. These allowed individuals to see what was recorded about them in local authority paper files.

It is generally agreed by those representing care leavers and those professionals working in the area of providing information that the DPA is not an effective way to meet the information needs of care leavers. This is primarily because, not having been designed with the needs of these adults in mind, the DPA makes restrictions on disclosing third party information. These restrictions can prevent care leavers from accessing significant family history information, including details of their parents, siblings and extended family. It can therefore be a real challenge for access to records officers (AROs) and social workers to provide meaningful and comprehensive information from childhood records. They can encounter many dilemmas when making decisions about whether or not to disclose third party personal information. However, statutory guidance recently published in England addresses this by encouraging local authorities to share information and support care leavers in accessing important information (DfE, 2014).

Considering what to disclose

Disclosing information under the Data Protection Act can be complex and may raise anxiety about what medical information can be disclosed, but the Information Commissioner's Office has useful guidance available at: www.ico.gov.uk/for_organisations/sector_guides/health.aspx.

Section 68(2) of the DPA states that a health record:

(a) consists of information relating to the physical or mental health or condition of an individual, and

(b) has been made by or on behalf of a health professional in connection with the care of that individual.

This is a definition that applies to health information contained within a social services file. It is recognised by the Information Commissioner that sharing basic medical information contained in records about a care leaver is acceptable, such as:

- height and weight;
- immunisations;
- childhood illnesses such as measles, chickenpox, etc;
- minor operations to remove appendix, tonsils/adenoids, etc;
- other routine medical matters;
- more serious matters where the individual can demonstrate some memories of the incident, or has been given some information about it.

Such information that is not contentious can be disclosed by the ARO or the social worker. Other medical matters, such as hereditary health conditions, are a difficult area. Whilst it is important to recognise the confidentiality of whichever living relative has the condition, it is important for the data controller (the organisation which holds the records) to understand that this information is also personal information for the care leaver. In most cases, this information should be disclosed. However, the ARO or social worker should seek the advice of the medical adviser/health professional to discuss how and by whom the information should be disclosed.

The Information Commissioner's Office *Data Protection Technical Guidance Note, Subject Access Request and Social Services Records* (2008), provides detail concerning the Statutory Instrument covering medical information and when to seek medical opinion on risk issues or explanation of medical conditions.

In considering a request made by an individual for disclosure of their own records relating to health, it is necessary to consider the Data Protection (Subject Access Modification) (Health) Order 2000, 2000/413. This is quite specific in prohibiting the disclosure of health information to a care leaver, or any other data subject, in cases where a health professional has been consulted and has determined that the disclosure is likely 'to cause serious harm to the physical or mental health or condition of the data subject or any other person'. Information can also be released if a medical practitioner has reviewed the file at any time during the six months prior to receipt of the subject access request and has determined that disclosure is unlikely 'to cause serious harm'.

Where medical information about a third party has a direct bearing on the physical or mental health or well-being of the care leaver then this information should only be withheld in those circumstances where a medical practitioner thinks disclosure *would* be likely to cause serious harm to the physical or mental health or condition of the data subject or any other person. The data controller should start with the assumption that most of this information should be disclosed and only potentially harmful information should be withheld. It is important for the worker to consult with the organisation's medical adviser as disclosure of medical information is a complex topic, which can cause some confusion.

Often, what may be deemed personal information of a parent or sibling may have significance for a care leaver. For example, if a parent had a history of mental illness or imprisonment, this is clearly personal information for the parent, but is also of great significance for the care leaver in understanding why he or she was placed in care. Similarly, knowing significant personal details of a sibling's history could give understanding of why they were separated and not placed together. The nature of the information, whether or not it was obtained in the expectation of confidentiality, and the needs of the subject are matters that will need to be taken into account when considering whether it is reasonable to disclose medical information about family members.

The guidance on the DPA to social services departments in England and Wales (Department of Health (DH), 2000) provides some general guidance. However, it does not specifically address the issue of care records, or the difficulties inherent in the data protection legislation about personal confidentiality when information relates to family members, and so is in effect relevant to more than one person. However, in 2008, the Information Commissioner's Office (ICO) issued some guidance specific to care records, available at: http://collections.europarchive.org/tna/20100423085705/http:/ico. gov.uk/upload/documents/library/data_protection/detailed_specialist_guides/sars_ social_services_v1.0_260808.pdf. See also: https://ico.org.uk/media/for-organisations/ documents/1065/subject-access-code-of-practice.pdf.

Guidance from the ICO, explaining the relationship between the DPA and monitoring under section 75 of the Northern Ireland Act 1998, and providing advice for public authorities that are required to carry out such monitoring, is available at: http://ico.org. uk/for_organisations/data_protection/topic_guides/~/media/documents/library/Data_ Protection/Detailed_specialist_guides/SECTION_75_MONITORING_GPN_V1.ashx.

Accessing information from care records

Once a written application has been made by the post-care adult (the subject), then the local authority/organisation that holds the records relating to the subject's time in care has a duty to respond to the subject access request within 40 days. If the response takes longer than this, then it is in breach of the Act.

The subject can be charged a fee of £10 and they have to produce proof of their identity before the local authority/voluntary agency can disclose information. Unlike adopted people, care leavers can insist on having the records sent to them by post without meeting with an ARO or social worker first to talk through some of the implications and impact that receiving records may have. However, most organisations encourage the care leaver to receive the care records during a face-to-face meeting, where other support can be offered. For information about accessing records of a deceased adult, see Chapter 6.

The availability of support, advice and help

Unlike adoption, there has been no specific legislation to govern the particular inform-ation needs of care leavers and the services they may require to access information and/or help them get in touch with family members, friends and staff members from the time they were in care across the lifespan.

It is important that the lifelong issues that may be a direct result of a person being brought up in care are addressed, and services should be provided by the local authority or the organisation where the care leaver was in care. Accessing services and support from organisations varies from agency to agency, with some providing services to assist the care leaver and others not, due to a lack of resources or recognition of the issues. However, there are a few self-help organisations that exist to provide information and advice to care leavers, in particular, the Care Leavers' Association.

Other helpful organisations are listed in *Access to Information for Post-Care Adults* (Feast, 2009). See also DfE, 2010 (to be updated in 2015).

The medical adviser's role

Medical matters, sometimes in depth, are often recorded in social care reports about the looked after child, and these may be accessed by the care leaver. If he or she does not know the details and if the record is complex and requires expert explanation, the agency medical adviser may be asked for advice about disclosing the information.

What health professionals should do

- Have a good understanding of the principles of confidentiality, information sharing, data protection and records management, and contribute to agency policy in these areas.
- Be familiar with legal statute and relevant guidance from professional organisations.
- Keep clear records and share information appropriately.
- Be aware of regulations regarding changing the name of an adopted child.
- Take a lead within health to ensure appropriate procedures are in place for managing paper and electronic health records when a child is adopted.
- Be available for discussion concerning what should be disclosed to adopted and post-care adults.

Key points

- Comprehensive and continuous health records are crucial for children separated from their birth families.
- Confidentiality is not the same as secrecy, and information should be shared appro-priately and in the best interests of children.

- Adoption and fostering agencies should have comprehensive policies regarding confidentiality of health information, sharing of information within the agency and with other agencies as relevant, as well as retention and access to health information included in records held by adoption and fostering agencies.
- The current practice of assigning a new NHS number when a child is adopted has contributed to fragmented health records. Since the introduction of electronic health records, recommendations have been made about management of health records in adoption, including a proposal that adopted children should retain their original NHS number, with appropriate safeguards in place to protect the placement.

Bibliography

Department for Children, Schools and Families (2008) *Information Sharing: Guidance for practitioners and managers*, London: DCSF, available at: www.education.gov.uk/childrenandyoung people/strategy/integratedworking/a0072915/information-sharing

Department for Children, Schools and Families (2009) *Promoting the Health and Wellbeing of Looked After Children: Statutory guidance*, London: DCSF

Department for Education (2010) *The Children Act 1989 Guidance and Regulations Volume 3: Planning transition to adulthood for care leavers*, London: DfE

Department of Health (2000) *Data Protection Act 1998: Guidance to Social Services*, London: DH

Department of Health, Social Services and Public Safety (2011) *Records Management: Good management, good records*, Belfast: DHSSPS

Feast J. (2009) *Access to Information for Post-Care Adults: A guide for social workers and Access to Records Officers* (AROs), BAAF: London

General Medical Council (1988) *Annual Report for 1987*, London; GMC

Health and Social Care Board (2010) *Adoption Regional Policy and Procedures*, Belfast, Health and Social Care Board

Information Commissioner's Office (ICO) (2008) *Data Protection Technical Guidance Note, Subject Access Request and Social Services Records*, London: ICO

Information Commissioner's Office (ICO) (2012) *Monitoring under section 75 of the Northern Ireland Act 1998*, London: ICO, available at: http://ico.org.uk/for_organisations/data_protection/topic_guides/~/media/documents/library/Data_Protection/Detailed_specialist_guides/SECTION_75_MONITORING_GPN_V1.ashx

Information Commissioner's Office (ICO) (2014) *Subject Access Code of Practice: Dealing with requests from individuals for personal information*, London: ICO

Mather M. (2000) *Doctors for Children in Public Care*, London: BAAF

Payne H. (1992) 'Medical records on adopted children', *Adoption & Fostering*, 16:3, pp 43–5

Useful resources

Information Commissioner's Office (ICO): www.ico.gov.uk/for_organisations/sector_guides/health.aspx

BAAF Adoption Search Reunion (ASR) website: www.adoptionsearchreunion.org.uk/Channels/

The Care Leavers' Association: www.careleavers.com/

GP to GP service: www.ic.nhs.uk/services/adoption-registration-service

17 Quality assurance and service commissioning

Peter Barnes and Florence Merredew

Clinical governance is the system through which NHS organisations are accountable for continuously improving the quality of their services and safeguarding high standards of care, by creating an environment in which clinical excellence can flourish.
(Department of Health (DH), 1998)

Although there are multiple components to clinical governance, this chapter is concerned with commissioning functions that determine standards and service specifications for looked after children, and the competencies of health care professionals working within those services. It looks first at what health care professionals need to know about this area, followed by issues to be considered by commissioners.

Health care professionals

Competencies – a "knowledge/skill base"

In order to provide a service of high quality, it is crucial that health professionals are adequately and appropriately trained for their role. For doctors working in this field, generic standards of good medical practice (General Medical Council (GMC), 2013), including the complex area of confidentiality (GMC, 2009), must be maintained as laid down by the GMC, and which, in the future, doctors will need to evidence for the purpose of revalidation. Nurses will be guided by *The Principles of Nursing Practice*, developed by the Royal College of Nursing (RCN) in partnership with the DH (England), the Nursing and Midwifery Council (NMC), and patient and service user organisations (RCN, 2010).

Paediatricians in training, who are likely to become the next generation of medical advisers and lead clinicians for looked after children, will need to be aware of the skills that they are going to need to acquire and develop in order to demonstrate their competence. The Royal College of Paediatrics and Child Health (RCPCH) has issued guidance for the training and supervision of paediatricians (2010).

Health professionals already working with looked after children will need to be familiar with the Intercollegiate Competences, published by the RCN and RCPCH (2012, revision expected in 2015), which highlight the knowledge, skills and competence expected of staff working in this field. They should also be familiar with the guidelines published by NICE/SCIE, aimed at improving outcomes for looked after children (2010;

2013) and the *Quality Standard for Health and Well-Being of Looked After Children and Young People* (NICE, 2013).

BAAF has also contributed to the development of a competence framework for those health professionals who take on the role of lead clinician for looked after children and/or the medical adviser to local authority adoption/fostering agencies. In addition, BAAF has developed model job descriptions and guidance to assist these professionals and their service managers/commissioners in the process of job planning, and identifying an appropriate workload for an individual undertaking this work, which is essential if a quality service is to be developed and maintained (BAAF, 2008).

Continuous professional development and training – "keeping up to date"

In order to provide a high quality service, health professionals need to keep up to date with best practice guidance and the available evidence base, and be prepared and willing to share this with partner agencies in order to influence their own practice and procedures. A recent example might be a knowledge of BAAF's Good Practice Guide *Evaluating Obesity in Substitute Carers* (Mather and Lehner, 2010), the evidence base for this and the implications this guidance has for agency policy, prospective substitute carer approval and placement practice.

Individual membership of BAAF provides access to a variety of training materials and practice guidance, informed by the best available evidence, and is strongly recommended. Doctors working in this field can access individual support and guidance through the national advisory committee and also regional health groups facilitated by BAAF, with similar arrangements in place to support colleagues from a nursing background. Attendance at BAAF-sponsored national and regional meetings offers an opportunity to network with colleagues with a similar specialist interest, which can help to avoid professional isolation, as well as providing an opportunity to discuss practice-related dilemmas and challenges. BAAF provides access to a range of publications and training events for those professionals working with looked after children, helping to maintain and develop their skills and knowledge.

Professional bodies now provide guidance to members regarding their own professional development and how to evidence this. Areas of specialist work need to be considered and included when an individual is developing their personal development plan, with a view to ensuring that they remain up to date. The RCPCH recommends that a paediatrician should record and evidence a total of 50 hours per year of "continuing professional development" activity, averaged over a five-year cycle, covering generic as well as specialist activity. The NMC requires a minimum of 35 hours of learning activity relevant to practice during the previous three years to maintain registration (2012). BAAF has provided further guidance, in their model job descriptions and competencies for medical advisers in adoption and fostering (BAAF, 2008), recommending at least 10 hours of personal learning activity per year in topics relevant to this specialist role, regardless of how many sessions are devoted to this work in an individual's job plan. This continuing professional development is likely to be available only through external opportunities and not provided by the doctors' employing organisations.

Health professionals who are members of adoption and fostering panels should participate in at least one panel training event each year, and be willing to contribute to these in order to share professional knowledge and expertise with other panel members, who may otherwise have a limited understanding of health issues and considerations relevant to their roles.

Health professionals should also contribute to the training of paediatric colleagues and trainees, GPs, prospective and approved substitute carers and professionals working for partner agencies. This will help to equip them for their roles both now and in the future in promoting the health and well-being of looked after children, in order to maintain and improve service standards in the years ahead.

Appraisal/revalidation – "evidencing personal standards"

There is now an acceptance that doctors, in order to maintain their licence to practice through the process of revalidation, should be able to demonstrate that they are meeting expected standards, including in their area of special interest/expertise. The GMC has provided guidance to doctors in relation to how they can collect evidence to confirm that they are "fit to practice" (www.gmc-uk.org/doctors/revalidation/12388.asp). The process of annual appraisal will be central to the process of revalidation. Those doctors who have a special interest in the health of looked after children will need to think about how, with the help of this guidance, they are going to demonstrate that they are maintaining appropriate professional standards in the service that they deliver. This is likely to involve evaluation of their contribution to looked after children's health services by partner agencies, and particularly social care professionals.

The NMC is currently considering the process of revalidation for nurses, which is not expected to be in place before 2015 (NMC, 2012).

The process of appraisal should be seen by health professionals as an opportunity to highlight those areas where they would like to develop professionally, with a plan agreed with their appraiser as to how this can be achieved. An effective process of appraisal is likely to have benefits not only for the appraisee, but also the service that they deliver.

Health professionals who act as advisers to adoption and fostering panels should ensure that they are also appraised as a panel member in accordance with statutory guidelines in the country where they are working. This appraisal should contribute to their overall appraisal undertaken by their employing Trust/Health Board.

The GMC has recently introduced a licensing and revalidation process for all doctors, which will be managed by their employing NHS organisation. For those doctors retired from the NHS, but still working part-time with voluntary adoption agencies and independent fostering providers, and who will be advising only on adult health issues, the process for revalidation is not yet clear. Government guidance concerning the revalidation of doctors employed only by agencies that do not have a Responsible Officer to oversee and recommend revalidation is expected.

Service evaluation and audit – "demonstrating and improving standards in service provision"

The process of appraisal already referred to is likely to require that an individual provides evidence of appropriate standards of practice in the service that they are helping to deliver.

The process of audit allows the quality of service provision to be compared to a set "benchmark" standard, with the development of a plan to address any areas where service provision is deemed to be falling short of chosen standards, with re-audit identifying whether or not this plan has in turn been effective. Health professionals should therefore view the audit process as an opportunity to improve service standards, as well as demonstrating to others, and particularly commissioners, where a high quality service is already being delivered, and where perhaps this could be further improved through investment.

Health professionals may consider working with partner agencies in auditing areas of service provision where they have a mutual interest, with a view to working collaboratively in order to deliver a service improvement plan to meet standards that may not have been achieved. Expectations and standards highlighted in various published guidelines and regulations offer an ideal opportunity to set audit benchmarks. Alternatively, health professionals may develop audit standards that are relevant in the face of local challenges and needs. Liaison with their local audit "lead" and audit department may offer further guidance, support and assistance.

The following are some suggested areas for consideration when planning an audit and "measuring" the quality of health services provided for looked after children, but these are not exhaustive and should ideally reflect the local needs assessment. Comments in relation to forms are with reference to the BAAF health assessment forms, which are recommended for national use (see Chapter 7).

- The initial health assessment (using Form IHA–C or IHA–YP) – whether a comprehensive health history is obtained, including the availability of a completed Form M/B (the obstetric and neonatal reports), or alternatively accessing information from hospital records with consent – Form PH (the self-completed parental health report), and whether this is available for each parent, and any other records of the child and parent deemed relevant in a particular case. Although the statutory guidance for England, *Promoting the Health and Well-being of Looked After Children* (Department for Children, Schools and Families (DCSF) and DH, 2009, revision expected in 2015) and *Towards a Stable Life and Brighter Future* in Wales (Welsh Assembly Government, 2007a), require a comprehensive health assessment on entry to care, not all looked after children's health services carry this out fully, perhaps only obtaining information on the health of birth parents and details relating to the pregnancy and the child's health in the early weeks of life when there is a plan for adoption.

- In England and Wales, whether a comprehensive health history as detailed above is available for the agency decision-maker when making a decision about adoption.

- Timeliness of notifications requesting a health assessment and in turn its completion – issues to consider and assess include when social care services notify health services; when consent is received; when the health assessment is undertaken; and when the health care plan is completed, all measured against the requirement for completion of the health care plan within 20 working days of the child becoming looked after.

- Whether consent for the health assessment has been obtained and how this has been recorded.

- When considering the mental health and emotional well-being of a looked after child, whether a written carer's report, for example, Form CR–C, and/or a Strengths and Difficulties Questionnaire (SDQ), has been completed, including what use has been made of the information, in terms of appropriate support when needs have been identified.

- The percentage of looked after children who are registered with a GP and/or dentist, and the timeliness of this registration.

- Whether immunisations are up to date. There is published evidence to indicate that looked after children have lower vaccination uptake rates than children in the general population (Barnes *et al*, 2005).

- In relation to the health care plan (HCP), whether all action points from the assessment are recorded on Part C (summary and recommendations) of Forms IHA (Initial Health Assessment) and RHA (Review Health Assessment) and whether the health care plan action points are subsequently carried out.

- What health promotion advice has been offered for different age groups of children and young people.

- For care leavers, whether they have an appointment for review of their health history and are provided with a written copy, and what referral/planning is carried out for adult services.

- Whether prospective adopters, at the point of being matched with a child, have a fuller understanding of the comprehensive needs of the child in question and have had their questions answered after discussion with the medical adviser responsible for preparing the child's adoption health report.

Commissioning

Those professionals who work to promote the health and well-being of looked after children are likely to be well aware of the disadvantages that many face, for example, as a result of their experiences of abuse and neglect. In order to improve outcomes for these children, health professionals need to work effectively with others, including carers and professionals in partner agencies, to provide a timely assessment of need and consider provision of services to address these needs. This work is often time-consuming and demanding, and may be constrained by resource limitations. It is important that health professionals highlight to commissioners the needs of this vulnerable group, given their corporate parenting responsibility.

There may be a lack of evidence and guidance to assist professionals in identifying the most appropriate intervention for a given child's needs. Where evidence and guidance are available, it is crucial that health professionals are aware of this in order to identify and provide a high quality service, and to influence commissioners in developing services. Health professionals need to continually update their own knowledge and skills, and in addition share best practice with other professionals in partner agencies who also have a crucial role in promoting the health and well-being of looked after children. It is becoming increasingly important that health professionals are able to demonstrate to service commissioners and their own regulatory professional bodies that they are offering a service of the highest quality.

Legal/policy framework/corporate parenting

It is well recognised that health and social care services, along with other relevant partners, share responsibility for the "corporate parenting" of looked after children, and effective joint working is required to fulfil this task and improve outcomes for this vulnerable group of children.

In England, responsibility for provision of healthcare services and promoting the health and well-being of looked after children is shared by local authorities, NHS England, Clinical Commissioning Groups, Health Trusts and other "relevant partners" that are bound by the duty, under Section 10 of the Children Act 2004, to promote co-operation and to co-operate to improve children's well-being. In Wales, the duties contained in the Children Act 2004 also apply to Welsh local authorities, local health boards and other statutory partners. NHS England (NHS, 2013a) will directly commission some public health services, including:

- the national immunisation programmes;
- the national screening programmes;
- public health services for offenders in custody;
- sexual assault referral centres;

- public health services for children aged 0–5 years (including health visiting, family nurse partnerships and much of the healthy child programme); and
- child health information systems.

In Northern Ireland, the Health and Social Care (Reform) Act (Northern Ireland) 2009 outlines the responsibility of the Department of Health and Social Services and Public Safety (DHSSPS) to promote and provide health care in Northern Ireland. The Act established both the Public Health Agency and Health and Social Care Board for Northern Ireland, which are responsible for commissioning services, resource management and performance management and service improvement. The HSC Board delegates relevant personal social services functions to the Trust. It works to identify and meet the needs of the Northern Ireland population, including looked after children.

There is much guidance on joint working, including:

- DCSF/DH (2009, revision expected in 2015) *Statutory Guidance on Promoting the Health and Well-being of Looked After Children*
- NICE (2010) *Promoting the Quality of Life of Looked After Children and Young People*, Public Health Guidance PH28 (revised 2013)
- NICE (2013) *Quality Standard for the Health and Well-Being of Looked After Children and Young People*, QS 31
- Welsh Assembly Government (2007a) *Towards a Stable Life and a Brighter Future*
- Office of the First Minister and Deputy First Minister (2006) *Our Children and Young People – Our Pledge: A ten year strategy for children and young people in Northern Ireland*, 2006–2016

Influencing commissioners

The starting point for commissioning health services for looked after children in England should be the Joint Strategic Needs Assessment (JSNA) and the Joint Health and Well-being Strategy, and in Wales, the strategy contained in *Towards a Stable Life and a Brighter Future* (Welsh Assembly Government, 2007a) and in Northern Ireland, the Healthy Child Healthy Future framework for the universal child health promotion programme in Northern Ireland (DHSSPS, 2010). Designated professionals have a crucial advocacy role in ensuring that the needs of looked after children, including those placed from other areas, are included when the JSNA is formulated. Both these documents should be developed in partnership with all members of the Children's Trust and should consider the health needs of all children and young people. Epidemiological information collected at a local level through health assessments and to inform government statistical returns should be used, at an aggregate level, to inform both these strategic documents. In addition, the views of local looked after children and young people should be sought to inform the design and delivery of their local health services.

The Designated Doctor* and Designated Nurse (for full details of these roles, see Chapter 7), with assistance from the looked after children's health team, should feed into the assessment and strategy through provision of the following information about looked after children in their region:

- analysis of their health inequalities and health needs, including children from groups with particular needs such as those with a plan for adoption, from minority ethnic backgrounds, with disabilities, preparing to leave care, unaccompanied asylum-seeking refugee children, and those adopted from abroad;
- data about provision of services for local looked after children, obtained through an effective system of audit;
- an annual report on the effectiveness of health services for looked after children.

In addition to providing the above information and reports, the Designated Doctor and Designated Nurse may advocate and influence on behalf of looked after children by undertaking the following.

- Ensuring that the annual report is shared as widely as possible with the Trust, corporate parenting board, all partner agencies and commissioners. Wherever possible, the annual report should be presented face to face for greater impact.
- Finding out about the local management structure, and clarifying roles and responsibilities, to understand how best to exert their influence. This may include the Local Safeguarding Children's Board (LSCB) in England and Wales, corporate parenting boards and, in Northern Ireland, the Safeguarding Board for Northern Ireland, and the Health and Social Care Board (HSCB). Ideally, designated professionals should sit on the corporate parenting board or at least have a mechanism for feeding into it, and should have links with the person on the commissioning board with responsibility for looked after children. In England, they should also work closely with their Director of Children's Services, who will be a member of the LSCB and Health and Well-being Board (HWB), and who should be aware of developments in Clinical Commissioning Groups (CCGs). The Director of Public Health (DPH) will also be influential as a statutory member of the Health and Well-being Board. In Wales, they should work closely with the Director of Social Services, who will be a statutory member of the LSCB. Similarly, in Northern Ireland Directors of Children's Services in each of the Health and Social Care Trusts are statutory members of the Safeguarding Board for Northern Ireland.
- Raising awareness of the needs of looked after children through being proactive in offering assistance and education to corporate parenting boards and commissioning bodies.

---

* Named doctor for looked after children strategic role in Wales.

- Training and advising new members of management structures that have responsibility for looked after children.
- Utilising all available levers such as Government guidance, NICE guidelines and results of service inspections, with reference to local data and audit, to advocate for service improvement.
- Training GPs and hospital-based health professionals to facilitate understanding of their roles in corporate parenting, and development of their clinical expertise with looked after children.
- Widespread sharing of health data on looked after children with corporate partners.

Out of area placements

The ideal scenario for children in most cases is that they are cared for within their local area. Under s.23(7) of the Children Act 1989, and s.27(8)(a) of the Children (Northern Ireland) Order 1995, local authorities/Trusts have a duty to place children near to their homes and the Responsible Commissioner Guidance (NHS, 2013b) and Welsh Guidance (Welsh Assembly Government, 2007a) support the principle that health and children's social care should work in partnership to meet children's needs locally, rather than having to seek out-of-area placements.

However, increasing demand and changing patterns of foster care provision mean that for many children and local authorities this is not possible, and significant numbers of children and young people in the care system are placed outside of their originating CCG/Trust/Health Board area.

Statutory duties and principles

The statutory duty for CCGs/Trusts/NHS England and local authorities to meet the health needs of looked after children is clearly laid out in the statutory guidance, *Promoting the Health and Well-being of Looked After Children* (DCSF/DH, 2009, revision expected in 2015).

NHS England guidance, *Who Pays? Determining responsibility for payments to providers* (NHS, 2013b) sets out a framework for establishing responsibility for the commissioning of, and payment for, individuals' care within the NHS. The responsibility for commissioning secondary care-type provision for looked after children in out of area placements sits with the originating CCG rather than the receiving CCG. The guidance recommends that the "originating CCG", those currently providing the health care, and the new provider should make arrangements to ensure continuity of provision of high quality, timely health care for the individual child. It is important to keep in mind that the CCG for the area in which the child is placed is responsible for provision of primary care services.

In Wales, the local/originating Health Board of origin also retains responsibility for the commissioning and resourcing of secondary health care for a looked after child placed out of area, following the LHB (Directed Functions) (Wales) (Amendment) Regulations 2009 and the guidance (Welsh Assembly Government, 2007b). The guidance contains the overriding principle of patient care that no treatment should be refused or delayed due to uncertainty or ambiguity as to which commissioning body is responsible for funding an individual's health care.

In Northern Ireland, arrangements for the provision of support services for children and young people placed out of their local Trust area are negotiated between the relevant Trusts and a formal agreement is required to be drawn up outlining responsibility for the provision and commissioning of services.

Local authorities are charged with the legal requirement of notifying the health provider in the area where a child is living, and in the event of the child moving out of the area, to notify both the health provider and local authority in the area where the child will be living. To ensure continuity of care, the local authority should have agreed local mechanisms with health providers to ensure compliance with regulations and guidance when making placement decisions, and to resolve any funding issues that arise.

Service provision in England

While the Responsible Commissioner guidance has clarified responsibility, there is considerable variation in implementation, with disagreement concerning who will carry out health assessments and to what standard, with resulting delays in service provision for individual children while negotiations between commissioners take place. Designated professionals will need to advocate for the child's needs to be met, and against delay due to funding decisions. In England, it is the role of NHS England to address disputes between the originating CCG, recipient CCG and providers in order to ensure access to provision for looked after children.

With the introduction of the new (and potentially more complex) commissioning arrangements of Clinical Commissioning Groups, NHS England and Health and Well-Being Boards in England, there is potential for further confusion. However, the reforms in the 2012 Health and Social Care Act provide an opportunity to resolve the issues of quality, access and resource variation in the drive to improve the health outcomes for this most vulnerable and mobile group of children, with longer term financial and societal benefits.

This has led to the introduction of a national tariff for looked after children placed out of area, which mandates national prices and sets out an agreed quality framework for statutory assessments based on NICE standards (NHS, 2013c). Annex 4A includes a checklist for various components of the assessment, and asks whether the examining health care professional is competent to Level 3 of the Intercollegiate Competencies for looked after children published by the Royal Colleges (RCPCH and RCN, 2012, revision expected in 2015). The Designated LAC Nurse or Doctor within the commissioning CCG is responsible for the quality assurance of out of area health assessments.

Post adoption

When a child is placed for adoption, they remain a looked after child and therefore remain the responsibility of their "home" authority. After the adoption order, the only responsibility of the original authority is that of ongoing adoption support services, but that responsibility falls away after three years, except for financial support. Every other responsibility for social, education and health needs will be the responsibility of the area in which the child and their adopters live once the order is made. All responsibility for primary and secondary health care will be based on the child's home address following the adoption order.

Common dilemmas

- This area of social paediatrics is often poorly understood by health colleagues and it can be particularly difficult to demonstrate to commissioners the complex nature of the work undertaken to promote the health and well-being of looked after children, the time needed, and the importance of this work (see section on IHA, in Chapter 7). Highlighting this work as a priority in order to secure resource allocation may be a challenge, but designated professionals have a crucial role in raising the profile of looked after children, especially with public health and commissioners.
- All doctors recognise the requirement to have a level of competency in safeguarding children, but recognition that similar levels of competency are required for looked after children is often lacking. This lack of awareness hinders essential information sharing, decision-making and allocation of resources. For example, hospital staff not understanding the importance of completing Form M/B when requested at the point of the initial health assessment potentially results in children with risk factors for blood-borne infection missing out on testing which may be life saving. Audit and training are potentially invaluable in highlighting and in turn addressing these areas.
- Health professionals working in this area are currently facing an increasing workload, without allocation of extra resources to keep pace with this. Whilst activity and outcome data collection may prove helpful in evidencing this, there may be real challenges in recording and collecting such data, which may not be routinely collected by health organisations.
- There may be challenges presented by joint agency working in promoting the health and well-being of looked after children. Partner agencies may have different priorities and also be subject to similar time/resource limitations to health professionals, which in turn will impact on working relationships.
- There is a limited evidence base to influence decision-making and planning around health care provision/service delivery for some looked after children. There are real challenges in obtaining evidence to demonstrate positive outcomes, particularly in the long term.

- Health professionals working in this area may have a unique role within their employing organisation, and this can bring challenges around professional isolation that can be a real issue when faced with problematic cases and a limited evidence base for decision-making. There is a danger that health professionals may be overwhelmed by ever-increasing workloads that they do not have time to address. Strategies to avoid these potential difficulties are required.
- Identifying who is best placed to undertake given roles within health care teams, and where professional boundaries lie, may be a source of tension within teams and between partner agencies. For example, should a specialist nurse be expected to provide medical advice and guidance as a member of a local authority fostering panel, in the absence of a doctor?
- Ensuring that an individual who is tasked with the role of appraising a doctor with a special interest in the health and well-being of looked after children has a good understanding of the nature of this work may be a challenge, and in turn this could hamper the effectiveness of the appraisal process.
- Recruitment difficulties in relation to vacant senior paediatrician posts with a special interest in the care of looked after children may compromise future service delivery and standards, with impending retirements potentially contributing further.

What health professionals should do

- Be aware of your own competencies and ensure that training needs are identified at appraisal.
- Identify gaps in health provision for looked after children, and relevant audit and evaluation opportunities.
- Contribute local data on the health needs, inequalities and service provision for looked after children to inform the annual report and local strategies for commissioning.
- Promote the health needs of looked after children at every opportunity.
- Develop close working relationships with partner agencies and be prepared to contribute to training on health.
- Raise concerns about the provision of health care for looked after children placed out of area.
- Ensure that robust systems are in place for notification and fast-tracking of the records of children moving out of or into the area.
- Ensure that clear pathways are in place for requesting health assessments of looked after children placed out of area.

Key points

- Health professionals who work to improve the health and well-being of looked after children require specialist skills and knowledge, that need to be enhanced through training and personal professional development. They must be prepared to demonstrate their competence to others, including to their professional regulatory body.
- An ability to work effectively with health professionals who have expertise in other areas and also with professionals in partner agencies sharing a corporate parenting responsibility is crucial for those undertaking this role. A willingness to contribute widely to the training of others is necessary.
- There are potential challenges for health practitioners in providing those who are responsible for commissioning services with evidence of need and the quality of the service that is already being offered. Auditing a local service against nationally recommended standards/regulations is important in this regard, and can also act as a driver to raise standards locally when deficiencies are identified. Health care professionals working with looked after children, particularly in designated posts, should have a good understanding of local management and commissioning structures, and must be prepared to develop close links with service commissioners and argue robustly for a share of scarce resources in order to maintain and improve service standards.
- Professional isolation is a potential risk for health care professionals, and establishing local and regional networks of support with colleagues who share a common area of special interest is helpful in addressing this. The support that is available through BAAF membership in terms of training, advice and practice guidance is an invaluable resource.

Bibliography

BAAF (2008) *Model Job Descriptions and Competencies for Medical Advisers in Adoption and Fostering*, London: BAAF

Barnes P., Price L., Maddocks A., Cheung W.Y., Williams J., Jackson S. and Mason B. (2005) 'Immunisation status in the public care system: a comparative study', *Vaccine*, 23:21, pp 2820–23

Department of Health (1998) *Clinical Governance: Moving from rhetoric to reality*, London: DH

Department of Health and Department for Children, Schools and Families (2009) *Promoting the Health and Well-being of Looked After Children*, London: DH/DCSF

Department for Health, Social and Services and Public Safety (2010) *Healthy Child, Healthy Future: A framework for the Universal Child Health Promosion Programme in Northern Ireland, Pregnancy to 19 Years*, Belfast: DHSSPS

General Medical Council (2009) *Confidentiality*, available at: www.gmc-uk.org/guidance/ethical_guidance/confidentiality.asp

General Medical Council (2013) *Good Medical Practice*, available at: www.gmc-uk.org/guidance/good_medical_practice/contents.asp

Mather M. and Lehner K. (2010) *Evaluating Obesity in Substitute Carers*, London: BAAF

NHS (2013a) *Direct Commissioning*, available at: www.england.nhs.uk/ourwork/d-com/

NHS (2013b) *Who Pays? Determining responsibility for payments to providers*, available at: www.england.nhs.uk/wp-content/uploads/2014/05/who-pays.pdf

NHS (2013c) *2014/15 National Tariff Payment System Monitor*, London: NHS

NICE (2013) *Quality Standard for the Health and Well-being of Looked After Children and Young People*, QS31, London: NICE

NICE/SCIE (2010) *Promoting the Quality of Life of Looked After Children and Young People*, PH28, London: NICE/SCIE

NICE/SCIE (2013) *Looked After Children and Young People*, London: NICE/SCIE

Nursing and Midwifery Council (2012) *Revalidation*, available at: www.nmc-uk.org/Registration/Revalidation/

Office of the First Minister and Deputy First Minister (2006) *Our Children and Young People – Our Pledge: A ten year strategy for children and young people in Northern Ireland, 2006–2016*, Belfast: Office of the First Minister and Deputy First Minister

Royal College of Nursing (2010) *Principles of Nursing Practice*, available at: www.rcn.org.uk/development/practice/principles

Royal College of Paediatrics and Child Health (2010) *Curriculum for Paediatric Training, Community Child Health*, Level 1, 2 and 3 training, London: RCPCH

Royal College of Nursing and Royal College of Paediatrics and Child Health (2012) *Looked After Children: Knowledge, skills and competences of health care staff*, Intercollegiate Role Framework, London: RCPCH

Welsh Assembly Government (2007a) *Towards a Stable Life and a Brighter Future*, Cardiff: Welsh Assembly Government

Welsh Assembly Government (2007b) *Local Health Board (Functions) (Wales) (Amendment) Regulations*, Cardiff: Welsh Assembly Government

Relevant legislation

Access to Health Records Act 1990

Access to Health Records (Northern Ireland) Order 1993

Adoption Agencies Regulations (Northern Ireland) 1989

Adoption Agencies Regulations 2005 (England)

Adoption Agencies (Wales) Regulations 2005

Adoption Agencies and Independent Review of Determinations (Amendment) Regulations 2011 (England)

Adoption Agencies (Panel and Consequential Amendments) Regulations 2012

Adoption Agencies (Amendment) (Wales) Regulations 2012

Adoption Agencies (Miscellaneous Amendments) Regulations 2013

Adoption and Children Act 2002 (England and Wales)

Adoption (Northern Ireland) Order 1987

Adoption: regional policy and procedures (Northern Ireland) 2010

Adoption Support Services (Local Authorities) (Wales) Regulations 2005

Adoption Support Services Regulations 2005 (England and Wales)

Adoption Support Services and Special Guardianship (Wales) (Amendment) Regulations 2013

Adoptions with a Foreign Element Regulations 2005

Arrangements for the Placement of Children (General) Regulations (Northern Ireland) 1996

Borders, Citizenship and Immigration Act 2009

Care Leavers (England) Regulations 2010

Care Planning, Placement and Case Review (England) Regulations 2010

Care Planning, Placement and Case Review and Fostering Services (Miscellaneous Amendments) Regulations 2013

Children Act 1989

Children and Families Act 2014

Children (Leaving Care) Act (Northern Ireland) 2002

Children (Leaving Care) Regulations (Northern Ireland) 2005

Children (Leaving Care) (Wales) Regulations 2001

Children (Leaving Care) (Amendment) (Wales) Regulations 2002

Children (Northern Ireland) Order 1995

Children (Private Arrangements for Fostering) Regulations 2005

Children (Private Arrangements for Fostering) Regulations (Northern Ireland) 1996

Children (Private Arrangements for Fostering) (Wales) Regulations 2006

Data Protection Act 1998

Data Protection (Miscellaneous Subject Access Exemptions) (Amendment) Order 2000

Disability Discrimination Act 2005

Equality Act 2010

Fostering Services (England) Regulations 2011

Fostering Services (Wales) Regulations 2003

Legal Aid, Sentencing and Punishment of Offenders Act 2012

Local Health Boards (Directed Functions) (Wales) (Amendment) Regulations 2009

Mental Capacity Act 2005 (England and Wales)

Mental Health Act 2007 (England and Wales)

Mental Health (Northern Ireland) Order 1986

National Health Service Act 1977

National Health Service (Functions of Strategic Health Authorities and the Primary Care Trusts and Administration Arrangements) (England) (Amendment) Regulations 2007

Northern Ireland Act 1998

Placement of Children (Wales) Regulations 2007

Race Relations Act 1976

Race Relations (Northern Ireland) Order 1997

Review of Children's Cases (Wales) Regulations 2007

Review of Children's Cases Regulations (Northern Ireland) 1996

Safeguarding Board Act (Northern Ireland) 2011

Social Services and Well-Being (Wales) Act 2014

Special Guardianship Regulations 2005

Special Guardianship (Wales) Regulations 2005

Notes about the contributors

Kamni Anand is a consultant community paediatrician. She commenced her career in community paediatric services in Northern Ireland, moving on to Scotland, then settling in England. She became lead clinician in the community paediatric service in Angus, Scotland, and was instrumental in developing secondary care services to children aged under five. Kamni took up the post of designated doctor, and developed and established a new health service for looked after children in Suffolk. Kamni has been a medical adviser in adoption and fostering for many years, both in Scotland and England.

Peter Barnes is a consultant community paediatrician, employed by Abertawe Bro Morgannwg Health Board in Swansea. He is also an honorary clinical tutor at Swansea Medical School, and a medical adviser for adoption and lead clinician for looked after children.

Melanie Bracewell has worked as a medical adviser for adoption within her role as a consultant community paediatrician since 2007, and provides advice to Nottingham City and Nottinghamshire County Council adoption and fostering agencies. She continues to work closely with the local designated lead for children in care to ensure adoption issues are not forgotten and the quality of work is maintained.

Stasia Brackenridge is a specialist nurse for looked after children and care leavers with Locala Community Partnership (co-located with Kirklees Council). She has been in post for 10 years, and has worked in health for 40 years.

Kath Burton is a community paediatrician in North Staffordshire; she has a special interest in adoption and fostering and has been medical adviser to Stoke adoption panel for 16 years. Kath chaired the BAAF North West Health Group from 2007 to 2014 and represented the region on the national BAAF Health Group Advisory Committee for 12 years.

Geraldine Casswell is a chartered clinical psychologist with many years of experience working in community and in-patient CAMHS. She was also chair of a fostering panel and provided expert witness reports to the family courts. Having recently left the NHS, she is now a consultant and trainer in dyadic developmental psychotherapy, a therapeutic approach developed for children who have experienced developmental trauma, and their carers.

Alexandra Conroy Harris was called to the Bar in 1989. She practised as a self-employed barrister in London and the South East, representing local authorities, children and parents in public and private law proceedings. She was employed for nine years as a social services lawyer for a London borough, representing the borough in cases involving children and vulnerable adults and providing training, support and advice to local authority social workers. Since 2008, she has been employed as the legal consultant to BAAF, providing advice to everyone involved in adoption and fostering. She is also the legal adviser to the IRM Cymru.

Judith Dennis joined the Refugee Council in 2000 as policy adviser – unaccompanied children. Since 2011, she has led all the policy work at the Refugee Council but takes a keen interest in the protection and care of separated children. She has recently completed research into the availability and quality of legal advice to separated children in a pan-European project. Prior to joining the Refugee Council, Judith worked directly with separated children in the social services departments of two London boroughs.

Kate Dickinson is a community paediatrician in Kent and has been the medical adviser for Dartford and Gravesham since 1995. Intercountry adoption is relatively prevalent in Kent, in comparison with other areas of the country, which has enabled Kate to gain a wide experience of the culture of intercountry adoption, trends in Kent and problems arising in children adopted from many parts of the world.

Julia Feast OBE is Policy, Research and Development Consultant at BAAF. She has been involved in a number of research studies on the subject of adoption, search and reunion. She has particular interests in the identity and information rights and needs of adopted people, care leavers and donor conceived people.

Nicola Feuchtwang is a consultant paediatrician in Barnet, North London. She has been involved in adoption and fostering work for over 20 years, including preparation groups for prospective adopters. She is currently the medical adviser to the adoption and fostering services in Barnet and Enfield.

Emma Fillmore is a consultant paediatrician with responsibility as designated doctor for children in care in Nottingham. Her specialist interest is the health needs of unaccompanied asylum-seeking children and young people, and children in detention.

Colin Flanagan is the lead in oral health promotion for Devon. The role involves teaching trainers, giving lectures, undertaking projects and coordinating oral health educators to undertake community work. He has been accepted as a Fellow of the Royal Society for Public Health (FRSPH) and is also a practising dentist.

Liz Gilmartin is a full-time specialist public health nurse for care leavers in Bradford and Airedale (within the looked after children health team), and part-time PhD student at the University of Huddersfield, in her final year. Her professional background is in nursing (for over 30 years) and midwifery (for 17 years). She has also undertaken safeguarding work for a number of years.

Judith Gould is the Associate Specialist in Paediatrics, Poole Hospital NHS Foundation Trust. Judith has also recently been appointed Dorset Clinical Commissioning Group designated doctor for looked after children. She has been the medical adviser for adoption and looked after children to Bournemouth Borough Council for 10 years, providing advice on adult health assessments to both adoption and fostering teams.

Emma Hedley has 17 years of experience as a paediatric nurse, and found her passion for health promotion whilst training in tropical medicine at St Mary's Hospital, London. Emma then had the opportunity to develop her skills working over a number of years in West Africa. This led to working in the community as a health visitor and for the past four years as a looked after children's nurse in Hillingdon, West London.

Efun Johnson currently works as the designated doctor for looked after children in Lambeth, a London borough with a large number of looked after children, including unaccompanied minors. In addition, she is the medical adviser for Action for Children, London Mosaic families' project and for the PACT panel. She has been a medical adviser since 1999 and a designated doctor since 2004. She has had significant experience in paediatrics and community paediatrics, working with vulnerable children and young people for over 15 years. She worked on the programme development group of the NICE/SCIE guidance, *Promoting the Quality of Life of Looked After Children and Young People*, and has served for two terms on the BAAF Health Group Advisory Committee.

Louise Large is a specialist nurse for vulnerable young people. She has worked with the Sheffield looked after children health team for the past seven years, with a remit to support the health needs of young people preparing to leave care aged 16–18, and young people involved in the youth justice service. She works with individuals and groups in a variety of settings, and in partnership with a range of support staff, social care practitioners, carers and parents.

Ann Lorek is a consultant community paediatrician in Lambeth, and co-director of interdisciplinary MA programmes in Child Studies and International Child Studies at King's College London. She has worked with refugee and asylum-seeking children for many years.

Florence Merredew was a GP and psychotherapist in Canada before moving to the UK and has worked as Health Group Development Officer at BAAF since 2001. Her remit is to promote the health of looked after children and their carers through co-ordination of the BAAF Health Group Advisory Committee, raising awareness, improving standards, and contributing to best practice and training.

Carolyn Sampeys is a community paediatrician and named doctor for adoption, fostering and looked after children for Cardiff and Vale University Health Board. She acts as medical adviser in adoption to Cardiff and the Vale of Glamorgan local authorities. She is also designated doctor for safeguarding children within the safeguarding children service, Public Health Wales, and has a particular remit for looked after children and adoption across Wales.

Carolyn has been instrumental in the development of the role of the specialist looked after children's nurse in Wales and has contributed to several consultations and changes in regulations and guidance relating to looked after children and adoption in England and Wales. She chairs the All-Wales Looked After Children's Health Exchange. Recently, Carolyn represented the NHS on the Wales National Adoption Service Task and Finish Group, and has been appointed to the Wales National Adoption Service Advisory Group. Carolyn has been a member of the BAAF Health Group Advisory Committee for several years. She is a past Chair of the BAAF Cymru Health Group and was elected Chair of the BAAF Health Group Advisory Committee in 2010. Carolyn is a member of BAAF's Board of Trustees.

Nikki Shepherd has worked with looked after children for 14 years. Her current role is as a designated nurse for looked after children. Previously, she worked with young people in residential care as a specialist nurse.

Hannah Smith qualified as a specialist practitioner in public health nursing (health visiting) in 1998 and became a designated nurse for looked after children and care leavers in 2002. She has been a member of the BAAF Health Group Advisory Committee for over six years and is an active member of the Yorkshire and Humberside regional health group. More recently, she has been appointed on a secondment basis as a specialist adviser to the Care Quality Commission.

Savita de Sousa is the Consultant, Black Minority Ethnic Issues and Private Fostering at BAAF. She coordinates the BAAF Black Minority Ethnic Perspectives Advisory Committee (BMEPAC) and chairs the BAAF Private Fostering Special Interest Groups in England. She provides advice, information, consultancy and training to practitioners, adopters and foster carers.

Appendix A
Statement on the use of DNA testing to determine racial background

BAAF and British Society for Human Genetics

Background

Some local authorities have begun commissioning DNA testing to determine racial backgrounds for some looked after children where parental racial group is uncertain. Popular interest in genetic testing to determine racial ancestry has also been sparked by various television programmes in recent years which have discussed the use of genetic testing to demonstrate geographic movements of people through history, and even to determine that given individuals today have markers for different ethnic groups or geographic regions.

Why ethnicity may be uncertain

Uncertainty about racial inheritance may arise in different situations, such as unknown paternity, or where a child's appearance does not seem to match the stated racial group of the parents. Sometimes children are conceived in situations where the biological parents do not know one another well, do not share much information about their backgrounds, or there may have been family secrets. Furthermore, some parents do not stay in contact, and the opportunity to later find out more for the sake of the child is lost.

Why knowledge about racial origin is important

For looked after children, there are both immediate and long-term reasons for wanting to know as much as possible about ethnic background. Here it is important to distinguish between DNA racial ancestry and ethnicity. DNA racial ancestry tells us simply about a genetic code, a blueprint for certain physical characteristics, whereas ethnicity tells us about the cultural identity of an individual. DNA ancestry does not necessarily predict ethnicity, thus knowing that a child's father was Asian does not tell us anything about that father's way of life, religion or culture. Certainly there is evidence that it is usually in the child's best interests to be in a placement which can reflect as fully as possible their ethnic background, culture, language and religion, and this becomes even more important for long-term and permanent placement. In addition, many children enter care with health inequalities, which must be addressed. Knowledge of a child's racial background can assist with appropriate screening for certain hereditary conditions which are prevalent in particular ethnic groups.

Learning about one's ethnic and cultural background and religion is a long-term process, which occurs naturally, over time, within a family. Yet for children who are separated from their birth family, particular care must be taken to seek a placement which can reflect these factors as closely as possible.

Developing a sense of "who I am", is a process which is ongoing throughout childhood, but comes into focus as adolescence approaches. One of the main developmental tasks of adolescence is the search for identity, which for any individual is a complex process. But for a young person whose racial and ethnic background is uncertain, this task is far more difficult. For example, for an individual whose appearance suggests a dual heritage of white and African or Asian, not knowing if one's roots lie in an African or Asian culture can make it impossible to move forward and explore an identity rooted in one or the other, or both. For all concerned, the "not knowing" can be the most difficult thing to deal with, for knowledge points in a certain direction and allows action. And this is where high quality social work practice by skilled and experienced professionals is crucial to support and assist young people through the process of exploring identity, including coping with uncertainty.

Use of DNA testing to determine racial background

Given the issues discussed above, it is understandable that professionals would wish to provide children and young people with as much information as possible about their ethnic background, including the use of DNA testing by commercial laboratories which offer results in the format of a percentage breakdown from different ethnic groups.

However, after wide-ranging consultation with colleagues in clinical genetics departments and the British Society for Human Genetics, the BAAF Health Group Advisory Committee **does not recommend the use of DNA testing to determine ethnicity, as these tests have not been adequately evaluated or validated as being accurate**. While the appeal of such a definitive numerical answer is understandable, practitioners must avoid the risk of making decisions about a child's future based on information from a non-validated test. Similarly, using possibly inaccurate information as a guide to assisting young people in identity formation is not acceptable. The reasons for this recommendation are outlined below:

1. *Ancestry categories may be misleading*
Standard testing will offer an estimate of percentage DNA ancestry make-up in the following categories:
   a) European
   b) Native American
   c) East Asian – including peoples from Japan, China, Mongolia, Korea, SE Asia, Pacific Islanders and Philippines
   d) Africa – including sub-Saharan peoples

What may be unclear to consumers of this service is that European categories include peoples from the Middle East and Indian subcontinent. Additional testing (for additional fees) can further discriminate Northern European, Southern European, Middle Eastern and South Asian ancestry.

2. *Ancestry does not determine racial appearance*

There is POOR correlation between DNA ancestry and colour of skin.

3. *There is no data on normal populations to help interpret the results of DNA ancestry testing.* In other words, many apparently white British people may have a mixed ancestry on genetic testing and yet have no identity with these non-European elements of their ancestry.

4. *DNA ancestry is not the same as ethnicity.* The former is simply a sequence of DNA, the latter is the socio-cultural context of a child's life. What is more relevant to the child is how they perceive themselves and how they are perceived by others. In other words, racial appearance is likely to be a more helpful guide to placement than a statistical account of their ancestry.

Case study

Baby Joel is born in Birmingham to a white mother who is half Irish and half Scottish. Paternity is unknown. Joel is six months old and has olive skin, brown eyes and dark brown hair. He has a care plan for adoption and is currently living with foster carers who are both white. His social worker is questioning whether the father may be Asian. There are several white couples who are a good match for Joel but linking has been deferred pending DNA ancestry testing as the social worker believes that Joel should have an opportunity to understand his ethnic inheritance should he prove to be of mixed race.

Testing results state that he is 50% European, 10% African, 40% East Asian.

Where does this leave Joel? Firstly, we do not know if this combination is feasible from two white parents – it probably is. Even assuming that Joel's father is Asian from Indian extraction, this would be reflected within the "European" component of the testing result. He could be mistakenly placed with a mixed race couple where one of the partners is East Asian. Finally, even if his father is Indian, DNA ancestry cannot tell us about ethnicity – in other words, what religious and cultural practices were important to his father. He could be mistakenly placed with a family of a completely different ethnic make-up. Most important for Joel is that he is placed in a family who are a good physical match to his size, skin colour and hair colour and that placement is not delayed by mistaken attempts to reflect an ethnicity that can only be best guessed.

Conclusion

The use of genetic testing to determine ethnic background is not recommended. High quality social work practice in collecting as much family background information as possible, and expertise in assessing and balancing the many competing factors relevant to child placement, along with sensitive and skilled life story work to assist with exploration of identity, remain the cornerstones of child placement work.

APPENDIX B
Adoption Agencies Regulations

England

Extracts from the Adoption Agencies Regulations 2005, as amended by the Adoption and Children (Miscellaneous Amendments) Regulations 2005 and the Adoption Agencies (Panel and Consequential Amendments) Regulations 2012

Other pre-assessment information

26. The adoption agency must—

(a) obtain the information about the prospective adopter which is specified in Part 1 of Schedule 4;

(b) obtain a written report from a registered medical practitioner about the health of the prospective adopter following a full examination which must include the matters specified in Part 2 of Schedule 4 unless the agency has received advice from its medical adviser that such an examination and report is unnecessary;

(c) obtain a written report of each of the interviews with the persons nominated by the prospective adopter to provide personal references for the prospective adopter;

(d) where the adoption agency considers it necessary, obtain a personal reference from the prospective adopter's former spouse, civil partner or partner; and

(e) where it is not the local authority in whose area the prospective adopter has their home, ascertain whether the local authority in whose area the prospective adopter has their home have any information about the prospective adopter which may be relevant to an assessment of the prospective adopter's suitability to adopt and if so obtain from that authority a written report setting out that information.

SCHEDULE 4
Regulation 26(a)
PART 1 Information to be provided during Stage 1

Information about the prospective adopter

5. Name and address of the prospective adopter's registered medical practitioner.

PART 2 Report on the Health of the Prospective Adopter

1. Name, date of birth, sex, weight and height.

2. A family health history of the parents, any brothers and sisters and the children of the

prospective adopter, with details of any serious physical or mental illness and any hereditary disease or disorder.

3. Infertility or reasons for deciding not to have children (if applicable).

4. Past health history, including details of any serious physical or mental illness, disability, accident, hospital admission or attendance at an out-patient department, and in each case any treatment given.

5. Obstetric history (if applicable).

6. Details of any present illness, including treatment and prognosis.

7. Details of any consumption of alcohol that may give cause for concern or whether the prospective adopter smokes or uses habit-forming drugs.

8. Any other relevant information which the adoption agency considers may assist the adoption panel and the adoption agency.

Requirement to obtain information about the child

15. 1) The adoption agency must obtain, so far as is reasonably practicable, the information about the child which is specified in Part 1 of Schedule 1.

   2) Subject to paragraph (4), the adoption agency must—

   (a) make arrangements for the child to be examined by a registered medical practitioner; and

   (b) obtain from that practitioner a written report ("the child's health report") on the state of the child's health which shall include any treatment which the child is receiving, any need for health care and the matters specified in Part 2 of Schedule 1, unless the agency has received advice from the medical adviser that such an examination and report is unnecessary.

   3) Subject to paragraph (4), the adoption agency must make arrangements—

   (a) for such other medical and psychiatric examinations of, and other tests on, the child to be carried out as are recommended by the agency's medical adviser; and

   (b) for written reports of such examinations and tests to be obtained.

   (4) Paragraphs (2) and (3) do not apply if the child is of sufficient understanding to make an informed decision and refuses to submit to the examinations or other tests.

Requirement to obtain information about the child's family

16. 1) The adoption agency must obtain, so far as is reasonably practicable, the information about the child's family which is specified in Part 3 of Schedule 1.

   2) The adoption agency must obtain, so far as is reasonably practicable, the information about the health of each of the child's natural parents and his brothers and sisters (of the full blood or half-blood) which is specified in Part 4 of Schedule 1.

Requirement to prepare child's permanence report

17. 1) The adoption agency must prepare a written report ("the child's permanence report") which shall include—

  (a) the information about the child and his family as specified in Parts 1 and 3 of Schedule 1;

  (b) a summary, written by the agency's medical adviser, of the state of the child's health, his health history and any need for health care which might arise in the future;

[......]

  (f) an assessment of the child's emotional and behavioural development and any related needs;

[.....]

  (j) any other information which the agency considers relevant.

2) In a case where—

  (a) the adoption agency is a local authority and is considering whether the child ought to be placed for adoption, and

  (b) either paragraph (2A) or paragraph (2B) applies, the adoption agency may not refer the case to the adoption panel.

2A) This paragraph applies where—

  (a) the child is placed for adoption by the adoption agency or is being provided with accommodation by them,

  (b) no adoption agency is authorised to place the child for adoption, and

  (c) the child has no parent or guardian, or the agency consider that the conditions in section 31(2) of the 1989 Act(1) are met in relation to the child.

2B) This paragraph applies where—

  (a) an application has been made, and has not been disposed of, on which a care order might be made in respect of the child, or

  (b) the child is subject to a care order and the adoption agency are not authorised to place the child for adoption.

2C) In a case not falling within paragraph (2), the adoption agency must send the information and reports referred to in paragraph (2D) to the adoption panel.

2D) For the purposes of paragraph (2C) and regulation 19(1A) the information and reports are—

  (i) the child's permanence report,

  (ii) the child's health report and any other reports referred to in regulation 15, and

  (iii) the information relating to the health of each of the child's natural parents, except that, in a case falling within paragraph (2C), the adoption agency may only send to the adoption panel the documents referred to in sub-paragraphs (ii) and (iii) if the agency's medical adviser advises it to do so.

SCHEDULE 1
PART 2 Matters to be included in the child's health report

1. Name, date of birth, sex, weight and height.
2. A neo-natal report on the child, including—
    (a) details of his birth and any complications;
    (b) the results of a physical examination and screening tests;
    (c) details of any treatment given;
    (d) details of any problem in management and feeding;
    (e) any other relevant information which may assist the adoption panel and the adoption agency; and
    (f) the name and address of any registered medical practitioner who may be able to provide further information about any of the above matters.
3. A full health history of the child, including—
    (a) details of any serious illness, disability, accident, hospital admission or attendance at an out-patient department, and in each case any treatment given;
    (b) details and dates of immunisations;
    (c) a physical and developmental assessment according to age, including an assessment of vision and hearing and of neurological, speech and language development and any evidence of emotional disorder;
    (d) for a child over five years of age, the school health history (if available);
    (e) how his physical and mental health and medical history have affected his physical, intellectual, emotional, social or behavioural development; and
    (f) any other relevant information which may assist the adoption panel and the adoption agency.

PART 4 Information relating to the health of the child's natural parents and brothers and sisters

1. Name, date of birth, sex, weight and height of each natural parent.
2. A health history of each of the child's natural parents, including details of any serious physical or mental illness, any hereditary disease or disorder, drug or alcohol misuse, disability, accident or hospital admission and in each case any treatment given where the agency consider such information to be relevant.
3. A health history of the child's brothers and sisters (of the full blood or half-blood), and the other children of each parent with details of any serious physical or mental illness and any hereditary disease or disorder.
4. A summary of the mother's obstetric history, including any problems in the

ante-natal, labour and post-natal periods, with the results of any tests carried out during or immediately after the pregnancy.

5. Details of any present illness, including treatment and prognosis.

6. Any other relevant information which the adoption agency considers may assist the adoption panel and the agency.

Wales

Extracts from the Adoption Agencies (Wales) Regulations 2005, as amended by the Adoption Agencies (Wales) (Amendment) Regulations 2012

Requirement to obtain information (including health information) about the child

15. 1) The adoption agency must, so far as is reasonably practicable, obtain the information about the child which is specified in Part 1 of Schedule 1.

(2) Subject to paragraph (4), the adoption agency must -

(a) make arrangements for the child to be examined by a registered medical practitioner; and

(b) obtain from that practitioner a written report on the state of the child's health which must include any treatment which the child is receiving, the child's needs for health care and the matters specified in Part 2 of Schedule 1, unless the agency has received advice from the medical adviser that such an examination and report is unnecessary.

(3) Subject to paragraph (4), the adoption agency must make arrangements -

(a) for such other medical and psychiatric examinations of, and other tests on, the child to be carried out as are recommended by the agency's medical adviser; and

(b) to obtain written reports of such examinations and tests.

(4) Paragraphs (2) and (3) do not apply if the child is of sufficient understanding to make an informed decision and refuses to submit to the examinations or other tests.

Requirement to obtain information (including health information) about the child's family

16. 1) The adoption agency must, so far as is reasonably practicable, obtain the inform-ation about the child's family which is specified in Parts 3 and 4 of Schedule 1.

2) The adoption agency must, so far as is reasonably practicable, obtain the information about the health of each of the child's natural parents and brothers and sisters which is specified in Part 5 of Schedule 1.

Requirement to prepare a written report

17. 1) Where the adoption agency consider in light of all the information obtained by virtue of regulations 12 to 16 that adoption is the preferred option for permanence for the child, the agency must prepare a written report which must include -

   (a) the information about the child and the child's family as specified in Parts 1, 3 and 4 of Schedule 1;

   (b) a summary, written by the agency's medical adviser, of the child's state of health, the child's health history and any need for health care which might arise in the future;

   (c) the wishes and feelings of the child regarding the matters set out in regulation 13(1)(c);

   (d) the wishes and feelings of the child's parent or guardian, and where regulation 14(2) applies, the child's father, and any other person the agency considers relevant, regarding the matters set out in regulation 14(1)(c);

   (e) the views of the agency about the child's need for contact with the child's parent or guardian or other relative or with any other person the agency considers relevant (including the child's father where regulation 14(2) applies) and the arrangements the agency proposes to make for allowing any person contact with the child;

   (f) an assessment of the child's emotional and behavioural development and any related needs;

   (g) an assessment of the parenting capacity of the child's parent or guardian, and if regulation 14(2) applies, the child's father;

   (h) a chronology of the decisions and actions taken by the agency with respect to the child;

   (i) an analysis of the options for the future care of the child which have been considered by the agency and why placement for adoption is considered the preferred option; and

   (j) any other information which the agency considers relevant.

   2) In a case where—

   (a) the adoption agency is a local authority and is considering whether the child ought to be placed for adoption, and

   (b) either paragraph (2A) or (2B) applies, the adoption agency may not refer the case to the adoption panel.

2A) This paragraph applies when—
- (a) the child is placed for adoption by the adoption agency or is being provided with accommodation by the local authority;
- (b) no adoption agency is authorised to place the child for adoption, and
- (c) the child has no parent or guardian, or the agency consider that the conditions in section 31(2) of the 1989 Act are met in relation to the child.

2B) This paragraph applies where—
- (a) an application has been made, and has not been disposed of, on which a care order might be made in respect of the child, or
- (b) the child is subject to a care order and the adoption agency are not authorised to place the child for adoption.

2C) In a case not falling within paragraph (2), the adoption agency must send the information and reports referred to in (2D) to the adoption panel.

2D) For the purposes of paragraph (2C) and regulation 19(1)(A) the information and reports are—
- (i) the written report referred to in regulation 17(1),
- (ii) the written report on the state of the child's health referred to in regulation 15(2)(b), unless the adoption agency has received advice from the medical adviser that such a report is unnecessary, and
- (iii) the information relating to the health of the child's natural parents.

(3) The adoption agency must obtain, so far as is reasonably practicable, any other relevant information which may be requested by the adoption panel and send that information to the panel.

PART 2 Regulation 15(2)
Matters to be included in the child's health report

1) Name, date of birth, gender, weight and height.
2) A neo-natal report on the child, including-
   - (a) details of the child's birth, and any complications;
   - (b) results of a physical examination and screening tests;
   - (c) details of any treatment given;
   - (d) details of any problem in management and feeding;
   - (e) any other relevant information which may assist the panel;
   - (f) the name and address of any doctor who may be able to provide further information about any of the above matters.
3) A full health history of the child, including-
   - (a) details of any serious illness, disability, accident, hospital admission or

attendance at an out-patient department, and in each case any treatment given;

(b) details and dates of immunisations;

(c) a physical and developmental assessment according to age, including an assessment of vision and hearing and of neurological, speech and language development and any evidence of emotional disorder;

(d) the school health history (if available);

(e) how the child's physical and mental health and medical history has affected his or her physical, intellectual, emotional, social or behavioural development;

(f) any other relevant information which may assist the adoption panel.

4) The signature, name, address and telephone number and qualifications of the registered medical practitioner who prepared the report, the date of the report and of the examinations carried out together with the name and address of any other doctor who may be able to provide further information about any of the above matters.

PART 5 Regulation 16(2)
Particulars relating to the health of the child's natural parents and brothers and sisters

1) Name, date of birth, gender, weight and height of each natural parent.

2) A family health history, covering each of the child's natural parents, the child's brothers and sisters (if any) and the other children (if any) of each parent with details of any serious physical or mental illness and any hereditary disease or disorder.

3) A health history of each of the child's natural parents, including details of any serious physical or mental illness, drug or alcohol misuse, disability, accident or hospital admission and in each case any treatment given where the agency consider such information to be relevant.

4) A summary of the mother's obstetric history, including any problems in the ante-natal, labour and post-natal periods, with the results of any tests carried out during or immediately after pregnancy.

5) Details of any present illness, including treatment and prognosis.

6) Any other relevant information which the agency considers may assist the panel.

7) The signature, name, address, telephone number and qualifications of any registered medical practitioner who supplied any of the information in this Part together with the name and address of any other doctor who may be able to provide further information about any of the above matters.

PART 4
Duties of adoption agency in respect of a prospective adopter

Procedure in respect of carrying out an assessment

26) 1) Where the adoption agency, after having followed the procedures referred to in regulations 23 and 25, consider the prospective adopter may be suitable to be an adoptive parent, it must carry out an assessment in accordance with this regulation.

2) The adoption agency must obtain such particulars about the prospective adopter as are referred to in Part 1 of Schedule 4.

3) The adoption agency must obtain—

(a) a written report from a registered medical practitioner about the health of the prospective adopter which must deal with the matters specified in Part 2 of Schedule 4 unless such a report has been made within 6 months of the panel's consideration of the case under regulation 27 and is available to the agency;

(b) a written report of each of the interviews with the persons nominated by the prospective adopter as personal referees; and

(c) a written report from the local authority in whose area the prospective adopter lives, and where the prospective adopter has lived in that area for a period of less than twelve months the agency must obtain a written report also from the local authority in whose area the prospective adopter lived previously.

(4) The adoption agency must prepare a written report which must include —

(a) the details of the prospective adopter as set out in Part 1 of Schedule 4;

(b) a summary, written by the agency's medical adviser, of the state of health of the prospective adopter;

(c) the agency's assessment of the prospective adopter's suitability to adopt a child, and in determining the suitability of a couple to adopt a child the agency must have proper regard to the need for stability and permanence in their relationship;

SCHEDULE 4
Regulation 26(2)
PART 1 Information about prospective adopter

11) Name and address of the prospective adopter's registered medical practitioner, if any.

PART 2 Regulation 26(3)(a)
Information about the health of the prospective adopter

1) Name, date of birth, gender, weight and height.
2) A family health history of the parents, the brothers and sisters (if any) and the children (if any) of the prospective adopter, with details of any serious physical or mental illness and inherited and congenital disease.
3) Infertility or reasons for deciding not to have children (if applicable).
4) Past health history, including details of any serious physical or mental illness, disability, accident, hospital admission or attendance at an out-patient department, and in each case any treatment given.
5) Obstetric history (if applicable).
6) Details of any present illness, including treatment and prognosis.
7) A full medical examination.
8) Details of any consumption of alcohol that may give cause for concern or whether the prospective adopter smokes or uses habit-forming drugs.
9) Any other relevant information which the agency considers may assist the panel.
10) The signature, name, address and qualifications of the registered medical practitioner who prepared the report, the date of the report and of the examinations carried out together with the name and address of any other doctor who may be able to provide further information about any of the above matters.

SCHEDULE 5 Regulation 32(1)
Information about the child to be given to the prospective adopter

1) Details of the child.
2) Photograph and physical description.
3) Details of the child's family circumstances and home environment, including details of the child's family (parents, siblings and significant others).
4) Chronology of the child's care.
5) The child's behaviour, how the child interacts with other children and relates to adults.
6) Whether the child is looked after by the local authority and, if so, the reasons and why the child is to be placed for adoption.
7) Details of the child's placement history including reasons for any placement breakdowns.
8) Details of the child's state of health, health history and any need for health care which might arise in the future.

9) Details of the child's educational history, a summary of the child's progress to date and whether assessed or likely to be assessed for special educational needs under the Education Act 1996.

10) The child's ascertainable wishes and feelings in relation to adoption, and contact with the child's parent, guardian, relative or other significant person.

11) The wishes and feelings of the child's parent, guardian, relative or other significant person in relation to adoption and contact.

12) The views of the person with whom the child is living about adoption.

13) The assessment of the child's needs for adoption support services and the agency's proposals for meeting those needs.

14) The agency's proposals for allowing any person contact with the child.

15) The proposed timescale for placement.

16) Any other information which the agency considers relevant.

Northern Ireland

Adoption Agencies (NI) Regulations (1989)

Adoption agency's duties in respect of a child and his parents or guardian

7 2) Where, following the procedure referred to in paragraph (1), an adoption agency is considering adoption for a child, the agency shall—

(a) set up a case record of the child and place on it any information obtained by virtue of this regulation;

(b) obtain, so far as is reasonably practicable, such particulars of the parents or guardian and, having regard to his age and understanding, the child, as are referred to in Parts l and Ill to· V of the Schedule together with any other relevant information which may be requested by the adoption panel;

(c) arrange and obtain a written report by a medical practitioner on the child's health which shall deal with the matters specified in Part II of the Schedule, unless such a report has been made within six months before the setting up of the case record under sub-paragraph (a) and is available to the agency;

(d) arrange such other examinations and screening procedures of, and tests on, the child and, so far as is reasonably practicable, his parents, as are recommended by the adoption agency's medical adviser, and obtain a copy of the written report of such examinations, screening procedures and tests; and

(e) prepare a written report containing the agency's observations on the matters referred to in this regulation, which shall be passed, together with all information obtained by it by virtue of this regulation, to the adoption panel or to another adoption agency.

Adoption agency's duties in respect of a prospective adopter

8   (2)   Where, following the procedure referred to in paragraph (1), an adoption agency considers that a person may be suitable to be an adoptive parent, it shall-

      (a)   set up a case record in respect of him and place on it any information obtained by virtue of this regulation;

      (b)   obtain such particulars as are referred to in Part VI of the Schedule together with, so far as is reasonably practicable, any other relevant information which may be requested by the adoption panel;

      (c)   obtain a written report by a medical practitioner on the prospective adopter's health which shall deal with the matters specified in Part VII of the Schedule, unless such a report has been made within six months before the setting up of the case record under sub-paragraph (a) and is available to the agency;

Placement for adoption

12. 1)   Where an adoption agency has decided in accordance with regulation 11 (1) that a prospective adopter would be a suitable adoptive parent for a particular child it shall provide the prospective adopter with written information about the child, his personal history and background, including his religious and cultural background, his health history and current state of health together with details of any condition as to religious upbringing of the child under Article 1 6(I)(b) (i)(ab), if applicable, and the adoption agency's written proposals in respect of the adoption, including proposals as to the date of placement for adoption with the prospective adopter.

     2)   If the prospective adopter accepts the adoption agency's proposals the agency shall—

      (a)   inform the child of the proposed placement for adoption with the prospective adopter where the child is capable of understanding the proposal;

      (b)   send a written report of the child's health history and current state of health to the prospective adopter's medical practitioner, if any, before the proposed placement, together with particulars of the proposed placement;

      (c)   notify in writing the Board in whose area the prospective adopter resides, before the placement, with particulars of the proposed placement;

      (d)   notify in writing the Education and Library Board in whose area the prospective adopter resides, before the placement, with particulars of the proposed placement if the child is of compulsory school age within the meaning of Article 46 of the Education and Libraries (Northern Ireland)

Order 1986 or if the adoption agency's medical adviser considers the child to be handicapped;

[....]

(i)   provide such advice and assistance to the prospective adopter as the agency considers necessary;

(j)   monitor the child's health during the placement to the extent that the adoption agency's medical adviser considers necessary

SCHEDULE

PART I
Particulars relating to the child

12)   Any special needs in relation to the child's health (whether physical or mental) and his emotional and behavioural development and whether he is subject to a statement under the Education and Libraries (Northern Ireland) Order 1986(a).

PART II
Matters to be covered in report on the child's health

1)   Name, date of birth, sex, weight and height.
2)   A neo-natal report on the child, including
   (a)   details of the birth, and any complications;
   (b)   results of a physical examination and screening tests;
   (c)   details of any treatment given;
   (d)   details of any problem in management and feeding;
   (e)   any other relevant information which may assist the panel;
   (f)   the name and address of any medical practitioner who may be able to provide further information about any of the above matters.
3)   A full health history and examination of the child, including-
   (a)   details of any serious illness, disability, accident, hospital admission or attendance at an out-patient department, and in each case any treatment given;
   (b)   details and dates of immunisations;
   (c)   a physical and developmental assessment according to age, including an assessment of vision and hearing and of neurological, speech and language development and any evidence of emotional disorder;
   (d)   for a child over five years of age, the school health history (if available);

(e)   any other relevant information which may assist the panel.

4)   The signature, name, address and qualifications of the medical practitioner who prepared the report, the date of the report and of the examinations carried out together with the name and address of any medical practitioner (if different) who may be able to provide further information about any of the above matters.

PART IV
Particulars relating to the health of each natural parent, including where appropriate the father of an illegitimate child

1)   Name, date of birth, sex, weight and height.

2)   A family health history, covering the parents, the brothers and sisters (if any) and the other children (if any) of the natural parent with details of any serious physical or mental illness and inherited and congenital disease.

3)   Past health history, including details of any serious physical or mental illness, disability, accident, hospital admission or attendance at an out-patient department, and in each case any treatment given.

4)   A full obstetric history of the mother, including any problems in the antenatal, labour and postnatal periods, with the results of any tests carried out during or immediately after pregnancy.

5)   Details of any present illness, including treatment and prognosis.

6)   Any other relevant information which the agency considers may assist the panel.

7)   The signature, name, address and qualifications of any medical practitioner who supplied any of the information in this Part together with the name and address of any medical practitioner (if different) who may be able to provide further information about any of the above matters.

PART VII
Matters to be covered in report on health of the prospective adopter

1)   Name, date of birth, sex, weight and height.

2)   A family health history, covering the parents, the brothers and sisters (if any) and the children (if any) of the prospective adopter, with details of any serious physical or mental illness and inherited and congenital disease.

3)   Marital history, including (if applicable) reasons for inability to have children.

4)   Past health history, including details of any serious physical or mental illness, disability, accident, hospital admission or attendance at an out-patient department, and in each case any treatment given.

5) Obstetric history (if applicable).

6) Details of any present illness, including treatment and prognosis.

7) A full medical examination.

8) Detail of any daily consumption of alcohol, tobacco and habit-forming drugs.

9) Any other relevant information which the agency considers may assist the panel.

10) The signature, name, address and qualifications of the medical practitioner when prepared the report, the date of the report and of the examinations tarried out together with the name and address of any medical practitioner (if different) who may be able to provide .further information about any of the above matters.